EF LENS WORK III

The Eyes of EOS

EF LENS WORK III

Contents

The Eyes of EOS ———————————————

The eye sees reality. The lens sees beyond reality to capture the truth.

The EF Lens Concept

Approaching the human eye

How far can an SLR lens actually succeed in duplicating the characteristics of the human eye? The natural colors of the subject seen by a clear eye, precise expression that can focus directly on what it wants to look at, a swift angle of vision that loses no time in catching even the fastest moving objects. Canon's pursuit of the techniques and technologies that will allow photographic lenses to approach the purity, expression, and dynamism of the human eye will never be tarnished by compromise.

Beyond human perspective

Why does that world we glimpse through the eye of an SLR lens appeal to so many people? Events so rapid they leave no visual impression, wondrous landscapes that peek out from unusual angles, distances and details invisible no matter how much you squint. Faster, wider, farther. There is no limit to the goals of Canon lenses, blazing trails into a photogenic world of expressiveness that ventures beyond human perspective.

Taking up the challenge of Canon lenses

24-70mm 1:2.8 L

Φ77mm

16-35mm 1 : 2.8

Already more than half a century has passed since Canon developed its first camera lens. And now, while making astounding breakthroughs in cutting edge digital technology, Canon is raising the design specification bar for the possibilities expected of each lens in the world of SLR cameras, already advancing by leaps and bounds. Our challenge now is to make the perfect lens, to meet the high level needs and desires of photographers who want the best from their EOS cameras. The Canon EF Lens. The Eyes of EOS.

The Professional Eye

Canon's Challenges

Canon's roots lie in Kwanon

Kwanon, the Buddhist Goddess of Mercy, was chosen as the name for the first Japanese 35mm focal plane shutter camera. Here is the story of how the Kwanon came to be developed and how it got its name.

A magazine ad for KWANON

The KWANON logo

In the 1930s, the two best 35mm focal plane shutter cameras were made by Leica and Contax. In 1932 the Leica II went on sale, followed the next year by the Contax I. These two cameras were produced in Germany, which boasted the world's finest precision machinery industry at that time, and they immediately became the object of desire of avid camera lovers throughout the world. In the meantime, Japan, with little or no technological power to speak of, was using foreign cameras as models.

At that time, the starting salary of a college graduate in a prestigious company was 70 yen per month, while a D-model Leica with a 50mm f/3.5 lens was priced at 420 yen. In other words, Leica and Contax cameras were far beyond the reach of the average person wanting to purchase a good camera.

At around this time, Goro Yoshida (1900-1993) attempted to build his own (and Japan's first) 35mm focal-plane shutter camera with a rangefinder (a 35mm rangefinder camera), just by taking apart a Leica II and studying its design. Yoshida, who had always been fascinated by cameras, taking them apart and putting them back together when still a schoolboy, dropped out of junior high school and began working as a repairman and remodeler working on movie cameras and movie projectors. In the mid-1920s, before he had even reached 30 years of age, he was often traveling back and forth between Japan and Shanghai to get parts for movie projectors. What made him decide to make a high-quality 35mm camera was something an American trader he met in Shanghai told

him. He said, "Why do you have to come all the way to Shanghai to get parts? Japan makes some of the best warships in the world, and if you can make those, there's no reason you can't make something as simple as parts for cameras. Save yourself some time and make them yourself." A born tinkerer, Yoshida's imagination was set aflame. Besides, his work involved repairing and remodeling movie cameras, so it is no surprise that he decided to build a camera himself. And while that is the story of how the idea for the first Canon camera was born, the lesson is one of equality: that everyone, even the Japanese at that time, could do something if they tried hard enough.

In 1933, the Precision Engineering Research Laboratory (later changed to "Canon") was established in a room in a three-floor apartment building in Roppongi in Tokyo, as a workshop for building high-quality 35mm cameras. The first glimpse the world got of this new company was an advertisement in the June 1934 issue of Asahi Camera, which even today remains one of Japan's top photography magazines. The gutsy ad copy under a picture of the Kwanon prototype read: "The "I" class submarine, the "92-Type" airplane, and the Kwanon camera: all world leaders." Japan developed several variants of the "I" class submarine in the 1920s, and the "92-Type" referred to the Japanese Imperial Army's air-cooled warplane. Both the vessel and plane were trumpeted in Japan as symbols of state-of-the-art weaponry. So Canon's advertisement linked Japan's first 35mm camera with top examples of the nation's technological prowess.

The Kwanon name itself originates in the Buddhist Goddess of Mercy, known as Kwanon in Japanese, and the logo pictured the thousand-armed Kwanon with the letters KWANON in the flames above her head. The name of the lens, on the other hand, came from Mahakashapa, one of the Buddha's disciples and leader of a religious group. It was chosen because of its similarity to the words the Japanese use when imitating the sounds the shutter makes – "kasha" (as it slides open) and "pa" (as it snaps shut).

The manufacture of the first high-quality 35mm rangefinder camera in Japan was the result of one man's dream to prove Japan's technological equality with Germany and all other western countries. That passion and pride continue to be passed on today in Canon EF lenses, which are the crystallization of the newest technologies and uncompromising craftsmanship.

Changing the way people think about lenses: the new DO lens optical element.

A challenge by Canon's technical team to the future of optical technology

The ultra telephoto EF400mm f/4 DO IS USM lens turns the old "big and heavy" image of telephoto lenses on its head, achieving a significantly lighter and more compact design than conventional models. And behind the appearance of the innovative new "DO Lens (multi-layered diffractive optical elements)" used in this lens lies the bold efforts by members of the Canon Development and Production teams.

In the mid 1990s, some of the young optical engineers at Canon noticed the possibilities available for a new optical system using "diffractive optical elements" which apply "wave optics," a way of treating light as waves. Diffractive optical elements are known to be much better at compensating for color aberration than conventional optical elements, so the engineers thought that using diffractive optical elements in telephoto lenses would make it possible to design much smaller and lighter lenses, while at the same time endowing them with very effective color aberration compensation.

However, the single-layered diffractive optical element which existed at that time caused much unnecessary flare (diffraction flare) when taking photographs using natural light, and were therefore not usable for photographic lenses. One of the engineers working on the design commented about the trouble the design team had, saying, "Everything we were attempting had never been tried before. For instance, we had a lot of trouble figuring out the complex formulas for calculating the diffraction flare accurately and establishing color canceling techniques for each instance of diffraction and methods for correcting chromatic aberration." As a result of the team's persistent efforts, however, the first prototype for the "DO lens" with an original multi-layer construction was produced, five years after design started, and it succeeded in rendering almost all light entering the lens usable for photographic purposes.

Meanwhile, the production team was working in tandem with the design team to develop techniques to mass-produce the new elements. For example, a diffractive optical element has a diffraction grating which stands 10 micro-millimeters high in a concentric circle. They successfully formed this very fine shape by greatly improving the replica aspherical lens technology, accuracy, and process, which were successfully used to produce the EF lenses. And while normal lens molds have ground surfaces on the lens side, the surfaces of the molds for the diffraction grating required a convex-concave pattern, so grinding them was out of the question. In order to solve this problem they developed an original 3D ultra high-precision micro-machining tool which could be controlled on the order of several nanometers, in order to produce a lens surface employing only cutting and no grinding or polishing. Not only that, but a new ultra-high-precision position technology was incorporated, on a micrometer scale, for joining the diffractive optical elements together – a key aspect of the design. It took five years to establish this mass-production system. And the result of the strenuous efforts by the design and manufacturing teams was the "DO lens," the first photographic lens in the world to incorporate diffractive optical elements.

Canon has in the past spared no effort in developing advanced original optical elements such as fluorite and wide-angle aspherical lenses, and by incorporating them immediately into products has worked to increase the performance of its optical systems, but of all these achievements, it is probably the DO lens that has the greatest chance of turning the world of interchangeable lenses on its head. These technologies keep being developed because of the atmosphere of challenge among Canon's engineers, passed down over the years. And that challenge will go on as Canon continues to develop new and innovative technologies.

Grinding on the order of nuclear particles.
The craftsman's skill delivers high-performance EF lenses.

EF lenses boast ultra-high resolution and picture quality with very high contrast. Behind the achievement of such high levels of performance lie advances in design technology using computers and design software, themselves the object of relentless advances. Yet, no matter how advanced or new the technology may be that an engineer uses to design a high-performance optical system, if the lenses to be mass-produced are not ground and polished with very high precision, the target optical performance cannot be reached. For this reason, the ground and polished lenses are inspected using a reference tool known as a "prototype standard," an instrument which must be made using the fine craftsmanship of an experienced grinding engineer - a skill which today is believed to have little or nothing to do with technology.

The prototype standard is actually a special lens which contains a mirror image of the convex and concave parts of the ground lens. It could be thought of as the yardstick against which the lens is measured. Any disparities in the curvature of the surfaces of the prototype standard and the ground lens cause striped patterns called Newton rings to appear. These rings are used to judge the precision with which the lens was ground - the fewer the better. For the prototype standard to work as a yardstick in this manner, however, it itself must be ground at extremely exacting standards, on the order of less than 0.03 micrometers for the roundness (3/100,000th of a millimeter), and $\pm$ 1 micrometer for the curvature radius. However, this level of precision cannot be achieved simply by punching a few numbers into a computer. As one grinding engineer puts it, "the condition of

the grind of the lens surface is judged by looking at the color and shape of the Newton rings, and the grinding machine is adjusted accordingly. It's a very difficult process." In other words, it is nothing but the grinding engineer's own knowledge and "feel" that make it possible to grind at a precision unattainable by a machine tool.

These remarkable engineers grind and polish lenses in accordance to minute factors, such as determining the condition of the surface by placing their hands on the grinding machine when it is running and fine-tuning it accordingly, or adjusting the amount of grind by factoring in the amount the glass has swollen from the heat of the grinding. In the hands of one of these remarkable engineers, the surface roughness of the finished prototype standard attains a fineness measured in angstroms, or in the magnitude of atomic particles, since one angstrom is 1/10 billionth of a meter. This is only possible for a very experienced craftsman, and is definitely not the work of a typical grinding engineer.

The prototype standards that they polish for use with optical equipment come in over 3,000 varieties, ranging from a curvature radius of less than 1 mm to infinity (flat surface), and more are being made to meet the continuing demand from the production floor.

Canon technology, which has created so many outstanding lenses, is only made possible by the grinding engineer's skill as a craftsman, which turns the design concept into a real object. Canon lenses, blazing trails in the world of imaging, derive their unrivalled levels of performance from the handiwork of the people who make them.

L Lenses
Where Dreams Are Crystal Clear.

The bright red line engraved on the lens barrel. And an L for "luxury."
The Canon EF lens L series possesses a level of quality sufficiently high to be called professional,
designed to include groundbreaking image performance, outstanding operability, and resistance to weather and aging.
"L." This name is reserved only for those few lenses that can meet stringent standards of performance,
using fluorite (an artificial crystal), a ground and polished aspherical surface,
UD, super UD lenses, or other special optical materials.
Optical design without compromise together with optical theory and precision engineering
technologies that are as steeped in tradition as they are cutting edge.
And the result of our relentless pursuit of these ideals is the L series of Canon EF lenses.

* The lenses have been specially set up to facilitate photography.

The Never Ending Challenge – The History of Canon Lenses

The history of Canon Lenses has undergone several transitions – from the range finder to the R Series,
the FL Series, the FD Series, and now the EF Series. No matter the age,
Canon has always focused on development that pursues further evolution.
Aspherical lenses, fluorite, USM, IS, and DO lenses,
and other new technologies are actively incorporated,
helping Canon maintain its position as world leader
in lens development.
Let us present to you some of our lenses which have made
their mark in the history of lens development.

1946

Canon's first camera lens
Serenar 50mm f/3.5 I

Canon first began working on lenses not long after the end of WWII. Developed and produced completely in-house, the first lens to see the light of day was the Serenar 50mm f/3.5. Serenar means "clear," symbolizing the clarity that the development team was aiming for.

1951

Recognized as a first-class lens
Serenar 50mm f/1.8 I

Five years after starting production, a lens appeared which could truly be called a classic. Taking a Gauss-type lens (one of the basic types of lens construction) and developing it further, we achieved crystal-clear imaging performance even at full aperture. Lens designers throughout the world were amazed with the result, and Canon lenses quickly gained recognition for their world-class quality.

1953

Lightweight and compact design
Serenar 100mm f/3.5 I

The first 100mm Canon lens was the long-focus type f/4 Triotar with a construction of three lens elements in three groups. Fame came with the telephoto type 100mm f/3.5 with five lens elements in four groups – a lightweight, compact medium telephoto lens only 69.5 mm long, 205 g/7.2 oz. in weight, and with a maximum diameter of 44mm. The model II was further reduced in weight to 184 g/6.5 oz., and became a hit among camera lovers.

1961

Largest aperture in the world for a camera lens
Canon 50mm f/0.95

In 1961 the 50mm f/0.95 went on sale, boasting the largest aperture of any photographic camera lens in the world. This legendary lens gained a reputation as being brighter than the human eye, and further strengthened Canon's international standing.

1964

Largest angle of view in the world for a camera lens
FL19mm f/3.5

This super wide-angle 19mm lens boasted the largest angle of view of any lens for SLR cameras at the time. The symmetrical arrangement in the optical system with concave lens elements in the front and back and convex lens elements in the center made it possible to eliminate distortion, chromatic difference of magnification, and comatic aberration, known as astigmatism. The concave lenses help achieve sufficient peripheral illumination while delivering a super wide angle. It was often said to be difficult to achieve a small lens size, correct spherical aberration, and deliver sufficient brightness from corner to corner with this type of optical system, but the FL19mm f/3.5 succeeded thanks to the incorporation of the convex lens group. It was sold with a special finder, as attaching the lens required the mirror to be raised, and it was also used for portraits of women with a slightly surreal effect.

1969

World's first* camera lens to use fluorite
FL-F300mm f/5.6

From early on Canon undertook research to make fluorite, which has characteristics not possessed by optical glass, into a material for camera lenses. Natural fluorite, however, is difficult to find in large crystals and is filled with impurities, making it impossible to use in a lens. Canon succeeded in beating the competition to development of techniques to eliminate the impurities and artificially grow crystals. The first lens in the world to use fluorite was the FL-F300mm f/5.6. Not only did fluorite succeed in eliminating color aberration, but it also made it possible to design shorter lenses. This 300mm was an innovative compact super telephoto lens in its day. These fluorite lens elements have been incorporated into many EF lenses as well as many of the lenses in the super telephoto high-performance L Lens Series.

* Among photographic lenses

1971

World's first large-aperture aspherical SLR lens with automatic diaphragm control

FD55mm f/1.2 AL

1971 saw the birth of the F-1, a real system SLR camera with professional specifications, and this was accompanied by the FD Series of lenses, which received high marks for their optical performance, including high contrast, sharpness, and outstanding color balance, as well as excellent mechanical performance and ease of use. The FD55mm f/1.2 AL was the world's first aspherical lens to support SLR viewing and auto-diaphragm control. Light rays entering the edge of a spherical lens are refracted differently than those passing through the center. For this reason the position of focus becomes misaligned causing spherical aberration, which in large-aperture lenses can lead to flaring. Aspherical lenses solve this problem, with no flaring at full aperture while nevertheless achieving high contrast images. Canon had to develop the machine tools required to make these lenses. Incorporating new technologies into products is the result of constant development from beginning to end.

1973

World's first* tilt-shift lens for 35mm cameras

TS35mm f/2.8 SSC

This was the first 35mm camera lens with tilt and shift functionality, and was ideal for architectural and commercial photography, which until then had been monopolized by large-format view cameras. This lens acted as the springboard for the EF Series TS-E.

* For 35mm camera lenses

1973

Innovative short zoom lens that made history

FD35-70mm f/2.8-3.5 SSC

This lens was a pioneer in short zoom lenses, thanks to its unique and simple two-lens-group design. It was equipped with a precise barrel construction in which zooming would move the front and rear lens groups at the same time in a non-linear fashion, with the positions of the front and rear lens groups moving apart at wide angles and coming together at telephoto angles, but without the barrel changing length. Also, the diaphragm in the rear lens group would move with it, and the aperture diameter changed in accordance with the zoom. Not only that, but it also came with a macro mechanism. This was truly an innovative lens. At that time zoom lenses were said to be lacking in comparison with single focal length lenses and were therefore rarely used by professional photographers, but as the exceptional performance of this lens gained recognition, it became a standard piece of equipment for the professional.

1975

First Canon lens to employ rear focusing

FD400mm f/4.5 SSC

Since conventional telephoto lenses required the entire lens to extend when focusing, the mechanical structure inevitably became very large. However, this lens adopted a rear-focusing system in which only part of the lens moved during focusing, thereby offering smooth operability. Another feature was the variable focus pitch system, which focused on the subject slowly for distant shots and swiftly for close-ups, just like the human eye. It was also compact and lightweight. The rear focusing system has since been employed in many lenses, and has contributed greatly to the creation of the high-speed autofocus used in EF lenses.

1982

Super wide-angle lens designed with leading-edge Canon software

New FD14mm f/2.8L

This was the lens with the widest angle in the FD lens series, employing aspherical lens elements to eliminate distortion. Canon developed the software to design the aspherical lens using computers. It was necessary to start with the basic and peripheral technologies in order to continue to produce cutting-edge technologies.

1989

World's largest aperture AF SLR lens

EF50mm f/1.0L USM

This standard lens boasted the largest aperture of any 35mm SLR camera lens when it went on sale. With two ground and polished aspherical elements and four high-index refractive glass lens elements, it delivered outstanding imaging performance with high contrast and minimal flare, even at the maximum aperture of f/1.0. The floating mechanism helped maintain high picture quality even at close focusing distances, while the electronic manual focus function allowed full-time manual focusing with a very light touch even in autofocus mode. This worked to enhance the already quick and rapid autofocus which employed a ring-type USM (Ultrasonic Motor) for the drive.

1993

World's first* interchangeable zoom lens for SLR cameras with a 10x magnification ratio

EF35-350mm f/3.5-5.6L USM

The expansive 10x zoom ratio was a first for SLR camera zoom lenses. Featuring coverage from wide-angle to super-telephoto, this lens delivered reliable performance in situations that required high mobility, such as sports photography. With its 6-group zoom system with 5 moving groups, the design successfully combined a high zoom ratio with compactness. Two UD lenses were incorporated to correct for color aberrations, which resulted in high-resolution images and outstanding contrast. Moreover, this lens was known for features such as a smoothly rotating tripod collar, a special ring to adjust zooming friction, full-time manual focus, and other conveniences.

* For SLR cameras with interchangeable lenses

1995

World's first*1 interchangeable lens for 35mm cameras with an image stabilizer

EF75-300mm f/4-5.6 IS USM

This was the first interchangeable telephoto lens for SLRs equipped with an image stabilizing function. A pair of gyro sensors detects the movement of the camera and moves the corrective optics (the second lens group) in the opposite direction to cancel any possible blurring of the image, making this an innovative lens. The image stabilization effect is good for the equivalent of two shutter speeds.*2 Silent autofocus is achieved through the use of a micro USM for the autofocus drive.

*1 For 35mm SLR cameras with interchangeable lenses

*2 Based on a shutter speed of "1/focal length" seconds, said to be the limit for hand-held photography without image stabilization.

1999

First L-series lens with an image stabilizer

EF300mm f/2.8L IS USM

This lens has achieved such a high reputation that it has come to be known as the symbol of Canon's professional lenses. In 1974 the FL 300mm f/2.8 SSC Fluorite lens was created, a high-performance, large-aperture telephoto lens. That lens blazed the trail to be followed by the FD 300mm f/2.8 SSC and eventually the EF300mm f/2.8L IS USM. Its innovative performance has produced numerous classic photographs in the fields of sports, journalism, and advertising. The EF300mm f/2.8L IS USM is equipped with an image stabilizing mechanism to greatly improve mobility. The optical system achieves outstanding image quality thanks to the inclusion of one fluorite lens element and two UD lens elements. Reduced weight in the focus lens group and improvements to the autofocus drive algorithm make the autofocus extremely fast, while additional functions include a new function which makes instantaneous focus adjustments as well as a new autofocus stop function. Use of magnesium and a lighter weight optical system give the lens an overall reduced weight compared to previous models, while the rubber used on the mount and switches endows the lens with outstanding dust-proof and drip-proof characteristics.

2001

World's first*1 camera lens to incorporate Canon's DO lens elements (multi-layered diffractive optical elements)

EF400mm f/4 DO IS USM

The EF400mm f/4 DO IS USM is a super telephoto lens which incorporates in part of the optical system Canon's own "DO lens (multi-layered diffractive optical elements)." Compared with lenses that have the same design specifications using only refractive optical elements, it not only maintains the same high image quality, but also delivers a 27% shorter length and 31% lighter weight. It is also equipped with an image stabilizing mechanism which corrects blurring during hand-held photography for the equivalent of two shutter speeds*2, as well as an AF stop function, and a dust-proof and drip-proof construction, giving it almost the same performance as the Super Telephoto L-Type IS Lens Series.

*1 For 35mm SLR cameras with interchangeable lenses

*2 Based on a shutter speed of "1/focal length" seconds, said to be the limit for hand-held photography without image stabilization.

2008

World's first* camera lens to employ SWC (Subwavelength Structure Coating)

EF24mm f/1.4L II USM

This large-diameter 24mm wide-angle lens employs revolutionary SWC (Subwavelength Structure Coating) anti-reflection technology for the first time in the world*. Utilizing nanometer-scale constructions even smaller than the wavelengths of visible light, SWC effectively minimizes lens flare and ghosting caused by extremely large-angle incidence of light, which is difficult to prevent with conventional coatings of vapor-deposited film. SWC proves the effectiveness of a new method of anti-reflection technology that takes advantage of microscopic construction on a lens surface. In addition, the EF24mm f/1.4L II USM employs two high-precision glass-mold aspherical lens elements and two UD lens elements to effectively eliminate various types of aberrations. Moreover, the featured floating mechanism provides high-resolution, high-contrast corner-to-corner image quality throughout the entire picture area. Canon will continue its development advances through related know-how, using SWC as a key technology to expand the freedom of optical product design.

* Among photographic lenses

2009

World's first* interchangeable SLR camera lens to employ Hybrid IS

EF100mm f/2.8L Macro IS USM

This medium telephoto macro lens features Canon's Hybrid IS (Image Stabilizer) – the world's first* optical image stabilizer capable of compensating for both angle and shift camera shake. Angle shake compensation aids in most shooting situations while shift shake compensation is especially useful when photographing close-ups. In addition to the vibration gyro (angular velocity sensor) found in previous optical IS systems, Hybrid IS includes an acceleration sensor for detecting camera shake that occurs parallel to the focal plane. A new algorithm calculates shake based on readings taken from the two sensors, then adjusts lens elements to compensate for both angle and shift camera shake simultaneously. This two-pronged approach to minimizing the effects of camera shake greatly enhances handheld shooting capability in the macro realm. Furthermore, the EF100mm f/2.8L Macro IS USM includes a UD lens element to correct chromatic aberration. The end results are superb image quality, excellent durability and easy operability, all of which are expected in L-series lenses.

* For SLR cameras with interchangeable lenses

39

The Birth of the EF Lens

EF lenses, born of an active pursuit of new technologies and based on a foundation of expertise gained from 60 years of lens development experience, have equaled or exceeded the optical performance of the FD Lens Series to achieve a new level of precision in autofocus and fully electronic control and create the core of the EOS SLR camera system with next-generation design specifications. The lenses were designed with an eye on the future, not just focusing on image performance, but also keeping the entire system in mind — specifically, the large-diameter electronic mount which allows total computerization of data communication between the camera and lens, and the lens motor drive system which utilizes a high-precision electromagnetically driven diaphragm together with an ideal autofocus actuator (drive system) inside the lens.

One of these autofocus actuators was the world's first USM (UltraSonic Motor), which delivers high torque with no operating noise, is equipped with outstanding start and stop characteristics and is an ideal actuator which makes the autofocus speed and precision even greater. The USM was at first only included in L lenses, but is now found in almost all EF lenses. In 1995 the EF75-300mm f/4-5.6 IS USM was developed, the world's first[1] interchangeable SLR lens with a built-in image stabilizing mechanism. This mechanism is now found in the super telephoto L-Type IS Series, represented by the EF300mm f/2.8L IS USM, establishing a whole new category of lenses.

In 2009, Canon raised the bar for image stabilization technology by developing Hybrid IS, the world's first[2] optical image stabilizer designed for macro photography. The system initially appeared in the EF100mm f/2.8L Macro IS USM lens.

Canon is renowned for developing key technologies that enhance optical performance. For example, the DO lens and SWC (Subwavelength Structure Coating) were both groundbreaking achievements in interchangeable lenses and contributed greatly to the elevation of photographic standards. DO lenses were introduced in 2001 with the launch of the EF400mm f/4 DO IS USM while SWC first appeared in 2008 on the EF24mm f/1.4L II USM.

[1] For 35mm SLR cameras with interchangeable lenses
[2] For SLR cameras with interchangeable lenses

Our Memories ... Your Memories

1930

Kwanon (Prototype)

Original (Hansa Canon)

S

J

JS

NS

1940

JII

JII

S

SII

IIB

1950

IIC

III

IV

IIIA

IVS

IIA

IID

IVSb

IIF

IVSb2

IIS2

IID2

L2

VT Deluxe

L1

L3

VL

VL2

VIT

VIL

P

Canon Flex

1960

RP

R2000

VT

7

RM

FX

FP

7S

Pellix

FT QL

Pellix QL

TL

EX EE

1970

F-1

FTb

F-1 High speed Motor Drive Camera

EX AUTO

FTb-N (Later model)

EF

TX

AE-1

TLb

F-1(Later model)

AT-1

A-1

AV-1

1980

AE-1 Program

New F-1

AL-1

T50

New F-1 High Speed Motor Drive Camera

T70

T80

T90

EOS 650

EOS 620

EOS 100

EOS IX 50

EOS-1D

EOS-1Ds Mark II

EOS-1D Mark III

EOS 750

EOS 1000S

EOS-3

EOS D60

EOS 20D

EOS 40D

EOS 850

EOS 5

EOS 3000

EOS 630

EOS Kiss

EOS Kiss 5

EOS Kiss 7

EOS-1Ds Mark III

EOS-1

EOS D6000/2000

EOS-1Ds

EOS Kiss Digital N

EOS Kiss X2

EOS-1N

EOS 20Da

EOS Kiss F

EOS RT

EOS Kiss III

EOS 10D

1990

EOS 5000

2000

EOS Kiss Digital

EOS-1D Mark II N

EOS 50D

EOS 10

EOS 55

EOS-1V

EOS Kiss Lite

EOS 5D Mark II

EOS 700

EOS-DCS 1/3

EOS 7

EOS 5D

T60

EOS 3000 N

EOS-1D Mark II

EOS 30D

EOS Kiss X3

EOS 1000

New EOS Kiss

EOS Kiss III L

EOS Kiss Digital X

EOS 7D

EF-M

EOS IX E

EOS D30

EOS 7s

EOS-1D Mark IV

Canon interchangeable lens cameras produced since the 1930s.
• Products' names are those for the Japanese market.

43

White Canon lenses capturing the moment at a sporting event

The EF Lens World

Single focal-length lenses

An amazing world in 180°: a fisheye lens that goes beyond the limits of human vision and delights the eye.

Camera lenses have what is called an angle of view, which is the limit within which the subject can be photographed in accordance with the focal length and the imaging format, similar to human vision. The angle of view of standard lenses, which is thought to be near that of the human eye, is approximately 50°, while that of a 15mm fisheye lens is 180° (diagonally across the frame in the 35mm format). This means that almost everything that is in front of the camera is included in photographs taken by fisheye lenses, such as the sky above, the ground below, and surrounding scenery far to the left and right, which would normally have to be looked at by turning the head and would not therefore be visible in normal vision.

Since fisheye lenses put everything within an angle of view of 180° onto the film or a 24 x 36mm image sensor, there is much distortion around the edges of the photograph. All straight lines outside the center of the photograph become curved. The stronger the hyperfocal effect, which puts everything in the picture into focus, the larger the objects at the center appear. Meanwhile, objects near the edges of the frame are extremely warped, creating a tremendous feeling of perspective. Incidentally, the name fisheye was first applied to this type of lens because this is how a fish underwater sees the outside world when it looks up, an effect which is related to the ratio of refraction of light.

However, when using fisheye lenses, it is important to remember that the visual impact is so strong that photographers need to be careful not to let the lens choose the picture instead of their own

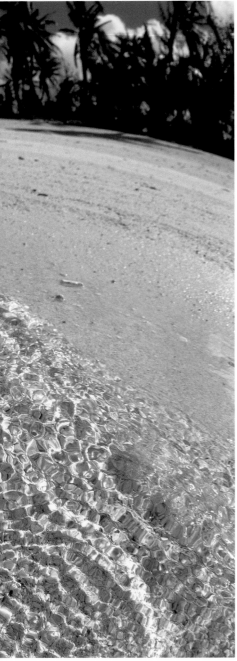

EF15mm f/2.8 Fisheye·1/640sec.·f/16

EF15mm f/2.8 Fisheye

- Focal length and maximum aperture: 15 mm 1:2.8
- Lens construction: 8 elements in 7 groups ● Diagonal angle of view: 180°
- Focus adjustment: Overall linear extension system with AFD
- Closest focusing distance: 0.2 m/ 0.7 ft., 0.14 x magnification
- Filter size: Rear drop-in gelatin filter holder
- Max. diameter x length, weight: ø 73 x 62.2 mm, 330 g/ 2.9" x 2.5", 11.6 oz.

artistic or photographic sensibility. Used skillfully, this type of lens can open unique vistas of expressive possibility, as well as being able to act as an ultra-wide-angle lens thanks to the fact that lines in the center of the picture are not deformed.

■EF15mm f/2.8 Fisheye
This fisheye lens with an 180° diagonal view can impart an extraordinary expressiveness to photographs. Even under conditions where manual focus would be difficult, the autofocus delivers sharp focus quickly and accurately. Fisheye lenses are in a class of their own for specialized photographic situations, demonstrating their unique perspective and hyperfocal effect when photographing objects as close as 0.2m/0.7ft. from the focal plane. The rear drop-in gelatin filter holder makes for easy filter work.

A 14mm lens covers a tremendous field of view in the 35mm format: creating a surreal effect only possible in photographs that go beyond a human perspective

Lenses with an ultra-wide focal length of 14mm can photograph an entire 114° wide-angle view in the 35mm format, equivalent to looking out the windshield of your car and seeing everything in one glance. This wide-angle view is most effective for photographing buildings from which you cannot get far enough away to take a good picture, as well as very small interiors. The strong perspective effect of this lens can also be seen in the daring expressiveness of landscape photographs. In portrait photography, the use of an ultra wide-angle lens can create a strong sense of separation between subject and background.

With this type of lens, the camera angle has a significant effect on the resulting photographic image, creating a very dynamic outcome. By holding the camera level, a more natural feeling with minimal perspective distortion results, but tilting the camera up or down even slightly causes vertical lines to appear to converge or taper dramatically. These results are particularly effective for artistic architectural photography.

■EF14mm f/2.8L II USM

Employing a newly designed optical system that corrects aberrations common to wide-angle lenses, this ultra wide-angle delivers sharp, high-resolution images over the entire image area along with outstanding contrast. Thanks to the precise, large-diameter GMo aspherical characteristics of the 3rd and 14th elements, distortion is effectively eliminated despite the 114°

EF14mm f/2.8L II USM·1/640sec.·f/11

angle of view. In addition, two UD elements reduce chromatic aberration of magnification for clean images and vastly reduced color bleeding. Ultrasonic rear focus allows manual focus at any time and combines with a high-speed CPU for fast autofocus. The circular aperture produces beautiful background blur effects and the dust- and drip-proof design is a nice touch when working in harsh environments. Flare and ghost, problems often associated with digital SLR photography, are also noticeably reduced. This lens is excellent for situations requiring crisp, precise full-frame imaging.

EF14mm f/2.8L II USM

● Focal length and maximum aperture: 14 mm 1:2.8
● Lens construction: 14 elements in 11 groups ● Diagonal angle of view: 114°
● Focus adjustment: Ring-type USM, rear focusing system, full-time manual focus
● Closest focusing distance: 0.2 m/ 0.66 ft., 0.15 x magnification
● Filter size: Rear drop-in gelatin filter holder
● Max. diameter x length, weight: ø 80 x 94 mm, 645 g/ 3.2" x 3.7", 1.4 lbs.

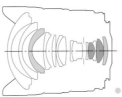

● Aspherical lens ● UD lens

Wide angle. Extreme depth of field.
The ultra wide-angle 20mm lens can be used almost anywhere.
Ultra wide-angle lenses are characterized by a dynamic wide-angle effect which goes beyond human visual perspective. Exaggerated perspective foreshortening makes subjects nearer to the camera appear very large, with a rapid decrease in size as they move further away. A pan-focus effect with everything appearing sharp from foreground to background is thus easily achieved, even when shooting at large apertures.

While delivering a wide-angle view of 94°, which puts everything inside the human field of vision into the photograph, the 20mm lens nevertheless allows a more natural feeling to be achieved, without the extreme foreshortening effect which dominates photographs taken by the 14mm lens. This lens is ideal if you want to take documentary photographs or portraits that have a slightly out-of-the-ordinary feel and a strong sense of presence, without losing their realism. This lens has a broad range of uses as an ultra wide-angle lens, good for everything from architectural and interior photography to general snapshots and landscape photography.

■EF20mm f/2.8 USM
A rear focus mechanism with a floating effect moves the rear lens group internally to correct close-distance aberrations while focusing the subject. Crisp, sharp images are possible from the minimum focusing distance of 0.25m/0.8ft. to infinity. The combination of the rear focusing design with an ultrasonic motor achieves fast and silent autofocusing. Of course, manual focusing

EF20mm f/2.8 USM·1/350sec.·f/5.6

is possible at all times without switching modes. Since the front of the lens does not rotate during focusing, superior operability is obtained with circular polarizing filters. This lens is good for active photographers who already have a standard zoom lens but want a lens that will give their landscape photography and snapshots a broader feeling.

EF20mm f/2.8 USM

● Focal length and maximum aperture: 20 mm 1:2.8
● Lens construction: 11 elements in 9 groups ● Diagonal angle of view: 94°
● Focus adjustment: Ring-type USM,rear focusing system, full-time manual focus
● Closest focusing distance: 0.25 m/ 0.8 ft., 0.14 x magnification ● Filter size: 72 mm
● Max. diameter x length, weight: ø 77.5 x 70.6 mm, 405 g/ 3.1" x 2.8", 14.3 oz.

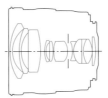

A 24mm lens adds a powerful sense of presence to subjects photographed up close. An impressive range of photographic expression broadened by the availability of large apertures.

The wide-angle 24mm lens delivers a broad angle of view, so proper use of its strong perspective and clear imaging performance allows a real sense of separation to be achieved between the subject and its background. While offering less dynamic effects than its super-wide-angle counterparts, this lens provides a beautiful blur effect in the background when the lens aperture is opened up fully, while at the same time offering outstanding imaging performance emphasizing the unique perspective available with wide-angle lenses. Taking portraits very close to the subject can also add a tinge of other-worldliness to the image – an effect typical of wide-angle lenses. Of course, these lenses are at their best when photographing expansive landscapes without losing the vastness of the image.

■EF24mm f/1.4L II USM

A large-diameter lens with a brightness of f/1.4. Making full use of advanced optical technology, this lens surpasses conventional models in realizing high image quality with high resolution and high contrast over its entire area, including the periphery. The EF24mm f/1.4L II USM uses two molded glass aspheric lenses to correct various aberrations such as field curvature and distortion, as well as two UD lenses that effectively control lateral chromatic aberration, which easily occurs in wide-angle lenses. In addition, this lens is the first in the world[*1] to make practical use of SWC (Subwavelength Structure Coating), an anti-reflective coating based on a microscopic structure even smaller than optical wavelengths. The EF24mm f/1.4L II USM also controls occurrence of flare and ghost images caused by a particularly large angle of incidence of light. Supporting the demanding requirements of professionals and advanced amateur photographers, the lens

EF24mm f/1.4L II USM

- Focal length and maximum aperture: 24 mm 1:1.4
- Lens construction: 13 elements in 10 groups ● Diagonal angle of view: 84°
- Focus adjustment: Ring-type USM, rear focusing system, full-time manual focus
- Closest focusing distance: 0.25 m/ 0.8 ft., 0.17 x magnification ● Filter size: 77 mm
- Max. diameter x length, weight: ø 83.5 x 86.9 mm, 650 g/ 3.4" x 4.0", 1.4 lbs.

● Aspherical lens ● UD lens

EF24mm f/1.4L II USM·2sec.·f/8

provides high-performance specifications, such as high-speed AF, a full-time manual focus mechanism, high dust- and drip-proof*[2] performance, etc.

■EF24mm f/2.8

Incorporation of rear focusing superbly compensates for all aberrations at any shooting distance, including extreme close-up, achieving very clear images. Since the length of the lens is always the same and the hood and filter mounts are designed not to rotate, operability with circular polarizing filters is sublime. Compact and easy to use, this is a fast, accurate autofocusing lens with unrivalled maneuverability.

*1 Among photographic lenses
*2 Camera models that support dust- and drip-proof performance: EOS-1Ds Mark III, EOS-1Ds Mark II, EOS-1Ds, EOS-1D Mark IV, EOS-1D Mark III, EOS-1D Mark II N, EOS-1D Mark II, EOS-1D, EOS-1V/HS

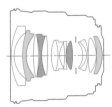

EF24mm f/2.8

- Focal length and maximum aperture: 24 mm 1:2.8
- Lens construction: 10 elements in 10 groups ● Diagonal angle of view: 84°
- Focus adjustment: Rear focusing system with AFD
- Closest focusing distance: 0.25 m/ 0.8 ft., 0.16 x magnification ● Filter size: 58 mm
- Max. diameter x length, weight: ø 67.5 x 48.5 mm, 270 g/ 2.7" x 1.9", 9.5 oz.

A 28mm lens providing photography with high mobility while utilizing visual effects typical of a wide-angle lens

Objects photographed with a wide-angle lens appear larger the closer they are to the camera, so use of wide-angle lenses is ideal for maintaining an ample perspective balance between subject and background. Of all the wide-angle lenses available, however, 28mm lenses are the most effective in this regard, not only for landscapes, of course, but also when moving in on the subject for portraits, delivering a strong sense of presence for the objects surrounding the subject while also giving even everyday subjects a hint of something different.

It goes without saying that 28mm lenses are also very useful for indoor snapshots that require a wide angle of view or for photographs of large groups of people. And since astigmatism and distortion are very low due to their fixed focal length, these lenses are useful for architectural photography.

■EF28mm f/1.8 USM

This is a large aperture lens that provides impressively natural delineation and beautiful shading, as well as excellent performance for indoor photography taking advantage of the bright maximum aperture of f/1.8. The optical system incorporates aspherical lenses, which not only keep the lens size down but also reduce spherical aberration and deliver sharp picture quality. A flare-cut diaphragm installed behind group 1 blocks unwanted light to ensure highest contrast. Operability is enhanced by inclusion of a ring-type USM for silent, high-speed AF with full-time manual focus and a non-rotating filter mount.

EF28mm f/1.8 USM·1/350sec.·f/11

EF28mm f/1.8 USM

- Focal length and maximum aperture: 28 mm 1:1.8
- Lens construction: 10 elements in 9 groups ● Diagonal angle of view: 75°
- Focus adjustment: Ring-type USM, rear focusing system, full-time manual focus
- Closest focusing distance: 0.25 m/ 0.8 ft., 0.18 x magnification ● Filter size: 58 mm
- Max. diameter x length, weight: ø 73.6 x 55.6 mm, 310 g/ 2.9" x 2.2", 10.9 oz.

● Aspherical lens

EF28mm f/2.8

- Focal length and maximum aperture: 28 mm 1:2.8
- Lens construction: 5 elements in 5 groups ● Diagonal angle of view: 75°
- Focus adjustment: overall linear extension system with AFD
- Closest focusing distance: 0.3 m/ 1 ft., 0.13 x magnification ● Filter size: 52 mm
- Max. diameter x length, weight: ø 67.4 x 42.5 mm, 185 g/ 2.7" x 1.7", 6.5 oz.

● Aspherical lens

■EF28mm f/2.8

Incorporation of a glass-molded aspherical lens element enables use of a simple yet effective 5-element, 5-group lens construction. This results in an extremely compact, lightweight optical system which achieves super-fast autofocusing with an extension type focusing system, while delivering sharp, high-contrast image quality. Distortion is virtually nonexistent, making this lens ideal for architectural photography and other scenes containing straight lines.

35mm: A focal length that delivers a subdued perspective and natural delineation similar to the human eye.

This lens offers a natural approach to subjects that is almost like that of a standard lens. But when you want to get a little more 'presence' in your photographs, with more breadth and depth in the visual plane, a 35mm lens is ideal. The expressive possibilities of these lenses range from sharply defined foreground and background utilizing a blur effect when the aperture is wide open or when taking close-up photographs, adding a different tone from that achievable with standard wide-angle lenses, and hyperfocal effects with the aperture stopped down all the way to give the photograph a sense of visual tension.

The slightly wider angle of view and the brightness of the maximum aperture values are also valuable assets for scenic photography using natural light. These lenses are particularly useful when photographing in low light conditions which would cause zoom lenses to lose effectiveness. These wide-angle, single focal length lenses can be used in many different situations, from indoor photography with straightforward perspective to portraits and snapshots.

■EF35mm f/1.4L USM

This lens boasts the brightness of the largest aperture in its class. Its 9th element is a ground aspherical lens that thoroughly eliminates spherical aberration and distortion. It achieves extremely sharp, faultless picture quality only possible with a single focal length lens. A floating mechanism maintains the lens's superior image quality from infinity to the closest shooting

EF35mm f/1.4L USM·0.6sec.·f/2.8

EF35mm f/1.4L USM

- Focal length and maximum aperture: 35 mm 1:1.4
- Lens construction: 11 elements in 9 groups ● Diagonal angle of view: 63°
- Focus adjustment: Ring-type USM, rear focusing system, full-time manual focus
- Closest focusing distance: 0.3 m/ 1 ft., 0.18 x magnification ● Filter size: 72 mm
- Max. diameter x length, weight: ø 79 x 86 mm, 580 g/ 3.1" x 3.4", 1.3 lbs.

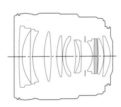

● Aspherical lens

distance of 0.3m/1ft. The non-rotating filter mount provides easy operability with circular polarizers and other types of filters.

■EF35mm f/2

The simple 7-elements, 5-groups lens construction utilizing a short zoom lens design method achieves a brightness of f/2 in a lightweight and compact design. This efficient lens construction combines with a multi-layer coating treatment to achieve very clear imaging performance with virtually no ghosting or flare. The minimum focusing distance is 0.25m/0.8ft. – the shortest in its class – making it possible to take close-ups at a magnification of 0.23x, despite the wide angle of the lens.

EF35mm f/2

- Focal length and maximum aperture: 35 mm 1:2
- Lens construction: 7 elements in 5 groups ● Diagonal angle of view: 63°
- Focus adjustment: Overall linear extension system with AFD
- Closest focusing distance: 0.25 m/ 0.8 ft., 0.23 x magnification ● Filter size: 52 mm
- Max. diameter x length, weight: ø 67.4 x 42.5 mm, 210 g/ 2.7" x 1.7", 7.4 oz.

EF50mm f/1.2L USM·1/800sec·f/1.2

EF50mm f/1.2L USM

- ● Focal length and maximum aperture: 50 mm 1:1.2
- ● Lens construction: 8 elements in 6 groups ● Diagonal angle of view: 46°
- ● Focus adjustment: Ring-type USM, overall linear extension system, full-time manual focus
- ● Closest focusing distance: 0.45 m/ 1.48 ft., 0.15 x magnification ● Filter size: 72 mm
- ● Max. diameter x length, weight: ø 85.8 x 65.5 mm, 590 g/ 3.4" x 2.6", 1.3 lbs.

● Aspherical lens

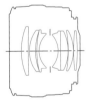

EF50mm f/1.4 USM

- ● Focal length and maximum aperture: 50 mm 1:1.4
- ● Lens construction: 7 elements in 6 groups ● Diagonal angle of view: 46°
- ● Focus adjustment: Micro USM, overall linear extension system, full-time manual focus
- ● Closest focusing distance: 0.45 m/ 1.5 ft., 0.15 x magnification ● Filter size: 58 mm
- ● Max. diameter x length, weight: ø 73.8 x 50.5 mm, 290 g/ 2.9" x 2", 10.2 oz.

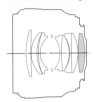

EF50mm f/1.8 Ⅱ

- ● Focal length and maximum aperture: 50 mm 1:1.8
- ● Lens construction: 6 elements in 5 groups ● Diagonal angle of view: 46°
- ● Focus adjustment: Overall linear extension system with Micromotor
- ● Closest focusing distance: 0.45 m/ 1.5 ft., 0.15 x magnification ● Filter size: 52 mm
- ● Max. diameter x length, weight: ø 68.2 x 41 mm, 130 g/ 2.7" x 1.6", 4.6 oz.

Natural images close to the perspective of the human eye.
A standard lens that, once mastered, proves its worth in any situation.

Photographs taken with a standard lens have a natural angle of view and an undistorted feeling of distance. And because the lens has about the same angle of view as the human eye, it demands much more from the photographer. The key to using a standard lens is to strike a winning combination of distance from the subject, perspective, and background blur. For example, by using a small aperture with low- or high-angle shots, you can create a feeling just as dynamic as that created with a wide-angle lens. Even when using a more conventional angle, a large aperture can be used to soften the background and obtain an image similar to the results obtained with a medium telephoto zoom lens. And by paying close attention to perspective and composition in close-ups, you can achieve professional-looking results. Indeed, the 50mm lens is the one lens that allows photographers to take advantage of all the principles of lens work.

■EF50mm f/1.2L USM

This standard lens features a super-wide maximum aperture of f/1.2. Taking advantage of shallow depth of field allows the photographer to capture subjects with impact, such as for wedding portraits. Use of an aspherical lens effectively corrects spherical aberrations and delivers sharp, high-contrast images even with the aperture fully open. Another attractive aspect of the lens is its circular aperture that creates beautiful background blur. Coupled with silent, high-speed autofocusing and full-time manual focus override for subtle focusing adjustment, this lens satisfies professionals both in image quality and operability.

■EF50mm f/1.4 USM

By optimally distributing power with a gauss type design and two high-refraction glass lenses, flare at maximum aperture is minimized and astigmatism is greatly reduced. Moreover, improvements in the quality of the focused image and the beautiful natural blur of the background are simultaneously achieved. Use of a Micro USM (Micro Ultrasonic Motor) provides fast, silent autofocusing, as well as full-time manual focus. The color balance is virtually identical to the ISO recommended reference values.

■EF50mm f/1.8 Ⅱ

An orthodox 6-element, 5-group construction allows high image quality and natural expressiveness throughout the entire focusing range from infinity to the closest focusing distance of 0.45m/1.5ft. A simple cam-type drive is used in the focusing system, providing quick, quiet autofocusing and achieving a light weight of 130g/4.6 oz. Neutral color balance achieves color reproduction that is nearly identical with the ISO recommended values. And with a price that won't break the bank, the fun of a single focal length lens with a different attitude from a standard zoom lens is available to everyone.

EF85mm f/1.2L II USM·1/640sec.·f/2

The 85mm medium telephoto lens is also known as the "portrait lens." It brings any image to life with a bright natural look.

With the perspective of the eye when looking closely at an object, 85mm lenses are often called "portrait lenses," because their natural perspective and blur effect makes them ideal for this purpose. Full-length photos of female models, head-and-shoulders portraits, and photographs that accentuate the subject by setting it off from the background are particularly well suited to this type of lens, with its natural feel. You can also take advantage of the brightness of the lens itself for taking naturally lit dusk and indoor shots – an appealing capability unavailable with zoom lenses.

■EF85mm f/1.2L II USM

An upgraded version of the EF85mm F/1.2L USM, widely deemed the "gold standard" for professional portrait work, this lens is the brightest in its class and offers beautiful out-of-focus effects. By virtue of its precisely ground aspherical lens, which adeptly compensates for spherical aberrations and other distortions, this lens displays exquisite detail and high contrast even at f/1.2. And with the incorporation of a floating lens mechanism, aberration fluctuations are substantially reduced at short and medium distance shots to ensure extremely sharp, quality images consistently at all shooting distances. We have also dramatically sped up AF performance in response to requests from professionals. A faster CPU and optimized AF algorithm allow the lens to focus instantaneously for reliable capture of fleeting photo opportunities. This lens is even more pleasant to use for portrait work because of the very shallow depth of field at f/1.2, coupled with full-time manual focusing for fine adjustment. Furthermore, Canon effectively reduced the flaring and ghosting common with digital cameras by optimizing internal lens placement and coatings. A circular aperture is also used to maximize the wonderful defocusing attributes of the lens at the maximum f/1.2 aperture. All told, this is the one lens that can meet the toughest demands of professional photographers, whether shooting female portraits with a masterful blur effect or natural scenes in natural lighting.

■EF85mm f/1.8 USM

This lens's most prominent feature is its outstanding portability. The rear focus system delivers sharp, clear images starting with the maximum aperture. The rapid, quiet, and accurate autofocusing is complemented by a full-time manual focus for subtle adjustments. When taking portraits even such fine adjustment as moving the focus from the tips of the eyelashes to the eye itself is possible, creating a subtle yet definite change in expressive tone. The natural soft blur effect is very attractive, and the lens's operability is outstanding, with a constant lens length as well as a non-rotating front lens group to make using circular polarizing filters even easier.

EF85mm f/1.2L II USM

- Focal length and maximum aperture: 85 mm 1:1.2
- Lens construction: 8 elements in 7 groups ● Diagonal angle of view: 28° 30'
- Focus adjustment: Ring-type USM, front group linear extension system, full-time manual focus
- Closest focusing distance: 0.95 m / 3.2 ft., 0.11 x magnification ● Filter size: 72 mm
- Max. diameter x length, weight: ø 91.5 x 84 mm, 1,025 g/ 3.6" x 3.3", 2.3 lbs.

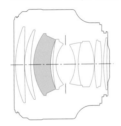

● Aspherical lens

EF85mm f/1.8 USM

- Focal length and maximum aperture: 85 mm 1:1.8
- Lens construction: 9 elements in 7 groups ● Diagonal angle of view: 28° 30'
- Focus adjustment: Ring-type USM, rear focusing system, full-time manual focus
- Closest focusing distance: 0.85 m/ 2.8 ft., 0.13 x magnification ● Filter size: 58 mm
- Max. diameter x length, weight: ø 75 x 71.5 mm, 425 g/ 3" x 2.8", 15 oz.

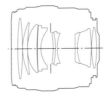

The 100mm telephoto lens clearly communicates the photographer's expressive intent by capturing the subject naturally using its slight telephoto effect.

Compared to the 85mm lens, the 100mm lens is characterized by an angle similar to that when you look closely at an object. It also provides a remarkable perspective compression effect, bringing the subject together with the background, making it possible to create photographs which seem to clip a certain composition out of reality in accordance with the photographer's will. And since the subject can be emphasized in the composition of the photograph without the necessity of being physically close to it, portrait photography becomes easier as the model can relax and achieve a more natural expression, without having to think about the camera in his or her face.

Uses also include image shot photographs utilizing pin-point focus, taking full advantage of the shallower depth of field at maximum aperture.

■EF100mm f/2 USM

For natural looking perspective in landscape photography, portraiture and snapshots, this large-aperture, medium telephoto lens is ideal, and easily portable. Equipped with a rear focusing optical system perfect for medium telephoto lenses, this lens compensates for all types of aberration, delivering outstanding image performance that is sharp and clear, even at maximum aperture. Designed with portrait photography in mind, a great deal of thought went into the natural, soft blur effect. The lens delivers quick, quiet USM autofocusing as well as smooth full-

EF100mm f/2 USM·1/45sec.·f/2.8

time manual focus. As with the EF85mm f/1.8 USM, the lens's operability is outstanding, with a constant lens length as well as a wide manual focus ring and non-rotating filter and hood mounts.

EF100mm f/2 USM

● Focal length and maximum aperture: 100 mm 1:2
● Lens construction: 8 elements in 6 groups ● Diagonal angle of view: 24°
● Focus adjustment: Ring-type USM, rear focusing system, full-time manual focus
● Closest focusing distance: 0.9 m/ 3 ft., 0.14 x magnification ● Filter size: 58 mm
● Max. diameter x length, weight: ø 75 x 73.5 mm, 460 g/ 3" x 2.9", 1 lb.

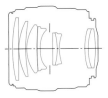

Isolating the most important part of the subject without losing the background.

The 135mm focal length delivers the best in telephoto lenses.

Telephoto lenses are great for transmitting the feeling of the photographer in a straight, unadorned manner. The intention behind the photograph is easily seen by the photographer's selection of what to include in the composition and how to include it, incorporating the background or emphasizing one part of the subject. The various effects of different telephoto lenses are contained in the 135mm lens, making it relatively easy to master. For instance, it is ideal for candid snapshots, such as shots of children playing from across the yard. Also possible are relatively orthodox photos, like rows of blooming flowers, taking advantage of the overlapping effect the lens's angle provides. And since the

shortness of the lens makes it easy to take with you, it is the ideal lens for learning the basics of how best to use telephoto lenses.

■EF135mm f/2L USM

This lens is perfect for indoor sports photography that takes advantage of the f/2 brightness, and for portrait photography that uses the beautiful shading only possible with a large aperture lens and the nearness of the closest focusing distance (0.9m/3ft.). The use of two UD elements effectively compensates for secondary spectrum and ensures sharp image quality. Light mechanical parts make this the lightest lens in its class at 750g/26.5oz. A ring-type USM and rear focusing guarantee quick and quiet autofocusing, and excellent performance-functionality balance makes this an easy-to-handle lens. Equipped with an Extender EF1.4×II or 2×II, it

EF135mm f/2L USM·1/60sec.·f/2

can be used for AF photography at 189mm f/2.8 and 270mm f/4. Operational ease is improved by the inclusion of full-time manual focusing which can be used in AF mode, and non-rotating filter and hood mounts.

EF135mm f/2L USM

- Focal length and maximum aperture: 135 mm 1:2
- Lens construction: 10 elements in 8 groups ● Diagonal angle of view: 18°
- Focus adjustment: Ring-type USM, rear focusing system, full-time manual focus
- Closest focusing distance: 0.9 m/ 3 ft., 0.19 x magnification ● Filter size: 72 mm
- Max. diameter x length, weight: ø 82.5 x 112 mm, 750 g/ 3.2" x 4.4", 1.7 lbs.

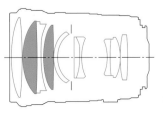

● UD lens

The expressive power of soft focus – Perfect for portraits and nature photography which stress the beauty of the subject.

Using the shallow depth of field characteristic of telephoto lenses, you can cut out all the unnecessary detail, and at the same time get the unforced expression you are looking for, thanks to the distance between the camera and the subject. These characteristics make the 135mm lens, along with medium telephoto lenses, very popular for portrait photography. They are also used for landscape photography, taking advantage of the close-up effect created by compressing the perspective and emphasizing the narrow angle of view. And to add a bit more flavor to the final product, it is not uncommon to use a filter to impart a soft touch to the whole composition. In portraits, the soft filter enhances the model's complexion and skin tone, and in landscapes and flower photography, it conveys a magical touch to the scene.

The soft focus technique used to draw out a mysterious beauty in portraits of female models and flowers can be achieved several

ways. The easiest is to use a soft focus filter. These filters have rough surfaces which disperse the light entering the lens (the photographic light), and the resulting photograph looks like a pale mist has enveloped the scene.

In contrast, soft focus lenses are specifically designed to use spherical aberration, which normally decreases sharpness in a lens and can cause "seeping," for its softening effect. Unlike soft filters, the image performance of soft focus lenses involves creating a unique and beautiful world which veils the subject in a soft fuzzy flare, while nevertheless maintaining the subject in sharp focus. The flare is controlled to round out the image. Soft focus lenses make taking this kind of photograph fun again.

■EF135mm f/2.8 with Softfocus

This unique lens is the only telephoto lens equipped with a built-in soft focus function to achieve very soft images by harnessing the effect of spherical aberration. There are two levels of softness

EF135mm f/2.8 with Softfocus·1/15sec.·f/3.5

which can be chosen (1 - weak, 2 - strong), in addition to level 0 which is for photographs with normal sharpness. The softness of levels 1 and 2 can be further controlled by careful selection of the aperture, making it possible to achieve very precise levels of softness. Image quality with the soft focus effect is ideal for flattering portraits and pictorial scenes, with the subject in focus but softened with an appropriate degree of flare. Not only can the ideal softness be achieved by moving the internal aspherical lens element in accordance with the amount of softness desired, aberration fluctuation caused by changes in distance is also eliminated. And there is no need to worry about trying to determine the correct focus position - the autofocusing system precisely focuses the subject for the optimum soft focus effect.

EF135mm f/2.8 with Softfocus

● Focal length and maximum aperture: 135 mm 1:2.8
● Lens construction: 7 elements in 6 groups ● Diagonal angle of view: 18°
● Focus adjustment: Rear focusing system with AFD
● Closest focusing distance: 1.3 m/ 4.3 ft., 0.12 x magnification ● Filter size: 52 mm
● Max. diameter x length, weight: ø 69.2 x 98.4 mm, 390 g/ 2.7" x 3.9", 13.8 oz.

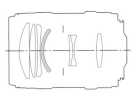

● Aspherical lens

EF200mm f/2L IS USM·1/80sec.·f/2

EF200mm f/2L IS USM

- Focal length and maximum aperture: 200 mm 1:2
- Lens construction: 17 elements in 12 groups ● Diagonal angle of view: 12°
- Focus adjustment distance: Ring-type USM, inner focusing system, full-time manual focus
- Closest focusing distance: 1.9 m/ 6.23 ft., 0.12 x magnification
- Filter size: 52 mm rear drop-in type
- Max. diameter x length, weight: ø 128 x 208 mm, 2,520 g/ 5" x 8.2", 5.6 lbs.

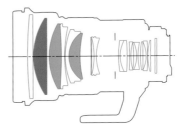

● UD lens ● Fluorite

Perspective compression makes subjects stand out with this 200mm lens.

A focal length of 200mm narrows angle of view considerably and emphasizes perspective compression – an effect unique to telephoto lenses that makes it possible to create powerful, intense images. For sports photography, rapidly moving subjects can be isolated within an uncluttered fragment of space to produce stunningly dynamic photos. When shooting fashion, a blurred background can be created by focusing on the foreground subject, taking advantage of the shallow depth of field characteristic of these lenses. The wider the aperture, the more pronounced this beautiful effect. When employed with a 200mm lens, this photographic technique makes it easy to separate subjects from the background.

■EF200mm f/2L IS USM

Featuring a circular aperture, this bright, fast telephoto lens produces a beautiful blur effect ideal for portraits or indoor sports photography. Its L-series optical system includes one fluorite and two UD elements, resulting in razor-sharp photos with minimal color bleeding. Advanced image stabilization that reduces camera shake by approximately five full shutter speed steps* combined with a compact, lightweight magnesium-alloy design makes this lens ideal for hand-held shooting. Additionally, it offers great operability and mobility via an AF stop button and other features. The dust- and drip-proof design delivers outstanding reliability in adverse environments.

* Base on a shutter speed of "1/focal length" seconds, said to be the limit for hand-held photography without image stabilization.

■EF200mm f/2.8L II USM

This is a lightweight, compact telephoto lens that was designed for mobility. Two UD lenses thoroughly eliminate secondary spectrum. The new rear focus design which reduces the overall weight of the moving lens elements and improves focusing precision also compensates for aberrations. The lens boasts excellent sharp, clear imaging performance at all focusing distances. The quick and quiet AF which uses a ring-type USM and the fine-tuned physical balance of the lens make operation a delight. It is equipped with a large separate hood which blocks out light very effectively. It is compatible with an optional detachable tripod collar, which provides a stable support and can be switched smoothly from vertical to horizontal positions and vice-versa.

EF200mm f/2.8L II USM

- Focal length and maximum aperture: 200 mm 1:2.8
- Lens construction: 9 elements in 7 groups ● Diagonal angle of view: 12°
- Focus adjustment: Ring-type USM, rear focusing system, full-time manual focus
- Closest focusing distance: 1.5 m/ 4.9 ft., 0.16 x magnification ● Filter size: 72 mm
- Max. diameter x length, weight: ø 83.2 x 136.2 mm, 765 g/ 3.3" x 5.4", 1.7 lbs.

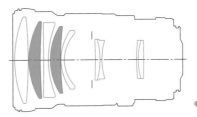

● UD lens

The appeal of a tightly compressed perspective.
A super telephoto lens that can bring life to any picture.

The ability of these lenses to go beyond the perspective of the human eye makes for photographs which bring a strongly compressed perspective to the viewer – and the 300mm is no exception, fully endowed with these characteristics, but also capable of handling fast-moving subjects thanks to its lightweight, compact design.

This lens is great for capturing fresh expressions, such as in natural portraits taken from a distance so as not to intrude on the model's frame of mind with the camera, and slightly magical close-ups of flowers which result in riotous or subdued splashes of color, depending on how the blur effect is used.

■EF300mm f/2.8L IS USM

This is the accumulation of all the new optical technologies Canon has, embodied in the next-generation L-type large-aperture 300mm, with a newly designed optical system. One fluorite lens element and two UD lens elements are used to thoroughly eliminate secondary spectrum. High picture quality with high resolution and high contrast is achieved. The world's fastest[*1] autofocusing has been achieved by employing a ring-type USM and improving the drive algorithm. Furthermore, equipping the lens with an image stabilizing mechanism that compensates for roughly two shutter speeds[*2] has made it possible to get the best performance out of it under all conditions. The closest focusing distance has also been reduced to 2.5m/8.2ft. Operability has been greatly advanced by adding an AF stop button and revamping the focus preset method. Using a magnesium alloy for the lens barrel has resulted in an ultra lightweight body which is 295 grams lighter than before. The body has outstanding dust-proof and drip-proof[*3] characteristics. It comes with a removable tripod collar.

EF300mm f/2.8L IS USM

- ● Focal length and maximum aperture: 300 mm 1:2.8
- ● Lens construction: 17 elements in 13 groups
- ● Diagonal angle of view: 8° 15'
- ● Focus adjustment: Ring-type USM, inner focusing system, full-time manual focus
- ● Closest focusing distance: 2.5 m/ 8.2 ft., 0.13 x magnification ● Filter size: 52 mm rear drop in
- ● Max. diameter x length, weight: ø 128 x 252 mm, 2,550 g/ 5" x 9.9", 5.6 lbs.

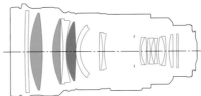

● UD lens ● Fluorite

EF300mm f/2.8L IS USM·1/25sec.·f/2.8

■EF300mm f/4L IS USM

In addition to the unrivalled optical performance, this 300mm lens is characterized by outstanding mobility thanks to the image stabilizing mechanism. In IS mode, the photographer has two options: mode 1, which is good for still shots, and mode 2, for many shots of moving objects. The optics includes two UD glass elements to thoroughly eliminate secondary spectrum. With a closest focusing distance of 1.5m/4.9ft, you can get in as close to the subject as possible in that unique way only possible with a macro lens. The image stabilizer also functions when using the Extender EF1.4xⅡ and Extender EF2xⅡ to provide that elusive 600 mm shooting capability.

*1 Bodies: EOS-1Ds Mark Ⅲ, EOS-1Ds Mark Ⅱ, EOS-1Ds, EOS-1D Mark Ⅳ, EOS-1D Mark Ⅲ, EOS-1D Mark Ⅱ N, EOS-1D Mark Ⅱ, EOS-1D, EOS-1V/HS, EOS-3 (all when using rechargeable battery pack)

*2 Based on a shutter speed of "1/focal length" seconds, said to be the limit for hand-held photography without image stabilization.

*3 Dust-proof and drip-proof models: EOS-1Ds Mark Ⅲ, EOS-1Ds Mark Ⅱ, EOS-1Ds, EOS-1D Mark Ⅳ, EOS-1D Mark Ⅲ, EOS-1D Mark Ⅱ N, EOS-1D Mark Ⅱ, EOS-1D, EOS-1V/HS, Extender EF1.4xⅡ, Extender EF2xⅡ

EF300mm f/4L IS USM

- ● Focal length and maximum aperture: 300 mm 1:4
- ● Lens construction: 15 elements in 11 groups (protective glass included)
- ● Diagonal angle of view: 8° 15'
- ● Focus adjustment: Ring-type USM, rear focusing system, full-time manual focus
- ● Closest focusing distance: 1.5 m/ 4.9 ft., 0.24 x magnification ● Filter size: 77 mm
- ● Max. diameter x length, weight: ø 90 x 221 mm, 1,190 g/ 3.5" x 8.7", 2.6 lbs.

● UD lens

The real attraction of super telephoto lenses.
400mm lenses with the impact of a compressed perspective.

400mm lenses are some of the most commonly used lenses for international sporting events such as the Olympics. These super telephoto lenses deliver shots which are both photogenic and have strong visual impact, such as a close-up of the focused concentration of a runner's expression on the starting line, or just the right way to frame the color and texture of a far-off mountaintop. 400mm lenses have an even more powerful compression effect than 300mm lenses, putting the subject and the background right next to each other, as it were, creating more tension in the composition of the photograph. This allows the photographer to bring immediacy to shots of wild animals and birds, which are generally difficult to photograph from up close, or the driving force of an F1 racecar as it comes around a corner.

■EF400mm f/2.8L IS USM

A 400mm super telephoto lens with a first-rate imaging performance, plus Image Stabilization effective over two shutter speeds. The image stabilizing mechanism used on IS lenses provides high-speed correction control whenever vertical or horizontal movement is detected, allowing for a greater range of hand-held photography. It provides reliable capabilities when used for fashion photography and sports photography performed indoors or at night. The optical system includes one fluorite and two UD lens elements that eliminate secondary spectrum, for ultra high contrast and image quality. With a ring-type USM and an improved drive algorithm, its autofocusing is the fastest in the world[*1]. The closest focusing distance has been reduced to 3m/9.8 ft., and it is equipped with full-time manual focus that does not consume electric power. It has both focus preset and AF Stop functions. This lens is lightweight due to the use of a magnesium alloy for its barrel and other external parts. It offers superior dust-

EF400mm f/2.8L IS USM

- Focal length and maximum aperture: 400 mm 1:2.8
- Lens construction: 17 elements in 13 groups
- Diagonal angle of view: 6° 10'
- Focus adjustment: Ring-type USM, inner focusing system, full-time manual focus
- Closest focusing distance: 3 m/ 9.8 ft., 0.15 x magnification ● Filter size: 52 mm rear drop in
- Max. diameter x length, weight: ø 163 x 349 mm, 5,370 g/ 6.4" x 13.7", 11.8 lbs.

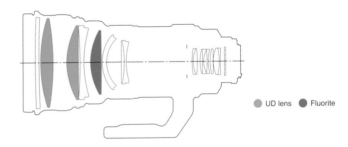

● UD lens ● Fluorite

EF400mm f/2.8L IS USM·1/250sec.·f/8

proof and drip-proof*² performance even under harsh conditions.

■EF400mm f/5.6L USM

This is a high-performance 400mm super telephoto lens featuring an extremely light and compact design ideal for photographers requiring high mobility and portability. The optical system incorporates one element made of Super UD glass and one element made of standard UD glass, thus effectively correcting color aberration and delivering extremely sharp, high-contrast imaging performance. Other features that ensure convenient operation include a built-in hood, a removable ring-type tripod mount, and a focus range selector that allows the user to select the full 3.5m/11.5ft.-to-infinity distance range or restrict the range to 8.5m/27.9ft.- to-infinity.

*1 Bodies: EOS-1Ds Mark III, EOS-1Ds Mark II, EOS-1Ds, EOS-1D Mark IV, EOS-1D Mark III, EOS-1D Mark II N, EOS-1D Mark II, EOS-1D, EOS-1V/HS, EOS-3 (all when using rechargeable battery pack)
*2 Dust-proof and drip-proof models: EOS-1Ds Mark III, EOS-1Ds Mark II, EOS-1Ds, EOS-1D Mark IV, EOS-1D Mark III, EOS-1D Mark II N, EOS-1D Mark II, EOS-1D, EOS-1V/HS, Extender EF1.4xII, Extender EF2xII

EF400mm f/5.6L USM

- Focal length and maximum aperture: 400 mm 1:5.6
- Lens construction: 7 elements in 6 groups ● Diagonal angle of view: 6° 10'
- Focus adjustment: Ring-type USM, rear focusing system, full-time manual focus
- Closest focusing distance: 3.5 m/ 11.5 ft., 0.12 x magnification ● Filter size: 77 mm
- Max. diameter x length, weight: ø 90 x 256.5 mm, 1,250 g/ 3.5" x 10.1", 2.8 lbs.

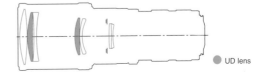

● UD lens

A new expressiveness and mobility in super telephoto lenses equipped with the new DO optical element that delivers compact size, light weight, and high picture quality.

It is a fact of life that the optical systems of super telephoto lenses grow in size and weight, which creates problems in terms of holding them, making it almost impossible to use them for hand-held photography as they cannot be held still enough. This causes blurry shots which ruin the impact and visual effect that the photographer was going after, and is a particular handicap for field sports which require much hand-held photography. Blurry shots are the enemy in this type of photography, so demand is high for super telephoto lenses that are light but still deliver high picture quality.

Big, heavy super telephoto lenses. The answer? A new technology embodied in DO lenses.

Many different technical approaches have been taken to try to solve the problem of how to make super telephoto lenses more compact and lighter. The latest solution is "diffractive optical elements" which allow interchangeable lenses for SLR cameras to be designed more compactly, lighter, and with high picture quality by applying optical characteristics which are unavailable in normal refraction lens elements. At the same time, however, if the light entering the lens is natural (white) light, part of that light becomes diffracted and appears as flares, which has made such characteristics difficult to apply to photographic lenses. Thanks to a newly developed original multi-layered construction, DO lenses have solved the problem of how to make super telephoto lenses smaller and lighter, without compromising picture quality.

■EF400mm f/4 DO IS USM

This is the first 400mm super telephoto lens for photography with the new multi-layered diffractive optical elements, or DO lens

EF400mm f/4 DO IS USM·1/320sec.·f/6.3

elements. It delivers unrivaled imaging performance while keeping size and weight down to manageable levels. By combining DO lens elements with normal refraction elements, color aberration is corrected to levels even higher than is possible with fluorite elements. This lens also has the fastest autofocusing in the world*¹. Equipped with an Image Stabilizing mechanism and a thoroughgoing dust-proof and drip-proof*² construction, it can be used in even the harshest weather conditions. It also comes with an AF Stop function for outstanding operability and mobility. The green line on the lens barrel is a symbol of the innovative technologies used to design and produce Canon lenses, and is shared by the Canon FL-F300mm f/5.6 which appeared in 1969, the first SLR lens in the world to use fluorite lens elements.

*1 Bodies: EOS-1Ds Mark III, EOS-1Ds Mark II, EOS-1Ds, EOS-1D Mark IV, EOS-1D Mark III, EOS-1D Mark II N, EOS-1D Mark II, EOS-1D, EOS-1V/HS, EOS-3 (all when using rechargeable battery pack)
*2 Dust-proof and drip-proof models: EOS-1Ds Mark III, EOS-1Ds Mark II, EOS-1Ds, EOS-1D Mark IV, EOS-1D Mark III, EOS-1D Mark II N, EOS-1D Mark II, EOS-1D, EOS-1V/HS, Extender EF1.4xII, Extender EF2xII

EF400mm f/4 DO IS USM

● Focal length and maximum aperture: 400 mm 1:4
● Lens construction: 17 elements in 13 groups
● Diagonal angle of view: 6° 10'
● Focus adjustment: Ring-type USM, inner focusing system, full-time manual focus
● Closest focusing distance: 3.5 m/ 11.5 ft., 0.12 x magnification ● Filter size: 52 mm rear drop-in type
● Max. diameter x length, weight: ø 128 x 232.7 mm, 1,940 g/ 5" x 9.4", 4.3 lbs.

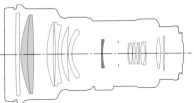

● Fluorite ● DO lens

Bringing out the lens's original performance by preventing unwanted blur.

The 500mm super telephoto lens, going beyond human perspective.

Follow the dynamic movement of the players on a field far away. Get right up into the powerful action of the teams as they interact on a soccer or rugby field. With the unique perspective compressing effect provided by a 500mm super telephoto lens, the photographer can put the subject and the background on almost the same visual plane, creating a visual tension and impact that are hard to imitate, and that make super telephoto lenses the pleasure they are.

With a 500mm lens, however, extreme attention needs to be paid to shaking of the hand or camera when following the movements of a moving subject, as this will result in a blurry shot – a common occurrence when trying to capture the action of a scene. Many professional photographers perform hand-held photography depending on the scene, but use of a monopod and an image stabilizing mechanism in such situations makes it possible to take extremely sharp photographs, even with a visual impact that is almost surreal, using only 1/10 of the 50mm lens's angle of view.

■EF500mm f/4L IS USM

This very mobile 500mm super telephoto lens has the double attraction of an original Image Stabilizing mechanism and a bright large aperture of f/4. Its newly designed optical system consists of 17 elements in 13 groups, including one fluorite lens element and two UD lens elements. These have eliminated virtually all aberrations to achieve a level of image quality previously impossible to attain with such high contrast and

EF500mm f/4L IS USM·1/30sec.·f/22

sharpness. With a ring-type USM and an improved drive algorithm, its autofocus is the fastest in the world*¹. The lens's closest focusing distance has been reduced to only 4.5m/14.8ft., and it is equipped with full-time mechanical manual focusing, focus preset, and an AF Stop function. The use of a magnesium alloy for the lens barrel minimizes weight and the lens offers superior dust-proof and drip-proof*² performance. The large f/4 aperture permits the use of autofocus when using an extender. Image Stabilization is even more effective when combined with a unipod, making shooting even more accurate.

*1 Bodies: EOS-1Ds Mark III, EOS-1Ds Mark II, EOS-1Ds, EOS-1D Mark IV, EOS-1D Mark III, EOS-1D Mark II N, EOS-1D Mark II, EOS-1D, EOS-1V/HS, EOS-3 (all when using rechargeable battery pack)
*2 Dust-proof and drip-proof models: EOS-1Ds Mark III, EOS-1Ds Mark II, EOS-1Ds, EOS-1D Mark IV, EOS-1D Mark III, EOS-1D Mark II N, EOS-1D Mark II, EOS-1D, EOS-1V/HS, Extender EF1.4xII, Extender EF2xII

EF500mm f/4L IS USM

- Focal length and maximum aperture: 500 mm 1:4
- Lens construction: 17 elements in 13 groups
- Diagonal angle of view: 5°
- Focus adjustment: Ring-type USM, inner focusing system, full-time manual focus
- Closest focusing distance: 4.5 m/ 14.8 ft., 0.12 x magnification ● Filter size: 52 mm rear drop in
- Max. diameter x length, weight: ⌀ 146 x 387 mm, 3,870 g/ 5.8" x 15.2", 8.5 lbs.

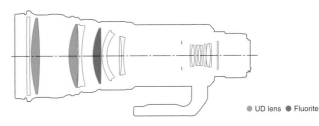

● UD lens ● Fluorite

Filling the frame with unapproachable subjects.

Excellent for photographing wild animals in the jungle or on the playing field.

The photographer's dream is to get right up close to the driver as his racecar careens around a corner at 200mph and capture the tension on his face, or sneak up on a hungry lion in the jungle and capture his subdued aggressiveness digitally or on film. For better or for worse, these acts are physically dangerous or simply impossible, but with a super telephoto lens, the photograph is not impossible. A 600mm lens lets you capture all those dramatic sports and wildlife moments with the visual impact of physical immediacy. The subtle movements of a subject moving far off in the distance can be brought in to fill the frame, with visual tension enhanced by the perspective compression that only a super telephoto lens can deliver.

Normally, this class of lens requires a tripod, but with the Image Stabilizing mechanism, all you need is a monopod for total mobility.

■EF600mm f/4L IS USM

This new 600mm super telephoto lens is equipped with an Image Stabilizer system and has a large aperture of f/4, providing the finest image performance in its class. It offers reliable capabilities when used to photograph wild animals or field sports. The optical system includes one fluorite lens element and two UD lens elements that eliminate secondary spectrum, resulting in a level of image quality with high contrast previously impossible to attain. With its improved drive algorithm, its autofocus is the fastest in

EF600mm f/4L IS USM·1/80sec.·f/9

EF600mm f/4L IS USM

- Focal length and maximum aperture: 600 mm 1:4
- Lens construction: 17 elements in 13 groups
- Diagonal angle of view: 4° 10'
- Focus adjustment: Ring-type USM, inner focusing system, full-time manual focus
- Closest focusing distance: 5.5 m/ 18 ft., 0.12 x magnification ● Filter size: 52 mm rear drop in
- Max. diameter x length, weight: ø 168 x 456 mm, 5,360 g/ 6.6" x 18", 11.8 lbs.

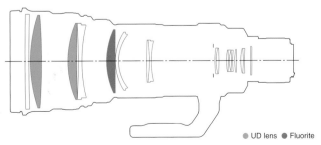

● UD lens ● Fluorite

the world*[1]. The closest focusing distance has been reduced to 5.5m/18ft. In addition to using a full-time mechanical manual focus and an AF stop function, the focus preset and other features were improved to make it easier to use. The use of a magnesium alloy for its principal parts has reduced its weight, making holding and mobility better than ever. It offers superior dust-proof and drip-proof*[2] performance for outstanding photography in the field.

*1 Bodies: EOS-1Ds Mark III, EOS-1Ds Mark II, EOS-1Ds, EOS-1D Mark IV, EOS-1D Mark III, EOS-1D Mark II N, EOS-1D Mark II, EOS-1D, EOS-1V/HS, EOS-3 (all when using rechargeable battery pack)
*2 Dust-proof and drip-proof models: EOS-1Ds Mark III, EOS-1Ds Mark II, EOS-1Ds, EOS-1D Mark IV, EOS-1D Mark III, EOS-1D Mark II N, EOS-1D Mark II, EOS-1D, EOS-1V/HS, Extender EF1.4xII, Extender EF2xII

EF800mm f/5.6L IS USM·1/320sec.·f/5.6

Tremendous magnification provided by the 800mm focal length expands creative possibilities for nature and sports photography.

With a tight angle of view of approximately 3° and extremely high magnification, 800mm super telephoto lenses vastly increase creative possibilities compared to 600mm lenses. Capture from shore the tense expression of a surfer about to challenge a huge wave, or fill the frame with the face of a sprinter at the starting line while shooting comfortably from the stands. Get in close to large, dangerous animals as well as the smaller, less threatening denizens of the wild. Because an 800mm lens dramatically compresses the perceived distance between subject and background, startling beautiful photos can be achieved by adding the sun or moon as dramatic elements to compositions. These lenses are highly prized by nature and sports photographers, who appreciate the ability to shoot from afar and still capture the essence of the scene.

■EF800mm f/5.6L IS USM

This 800mm super telephoto lens has the longest focal length[1] in the world for lenses equipped with image stabilization. Since long telephoto lenses are highly susceptible to color aberrations, the construction includes two fluorite elements as well as one super UD and one UD element. This minimizes aberrations, resulting in sharp, high-contrast images. Furthermore, the arrangement of the coated elements reduces lens flare and ghost, which often cause problems when using digital cameras, and provides excellent color balance. Despite the 800mm focal length, it is highly portable thanks to an advanced optical design and magnesium-alloy body. Comparable in size yet noticeably lighter than the EF600mm f/4L IS USM and easy to use, this 800mm lens is well suited for photography from a monopod. Additionally, the image stabilizer reduces camera shake by approximately four full shutter speed steps[2]. Offering AF stop, focus preset, full-time manual focus and a dust- and drip-proof design[3], this addition to the Canon EF L-series is great for getting the perfect shot, even in extreme environments.

*1 As of March 2008.
*2 Based on a shutter speed of "1/focal length" seconds, said to be the limit for hand-held photography without image stabilization.
*3 Dust-proof and drip-proof models: EOS-1Ds Mark III, EOS-1Ds Mark II, EOS-1Ds, EOS-1D Mark IV, EOS-1D Mark III, EOS-1D Mark II N, EOS-1D Mark II, EOS-1D, EOS-1V/HS, Extender EF1.4xII, Extender EF2xII.

EF800mm f/5.6L IS USM

- Focal length and maximum aperture: 800 mm 1:5.6
- Lens construction: 18 elements in 14 groups ● Diagonal angle of view: 3° 5'
- Focus adjustment distance: Ring-type USM, inner focusing system, full-time manual focus
- Closest focusing distance: 6 m/ 19.69 ft., 0.14 x magnification
- Filter size: 52 mm rear drop-in type
- Max. diameter x length, weight: ø 163 x 461 mm, 4,500 g/ 6.4" x 18.1", 9.9 lbs.

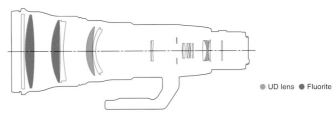

● UD lens ● Fluorite

Making the everyday dramatic.
A macro lens for a view of the world from a cat's point of view.

Get right up close to the plants and capture the beauty of the patterns created by nature. Catch the moment when a butterfly takes flight, flapping its lissome wings. For these situations, what you need most is a macro lens, which allows close-up photography at 1/2 magnification or life-size magnification, and which is optically designed to have characteristics ideal for image performance under these kinds of circumstances. With even color reproduction and sharpness throughout the frame, these lenses are ideal for scientific and academic uses as well.

■EF50mm f/2.5 Compact Macro

This compact 50mm macro lens is effective for close-up shots up to 0.5x (1/2 life-size) magnification. A floating element construction provides high-quality performance with sharp, clear images, from close-up photography to infinity. With the largest maximum aperture of any autofocus macro lens – f/2.5 – close-up shots with shallow depth of field and general portraits with pleasing background blur are possible.

■Life-Size Converter EF

This life-size converter is designed for exclusive use with the EF50mm f/2.5 Compact Macro. It allows photography with magnifications from 0.26x to life-size (1:1). The aperture drops one step, but the autofocusing is very fast, making for easy shooting in close-up situations where focusing tends to be difficult.

EF50mm Compact Macro
EF100mm Macro

EF50mm f/2.5 Compact Macro

- Focal length and maximum aperture: 50 mm 1:2.5
- Lens construction: 9 elements in 8 groups ● Diagonal angle of view: 46°
- Focus adjustment: Front group linear extension system with AFD
- Closest focusing distance: 0.23 m/ 0.8 ft., 0.5 x magnification ● Filter size: 52 mm
- Max. diameter x length, weight: ø 67.6 x 63 mm, 280 g/ 2.7" x 2.5", 9.9 oz.

Life-Size Converter EF

(designed for use with the EF50mm f/2.5 Compact Macro)

- Lens construction: 4 elements in 3 groups
- Max. diameter x length, weight: ø 67.6 x 34.9 mm, 160 g/ 2.7" x 1.4", 5.6 oz.

EF100mm f/2.8 Macro USM·1/6sec.·f/5.6

EF100mm f/2.8 Macro USM

- Focal length and maximum aperture: 100 mm 1:2.8
- Lens construction: 12 elements in 8 groups ● Diagonal angle of view: 24°
- Focus adjustment: Ring-type USM, inner focusing system, full-time manual focus
- Closest focusing distance: 0.31 m/ 1 ft., 1 x magnification ● Filter size: 58 mm
- Max. diameter x length, weight: ø 78.6 x 118.6 mm, 580 g/ 3.1" x 4.7", 1.3 lbs.

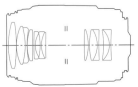

■**EF100mm f/2.8 Macro USM**

A medium telephoto macro lens offering excellent picture quality and close-up magnification up to life size (1:1). Optimizing the optical power distribution reduces spherical aberration fluctuation during close-up photography, delivering constant high picture quality over all focusing distances. The inner focusing system makes the working distance (the distance from the lens to the subject) 149mm during life-size photography – twice the distance of the 50mm macro lens. Convenient operability is achieved with the easy full-time manual focus ideal for subtle adjustments of the focus position (a task in macro photography) and the non-rotating front lens element. If the optional ring-type tripod mount B (B) (with an adapter for the EF100mm f/2.8 Macro USM) is used, switching between vertical and horizontal compositions without affecting the optical axis is a simple matter.

A medium telephoto macro lens equipped with Canon's advanced image stabilization system — Hybrid IS (image stabilizer) — that allows handheld shooting at 1:1.

One of the major benefits of a 100mm macro lens compared to other macro lenses is the comfortable working distance it allows between photographer and subject. This lessens the likelihood of the photographer's shadow intruding on a scene or scaring away easily frightened subjects such as insects. The extremely shallow depth of field of this lens produces the signature look of macro photography; namely, pinpoint focus on a subject set amongst a beautifully blurred foreground and background. However, the shallow depth of field and high magnification requires that extra attention be paid to stabilizing the camera when shooting. Hence, tripods are nearly indispensable in macro photography.

With the advent of Canon's Hybrid IS however, high-quality handheld macro photography is now possible. Hybrid IS has the distinction of being the world's first[1] image stabilization technology that supports both normal and macro photography. Since shooting with a tripod in confined spaces is difficult or else severely restricted in protected habitats, this functionality is certain to be welcomed by photographers who find themselves either without a tripod or in a situation where the use of one is not an option.

■EF100mm f/2.8L Macro IS USM

When shooting non-macro photos, angle camera shake can cause blurred images. For handheld close-ups, however, image quality can be adversely affected by not only angle camera shake, but also by shift camera shake which occurs parallel to the image plane. The advanced Hybrid IS system used in the EF100mm f/2.8L Macro IS USM effectively combats this, detecting and correcting for both types of camera shake.

To prevent camera shake from ruining close-ups, use a shutter speed

EF100mm f/2.8L Macro IS USM·1/320sec.·f/2.8

one or two steps faster than the generally recommended minimum shutter speed (i.e. 1/focal length of the lens in seconds). Hybrid IS achieves effective camera shake compensation[*2] that allows use of shutter speeds approximately three steps slower at 0.5x magnification and two steps slower at 1x, making possible handheld macro photos that are as easy to take as normal photos.

With an optical system boasting a UD lens element and inner focusing system, the EF100mm f/2.8L Macro IS USM delivers high-quality images that exhibit superb resolution, excellent contrast and minimal chromatic aberration. This outstanding L-series lens is also equipped with full-time manual focus and other functions useful for macro photography, as well as a dust- and drop-proof design. Optional accessories include Tripod Mount Ring D (B) and Macrolite Adapter 67.

*1 For interchangeable SLR camera lenses.
*2 Effects of IS may vary depending on shooting conditions.
  IS allows shooting normal photos using shutter speeds approximately 4 steps slower than with non-IS lenses.

EF100mm f/2.8L Macro IS USM

● Focal length and maximum aperture: 100 mm 1:2.8
● Lens construction: 15 elements in 12 groups ● Diagonal angle of view: 24°
● Focus adjustment: Ring-type USM, inner focusing system, full-time manual focus
● Closest focusing distance: 0.3 m/ 1.0 ft., 1 x magnification ● Filter size: 67 mm
● Max. diameter x length, weight: ø 77.7 x 123 mm, 625 g/ 3.1" x 4.8", 1.4 lbs.

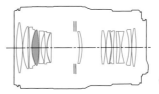

● UD lens

Discovering the beauty hidden in plants and bugs.
A telephoto macro lens that can peer into the universe of natural formations.

Close-up photography involves many different subjects and purposes, so you have to choose the macro lens best for the situation and use it to its fullest. One of the factors that needs to be considered is the relationship between photographic magnification and working distance. Working distance is the distance measured from the tip of the lens to the subject. For example, when you want to take a life-size photograph of a subject, the working distance for a 100mm medium telephoto lens is double that of a 50mm macro lens. While a 50mm macro lens is good for getting very close to the subject, if you are taking photographs of insects and small animals, which are not so easy

to approach, a 100mm or 180mm macro lens would be a more suitable option.

As with normal lenses, the longer the focal length becomes, the shallower the depth of field becomes, which makes camera movement a problem. One option is to use a 50mm with its wide range of use for snapshots and other general photographic purposes, a 100mm for portraits, and a 180mm for photography of animals and other subjects which are unapproachable.

■EF180mm f/3.5L Macro USM
This 180mm telephoto macro lens is capable of close-ups up to 1x. It is ideal for photographing insects and small animals, where a long working distance is desirable. The focusing range can easily be switched between 0.48m/1.6ft. to infinity and 1.5m/4.9ft.

EF180mm f/3.5L Macro USM·1/50sec.·f/3.5

to infinity. Use of three UD elements effectively corrects secondary spectrum. Employing an internal floating construction ensures sharp delineation at all subject distances. Since the length of the lens does not change when focusing, there is no need to worry about the lens coming in contact with the subject. The ring-type USM delivers quiet autofocusing. Full-time manual focus is also available. Maximum magnification can be raised to either 1.4x or 2x by using Extender EF1.4xII or 2xII.

EF180mm f/3.5L Macro USM

- Focal length and maximum aperture: 180 mm 1:3.5
- Lens construction: 14 elements in 12 groups ● Diagonal angle of view: 13° 40'
- Focus adjustment: Ring-type USM, inner focusing system, full-time manual focus
- Closest focusing distance: 0.48 m/ 1.6 ft., 1 x magnification ● Filter size: 72 mm
- Max. diameter x length, weight: ø 82.5 x 186.6 mm, 1,090 g/ 3.3" x 7.4", 2.4 lbs.

● UD lens

The true expression of a photograph – the world of macro photography.

A macrophoto lens specifically designed to bring out that appeal.

The fun of taking photographs is discovering whole worlds which are invisible to the naked eye, such as when using a telephoto lens or a macro lens. Getting right up close to a subject makes you feel like you've become a small animal yourself. This feeling of the unordinary often allows you to discover new ways of looking at subjects which you would normally pass over. Even the smallest movements of a bug on a rose petal or the delicate pattern on the surface of a ceramic plate can bring gasps of delight. Macrophoto lens are designed especially for this type of high-magnification photography. These lens are excellent for finding new forms of expression through macrophotography. Since they are specially designed, they reduce aberration fluctuation and distortion while providing good operability and

mobility for focusing and lighting. Using commercially available focusing rails when photographing makes it easier to capture the subject and make minor adjustments to the focus and magnification.

■MP-E65mm f/2.8 1-5× Macro Photo

This macrophoto lens allows expanded photography from life-size to 5× magnification. A floating system using three lens groups has been adopted to deliver high variable magnification in the macro region. It effectively corrects the aberration fluctuation which accompanies changes in magnification. With a UD lens element as the second element, secondary spectrum, a problem during high magnification, is minimized, guaranteeing outstanding imaging performance. The lens is equipped with an EMD (electromagnetic diaphragm) to deliver AE photography* Subtle adjustments to magnification are possible using the wide ring. A light-blocking line is incorporated into the front of the lens to

Macro photo lens

MP-E65mm f/2.8 1-5x Macro Photo·1/13sec.·f/14
(3x magnification)

reduce inclusion when very close to the subject. It is possible to use the Macro Ring Lite MR-14EX and the Macro Twin Lite MT-24EX. The lens comes with a removable tripod mount which allows smooth switching between vertical and horizontal photography and offers solid support.

Note: At Canon, a lens is called a macro photo lens if it is designed for high magnification with a maximum photographic magnification that exceeds life-size magnification.

* AE photography at all magnifications (1x – 5x) is available with the following cameras: EOS-1Ds Mark III, EOS-1Ds Mark II, EOS-1Ds, EOS-1D Mark IV, EOS-1D Mark III, EOS-1D Mark II N, EOS-1D Mark II, EOS-1D, EOS-1V/HS, EOS-1N/DP/HS, EOS-1, EOS-3 (laser matte screen must be replaced). For other EOS models, exposure compensation is required. The actual aperture rises as the magnification goes up, so we recommend using exposure compensation or the Macro Ring Lite MR-14EX or the Macro Twin Lite MT-24EX.

* We recommend using commercially available focusing rails for small focusing adjustments.

[Photograph] The Photographer placed a bottle behind a glass filled with sparkling water, and the bottle label seen through the bubbles created an interesting effect. The world of macrophoto lenses can open up beautiful and surprising vistas that are otherwise invisible to the human eye.

MP-E65mm f/2.8 1-5x Macro Photo

- ● Focal length and maximum aperture: 65 mm 1:2.8
- ● Lens construction: 10 elements in 8 groups ● Diagonal angle of view: 18° 40' at 1 x magnification
- ● Focus adjustment: Manual focus, front group linear extension
- ● Closest focusing distance: 0.24 m/ 0.8 ft., 5 x magnification ● Filter size: 58 mm
- ● Max. diameter x length, weight: ø 81 x 98 mm, 710 g/ 3.2" x 3.9", 1.6 lbs.

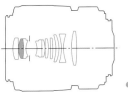

● UD lens

A super wide-angle TS-E lens for architectural photographers that combines wide coverage with tilt-shift functionality.

Tilt-shift functionality means a photographic system is capable of tilt (changing the lens axis angle relative to the focal plane) and shift (moving the lens parallel to the focal plane). Once the exclusive domain of large-format cameras, tilt-shift is now possible on SLR cameras thanks to TS-E lenses.

Shift is particularly useful for obtaining natural looking photos of buildings. Photographing a building using a wide-angle lens that is even slightly pointed up causes vertical lines to converge, resulting in a building that appears to taper off at the top. Properly leveling the camera then shifting the lens up solves this, maintaining the perpendicularity of walls relative to the base of the building.

Compared to other lenses in the series, the TS-E17mm f/4L provides an exceptionally wide diagonal angle of view of 125 degrees. This makes it a powerful tool for obtaining undistorted photos of buildings, especially in cities where limited space often

makes it impossible to move back far enough to record the entire building without angling the lens up. It also provides an alternative to the TS-E24mm f/3.5L II, allowing you to more easily capture super high-rise towers. Thanks to the dramatic perspective provided by its short focal length, the TS-E17mm f/4L is extremely valuable to architectural photographers, who frequently want to emphasize the depth of a building or size of a room.

■TS-E17mm f/4L

This super wide-angle TS-E lens combines conventional lens rotation with Canon's TS Revolving System, allowing the relationship between tilt and shift to be changed from perpendicular to parallel. As a result, the lens can control perspective and focus plane independently. The large, high-precision glass-molded aspherical lens element in the TS-E17mm f/4L produces an image circle that covers the entire shift range of ±12mm, and delivers images that exhibit outstanding quality

TS-E17mm f/4L·10sec.·f/11

from edge to edge with negligible distortion. Four UD lenses are also employed to reduce magnification chromatic aberration — a common issue with wide-angle lenses. In addition, SWC (Subwavelength Structure Coating), an innovative new anti-reflection layer, minimizes flare and ghosting caused by light entering the lens at large angles of incidence. To ensure easy operation, the TS-E17mm f/4L is outfitted with large controls, and a tilt lock function is included to securely fix tilt at a desired position.

[Photograph] Gold ornaments adorning the wall of a splendid cathedral caught the sharp eye of this photographer. Since the subject lay beyond a fence, a 17mm lens was chosen to capture the entire scene and shift was employed to prevent the walls from converging.

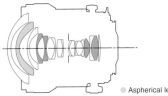

TS-E17mm f/4L

- Focal length and maximum aperture: 17 mm 1:4 ● Lens construction: 18 elements in 12 groups
- Diagonal angle of view: 104° ● Image circle diameter: 67.2 mm
- Tilt/shift amount: ±6.5°/±12 mm ● TS revolving system rotation angle: ±90°.
- Focus adjustment: Manual focus with a rear focusing system
- Closest focusing distance: 0.25 m/ 9.8 in., 0.14 x magnification ● Filter size: Filters not supported
- Max. diameter x length, weight: ø 88.9 x 106.7 mm, 820 g/ 3.5" x 4.2", 1.8 lbs.

● Aspherical lens ● UD lens

A wide-angle TS-E lens that brings the tilt-shift functionality of large-format cameras to the portable world of SLR photography.

Part of the TS-E lineup of tilt-shift lenses, the TS-E24mm f/3.5L II has a wide angle of view and produces images with excellent depth — an outstanding choice for photographing buildings as well as urban and rural landscapes. Since it has a more natural perspective than lenses with shorter focal lengths, it is an excellent complement to the TS-E17mm f/4L. Shift capability makes the TS-E24mm f/3.5L II a fine choice for photographing building interiors and exteriors, and is especially useful for handling low- to medium-rise structures when it is difficult to maintain sufficient camera-to-subject distance. Furthermore, horizontal shift can be employed to prevent the camera's reflection from appearing in a window or mirror without having to drastically alter the composition. This technique is handy when photographing interiors with large reflective surfaces or when shooting through windows.

This and other TS-E lenses are also invaluable for landscape photography, allowing you to create spectacular panoramas by taking multiple photos while shifting the lens horizontally, then stitching the photos together later.

■TS-E24mm f/3.5L II

Based on a completely new design, this wide-angle TS-E lens delivers optical performance ideally suited to the digital age, and offers superb functionality along with easy operation. Enhanced functionality includes wider tilt and shift ranges of ±8.5° and ±12mm, respectively, and Canon's TS Revolving System that changes the relationship between tilt and shift from perpendicular to parallel. Thanks to its large, high-precision glass-molded aspherical lens, the TS-E24mm f/3.5L II produces extremely high-quality images that exhibit minimal distortion, outstanding

TS-E24mm f/3.5L Ⅱ ·20sec.·f/11

resolution and excellent contrast. Furthermore, the lens includes three UD elements to correct various aberrations over the entire image in addition to SWC (Subwavelength Structure Coating), which minimizes flare and ghosting — common problems that occur when photographing buildings due to the lack of lighting control. The TS-E24mm f/3.5L II is also equipped with a tilt lock function to securely fix tilt at a desired position while large knobs and levers make for accurate and easy operation.

[Photograph] By waiting for sunset, the photographer was able to capture the grandeur of this beautiful architectural structure emerging from surrounding light. In order to avoid verticals from converging, vertical shift was employed while horizontal tilt was used to maintain sharp focus over the entire face of the building.

TS-E24mm f/3.5L Ⅱ

- Focal length and maximum aperture: 24 mm 1:3.5 ● Lens construction: 16 elements in 11 groups
- Diagonal angle of view: 84° ● Image circle diameter: 67.2 mm
- Tilt/shift amount: ±8.5°/±12 mm ● TS revolving system rotation angle: ±90°.
- Focus adjustment: Manual focus with a rear focusing system
- Closest focusing distance: 0.21 m/ 8.6 in., 0.34 x magnification ● Filter size: 82 mm
- Max. diameter x length, weight: ø 88.5 x 106.9 mm, 780 g/ 3.5" x 4.2", 1.7 lbs.

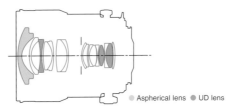

● Aspherical lens ● UD lens

TS-E45mm f/2.8·1/30sec.·f/4

Create an illusory world.
Only with the expressive power of a TS-E lens.

When performing tilt/shift photography, tilting is no less important than shifting. By changing the angle of the optical axis relative to the camera's focal plane, it is possible to take a photograph with everything in focus from near to far, as in, for instance, a photograph of a line of pillars receding away from the camera in an old European convent. With TS-E lenses, it is possible to tilt the optical axis ±8°. Tilting is useful when you want to achieve a pan-focus effect with a shallow aperture setting and a fast shutter speed, or, on the contrary, when you want to blur the background. Reversing the tilt drastically reduces the area of the picture that remains in focus, so if for example you want nothing but a person's face in focus in a photograph, tilting creates a unique effect.

The most important prerequisites for successful tilt/shift photography are making sure the camera is leveled on a tripod and checking the exact composition of the scene through the viewfinder. Cameras with 100% viewfinder coverage such as the EOS-1 series and/or 100% LCD monitor coverage such as EOS digital SLRs make this easier. On cameras with interchangeable focusing screens, a grid screen should be used to facilitate accurate alignment of horizontal and vertical lines in the scene.

■TS-E45mm f/2.8

When you want to maintain a natural perspective while photographing buildings and other structures with the shift function, this 45mm standard TS-E lens is just the answer. Its floating mechanism combines with its rear focusing system to ensure sharp, stable imaging performance at all shooting distances. And since the filter mount does not rotate during focusing, using a circular polarizer or graduated ND filter is no problem. The tilt and shift controls of TS-E lenses are set to bisect at right angles. However your Canon service center can set this to parallel.

[Photograph] The Photographer caught the color of French cuisine without a tripod. To get all the food in focus, the camera had to be placed at a steep angle diagonally above it, tilting the lens to get both the near and far sections into focus.

TS-E45mm f/2.8

● Focal length and maximum aperture: 45 mm 1:2.8
● Lens construction: 10 elements in 9 groups ● Diagonal angle of view: 51°
● Image circle diameter: 58.6 mm ● Tilt/shift amount: ±8°/±11 mm
● Angle of revolution: 0±90°
● Focus adjustment: Manual focus with a rear focusing system
● Closest focusing distance: 0.4 m/ 1.3 ft., 0.16 x magnification ● Filter size: 72 mm
● Max. diameter x length, weight: ø 81 x 90.1 mm, 645 g/ 3.2" x 3.5", 1.4 lbs.

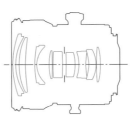

A lens that won't let you down when you need accuracy.
TS-E lenses – the appeal of being able to work in all situations.

TS-E lenses correct image distortion and adjust the area in focus by controlling the lens's optical axis. In order to get the best out of these lenses, however, you need to understand more than just making such corrections and adjustments – you have to keep a close eye on the subject's situation and the purpose of the shot in order to get a solid understanding of what the best focus distance is. The best lens for photography in places where sufficient distance between the camera and the object is not available, such as outside tall buildings or in small rooms, is the wide-angle TS-E 17mm and 24mm. If you want a more natural perspective, the TS-E 45mm is the lens for you. Besides being able to be used as a regular medium telephoto lens, the TS-E 90mm can also be used as a macro lens. With a maximum magnification of 0.29x, plenty of working distance can be attained, making photographs of food, to take one example, very easy to compose effectively. For

photographs of merchandise that require an accurate representation of the product without any distortion, these lenses are ideal for delivering effective tilt/shift photography with a natural perspective.

TS-E lenses feature fully automatic aperture control thanks to their built-in EMD (electromagnetic diaphragm). Although only manual focusing is available, only the TS-E series can offer tilt and shift photography with AE. This is the first successful attempt to incorporate automatic aperture control and AE photography with AEB using a fully electronic mount, and advanced imaging performance with easy exposure control is thereby guaranteed.

■TS-E90mm f/2.8

The world's first telephoto tilt/shift lens, useful for a wide variety of applications, from merchandise and food photography to portraiture and nature photography. The 6-element, 5-group Gauss-type optical system achieves outstanding imaging

TS-E90mm f/2.8·1/320sec.·f/2.8

performance and natural-looking blur. Focusing is possible down to an extremely close shooting distance of 0.5m/1.6ft., enabling effective close-up photography. A maximum magnification of 0.29x is available. Use of reverse tilt to adjust the positioning of depth of field allows the photographer to achieve unique and innovative photography unattainable with normal lenses even at large apertures. The tilt and shift controls of TS-E lenses are set to bisect at right angles. However your Canon service center can set this to parallel.

[Photograph] The Photographer captured the calmness of orchids floating in a flower vase placed on top of a blue piece of glass, caressed by the natural light coming in through the window. In order to capture the depth as well as the orchids all lined up in a row, the photographer revolved the lens 45° and tilted the focusing surface diagonally.

TS-E90mm f/2.8

● Focal length and maximum aperture: 90 mm 1:2.8
● Lens construction: 6 elements in 5 groups ● Diagonal angle of view: 27°
● Image circle diameter: 58.6 mm ● Tilt/shift amount: ±8°/±11 mm
● Angle of revolution: 0±90°
● Focus adjustment: Manual focus, overall linear extension system
● Closest focusing distance: 0.5 m/ 1.6 ft., 0.29 x magnification ● Filter size: 58 mm
● Max. diameter x length, weight: ø 73.6 x 88 mm, 565 g/ 2.9" x 3.5", 1.2 lbs.

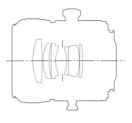

Extender EF1.4x II

● Lens construction: 5 elements in 4 groups
● Max. diameter x length, weight: 72.8 x 27.2 mm, 220 g/ 2.9" x 1.1", 7.8 oz.

Extender EF2x II

● Lens construction: 7 elements in 5 groups
● Max. diameter x length, weight: 71.8 x 57.9 mm, 265 g/ 2.8" x 2.3", 9.3 oz.

Maintains the imaging performance of a master lens while delivering focal length magnification of 1.4x and 2x.

Extenders are useful when you want to use a telephoto lens to increase the visual impact of the subject by getting in even closer to it, or when you simply want to reduce the number of telephoto lenses you carry around. Not only do they increase the telephoto effect, filling the frame with the sun, say, when taking shots of sunrises and sunsets, but they are also ideal for close-up photography, taking advantage of the fact that the closest focusing distance does not change.

The biggest advantage, however, is that with a single extender you can make more efficient use of your telephoto lens — especially a super-telephoto lens — without sacrificing compactness or portability. For instance, if you have a 300mm lens, you can use it for 420mm or 600mm super-telephoto shots simply by adding the Extender EF1.4x II or the EF2x II. Combining a 70-200mm zoom lens with the Extender EF2x II lets you put together a lens system that can efficiently deliver zooming up to 400mm, while keeping the size manageable. Depending on the camera, autofocusing with the center AF point is possible with effective maximum apertures as small as f/8. And if you are using an IS lens with the image stabilizing function, hand-held photography is no problem, since the function is effective for two shutter speeds[*1] less than 1/focal length seconds.

The dust-proof and drip-proof construction allows full utilization of the lens' capabilities for photography under the harshest conditions if combined with EOS cameras or EF lenses with the same dust-proof and drip-proof specifications.

■Extender EF1.4x II

This high-performance extender increases the lens's focal length by 1.4 times. Not only does the actual F-stop value drop only one step when the extender is used, but autofocusing is also maintained with most lenses, which makes the extender extremely useful when you need to maintain brightness or mobility. The interior of the lens barrel has been treated thoroughly against reflections, employing a flare-reducing high image quality design. The Extender EF1.4x II features dust-proof and drip-proof construction.

■Extender EF2x II

This extender doubles the lens's focal length, making it ideal for even greater visual impact during super-telephoto photography. It has the same weather-resistant and flare reducing design as the EF1.4x II. Because it reduces aberration fluctuation, it does not degrade the picture quality or performance of the master lens itself. The effective F-stop value drops two steps.

* Compatible lenses: single focal length L-series lenses 135mm and up, as well as the EF100-400mm f/4.5-5.6L IS USM, the EF70-200mm f/2.8L IS USM, the EF70-200mm f/2.8L USM, the EF70-200mm f/4L IS USM, and the EF70-200mm f/4L USM.

*1 Effective for approximately 3 shutter speeds with the EF70-200mm f/2.8L IS USM, 4 shutter speeds with the EF70-200mm f/4L IS USM.

Extender use:
1. When using the Extender EF1.4x II or EF2x II with the EF100-400mm f/4.5-5.6L IS USM, or when using the Extender EF2x II with the EF300mm f/4L IS USM, EF400mm f/4 DO IS USM, EF500mm f/4L IS USM, EF600mm f/4L IS USM, EF800mm f/5.6L IS USM, EF70-200mm f/4L IS USM camera bodies which offer image stabilization are the EOS-1Ds Mark III, EOS-1Ds Mark II, EOS-1Ds, EOS-1D Mark IV, EOS-1D Mark III, EOS-1D Mark II N, EOS-1D Mark II, EOS-1D, EOS 5D Mark II, EOS 5D, EOS 7D, EOS 50D, EOS 40D, EOS 30D, EOS 20D, EOS 20Da, EOS 10D, EOS D60, EOS D30, EOS Kiss X3/REBEL T1i/500D, EOS Kiss X2/DIGITAL REBEL XSi/450D, EOS Kiss F/DIGITAL REBEL XS/1000D, EOS Kiss Digital X/DIGITAL REBEL XTi/400D DIGITAL, EOS Kiss Digital N/DIGITAL REBEL XT/350D DIGITAL, EOS Kiss Digital/DIGITAL REBEL/300D DIGITAL, EOS D6000, EOS D2000, EOS-DCS 1, EOS-DCS 3, EOS-1V/HS, EOS-1N/DP/HS/RS, EOS 7s/ELAN 7NE/ELAN 7N/30V/33V, EOS 7/ELAN 7E/ELAN 7/33/30, EOS-3, EOS 55/ELAN II E/ELAN II/50E/50, EOS Kiss 7/REBEL T2/300X, EOS Kiss Lite/REBEL K2/3000V, EOS Kiss 5/REBEL Ti/300V, EOS Kiss III L, EOS Kiss III/REBEL 2000/300, New EOS Kiss/REBEL G/500N, EOS REBEL G II, EOS REBEL X, EOS Kiss/REBEL XS/500, EOS 3000N/XSN, EOS 3000/88, EOS 5000/888, EOS IX 50/Lite/7 and EOS IX E/IX.
2. When using the Extender EF1.4x II with the EF100-400mm f/4.5-5.6L IS USM, or when using the Extender EF2x II with the EF300mm f/4L IS USM, EF400mm f/4 DO IS USM, EF500mm f/4L IS USM, EF600mm f/4L IS USM, EF800mm f/5.6L IS USM, EF70-200mm f/4L IS USM or EF70-200mm f/4L USM, camera bodies which offer autofocus as long as the center measuring point is used are the EOS-1Ds Mark III, EOS-1Ds Mark II, EOS-1Ds, EOS-1D Mark IV, EOS-1D Mark III, EOS-1D Mark II N, EOS-1D Mark II, EOS-1D, EOS-1V/HS and EOS-3.
3. When using the Extender EF1.4x II or the EF2x II with the EF70-200mm f/2.8L USM, autofocus can only be used with the multi-point range finder EOS camera when using the center measuring point.

The EF Lens World

Zoom lenses

A unique visual world with a strong wide-angle perspective.
A super wide-angle zoom with dynamic expressive ability.

The greatest appeal of a wide-angle lens lies in the wide angle and the perspective, which become profoundly intriguing the more you learn about them. Super wide-angle zooms give you the pleasure of finding just the right framing while dynamically adjusting the perspective. Even with digital cameras, which often have a screen size even smaller than that of 35mm cameras, it is possible to enjoy photography over a wide range of angles and focusing distances.

Of course, to get the most out of these features and achieve the ultimate photographic expression, you need to have an experienced eye, but the process of accumulating that experience is fun in and of itself, because the deeper you dig, the more

effective the techniques become. Since the perspective, which is the most powerful effect of wide-angle photography, is stronger at shorter focusing distances, close objects appear closer and distant objects appear more distant. One example is photographing a vast landscape: you might, for instance, introduce some clouds behind the main subject to give it some depth, making the sky seem like it just goes on forever, or place a solitary withered tree in the composition to emphasize the loneliness of the spot. In portraiture, you can get two or three steps closer to the subject to give some unity to the subject and the background, giving the shot a documentary touch.

■EF16-35mm f/2.8L II USM

This super wide-angle zoom boasts the shortest minimum focal

EF16-35mm f/2.8L II USM·1/500sec.·f/10

length, largest aperture, and broadest zoom range in its class. In addition to three types of aspherical lens elements (ground, replica, glass mold), two UD lens elements are used to correct a variety of aberrations. To meet the strict demands of professionals and dedicated hobbyists, image quality on the wide-angle end has been greatly enhanced over conventional models for sharp, high-contrast image reproduction. Use of a circular aperture diaphragm brings out the beauty of blurred areas. Magnification-type chromatic aberrations, as well as the flare / ghosting common in digital cameras, are also thoroughly controlled. Moreover, uncompromising dust-proof and drip-proof* design specifications allow shooting in severe conditions.

* Dust-proof and drip-proof models: EOS-1Ds Mark III, EOS-1Ds Mark II, EOS-1Ds, EOS-1D Mark IV, EOS-1D Mark III, EOS-1D Mark II N, EOS-1D Mark II, EOS-1D, EOS-1V/HS

EF16-35mm f/2.8L II USM

- Focal length and maximum aperture: 16-35 mm 1:2.8
- Lens construction: 16 elements in 12 groups ● Diagonal angle of view: 108° 10' - 63°
- Focus adjustment: Ring-type USM, inner focusing system, full-time manual focus
- Closest focusing distance: 0.28 m/ 0.9 ft., 0.22 x magnification
- Zoom system: Rotation type ● Filter size: 82 mm
- Max. diameter x length, weight: ø 88.5 x 111.6 mm, 635 g/ 3.5" x 4.4", 1.4 lbs.

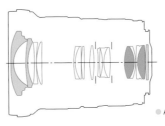

● Aspherical lens ● UD lens

A wide-angle zoom lens lets you get right up close to the subject, bringing out the breadth and depth of its uniqueness.
Using the broad angle of view of a zoom lens at short focal lengths makes it possible to capture not only landscapes but also narrow interiors as well as large groups of people – a truly versatile lens. In small interiors which do not allow you to get far enough away from the subject you can take advantage of the wide angle of view to not only photograph large groups of people but also capture the surroundings. For snapshots of moving objects you can follow the subject at the shortest focal length and then zoom in to frame it when the moment is just right. Of course, you can also bring out a contrast between the subject and its surroundings by using the short focal length effect to the fullest. In portraiture this effect can be used to bring out a sense of presence by getting in close to the subject. The possibilities are endless. One thing you should watch out for is taking photographs at the widest angle which wind up

"subject-less" and lacking a center of attention. You should avoid over-relying on the wideness of the angle of view, instead keeping in mind the three elements that will bring focus (no pun intended) to your photography: breadth, depth, and theme.

■EF17-40mm f/4L USM
This super wide-angle zoom lens allows you to take wide photographs even with digital SLR cameras which have a screen size smaller than 35mm, covering the range from a super wide-angle 17mm to a standard 40mm. Three aspherical lens elements which come in two types deliver both a wide zoom range and high image quality, while the super UD lens elements provide excellent correction of the magnification-type chromatic aberration. Innovations such as a lens coating optimized for digital photography help minimize flare and ghosts, which often occur with digital cameras. The circular aperture diaphragm

EF17-40mm f/4L USM·1/500sec.·f/11

EF17-40mm f/4L USM

● Focal length and maximum aperture: 17-40 mm 1:4
● Lens construction: 12 elements in 9 groups ● Diagonal angle of view: 104°-57° 30'
● Focus adjustment: Ring-type USM, inner focusing system, full-time manual focus
● Closest focusing distance: 0.28 m/ 0.9 ft., 024 x magnification ● Zoom system: Rotating type
● Filter size: 77 mm ● Max. diameter x length, weight: ø 83.5 x 96.8 mm, 475 g/ 3.3" x 3.8", 1 lb.

which brings out a nuanced blur and the achievement of a closest focusing distance of 0.28m over the whole range of the zoom, not only help you in composition, but the quiet, high-speed autofocus and the outstanding dust-proof and drip-proof* construction make this lens extremely mobile. The front filter mount does not rotate during focusing, so there is no problem when using circular PL filters or other filters, and in combination with the EF70-200mm f/4L IS USM you can get the right shot almost anywhere you go.

* Dust-proof and drip-proof models: EOS-1Ds Mark III, EOS-1Ds Mark II, EOS-1Ds, EOS-1D Mark IV, EOS-1D Mark III, EOS-1D Mark II N, EOS-1D Mark II, EOS-1D, EOS-1V/HS

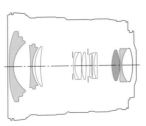

● Aspherical lens ● UD lens

EF24-70mm f/2.8L USM·1/160sec.·f/13

A standard zoom lens will give you your own voice.

The standard zoom lens, with coverage from wide-angle to standard and beyond to medium telephoto, is often a budding photographer's first step into the world of lenses. Centered on a focal length of 50mm, which is closest to the normal perspective of the human eye, the zoom region goes from an expansive wide angle which can take in a whole scene to concentrating on one particular spot – very much like the human eye.

You can take photographs of the world just as you see it with this lens, especially since it is so easy to use for shots of the family on vacation, and other situations you may encounter in everyday life. One handy way of using the lens is to take in the whole scene with the zoom set to wide angle, then zoom in on any particular detail that happens to catch your attention. As you get a feel for the lens, you'll learn your own preferences in terms of the different angles of view and perspectives at each focal length, and the changes in the blur quality of background items that are out of focus. That is one of the advantages of using a lens like this, because it is very good for expressing exactly what you see when you look at your subject.

■EF24-70mm f/2.8L USM

This is a large-aperture standard zoom with a short minimum focal length of 24mm. It is also good for wide-angle photography using digital SLR cameras which have a screen size smaller than 35mm. Use of two types of aspherical lens elements and a UD lens element corrects the magnification-type chromatic aberration often seen at wider angles, for extremely high picture quality. While on the one hand employing a no-compromise dust-proof and drip-proof* construction, on the other hand the quiet and fast autofocus, the mechanical full-time manual focus, and the broad zoom ring make the lens easy to use, while the circular diaphragm delivers a beautiful blur effect. The closest focusing distance is 0.38m, and the magnification is 0.29x, making the lens ideal for close-up photography.

* Dust-proof and drip-proof models: EOS-1Ds Mark III, EOS-1Ds Mark II, EOS-1Ds, EOS-1D Mark IV, EOS-1D Mark III, EOS-1D Mark II N, EOS-1D Mark II, EOS-1D, EOS-1V/HS

EF24-70mm f/2.8L USM

● Focal length and maximum aperture: 24-70 mm 1:2.8
● Lens construction: 16 elements in 13 groups ● Diagonal angle of view: 84° - 34°
● Focus adjustment: Ring-type USM, rear focusing system, full-time manual focus
● Closest focusing distance: 0.38 m/ 1.3 ft. (Macro), 0.29 x magnification
● Zoom system: Rotating type ● Filter size: 77 mm
● Max. diameter x length, weight: ø 83.2 x 123.5 mm, 950 g/ 3.3" x 4.9", 2.1 lbs.

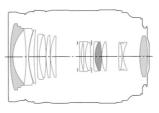

● Aspherical lens ● UD lens

Capturing impressive scenes close to the subject.
A high-performance standard zoom lens exhibiting strength under harsh conditions.

The lens covers a range from 24mm with the striking perspective effect of a wide-angle lens to 105mm, which is suitable for medium zoom portraiture and landscape photography. This is a standard zoom lens able to handle a broad range of photographic expression including impressive wide-angle shots that emphasize perspective by approaching the subject so that it fills the frame, standard photography with a similar definition to the human eye and medium telephoto shots that highlight the expressions of people by adding a beautiful blur to the background. In addition to achieving the high image quality typical of L-series lenses, the lens incorporates an image stabilizing mechanism effective for counteracting the effects of camera shake by approximately three shutter speed steps, enabling users to pursue subjects without missing any photo opportunities. Moreover, it offers excellent durability and weather resistance due to a highly dust-proof and drip-proof construction enabling shooting in harsh conditions such as deserts, jungles, beaches, glaciers and mountainous regions. In addition to professional news, sports and documentary photojournalism, it is also able to beautifully portray a variety of subjects in day-to-day life or on holidays including scenery shots, souvenir shots of the family, snap shots in town, portraits and indoor photography.

■EF24-105mm f/4L IS USM

This is a standard zoom lens covering a wide range from 24mm wide-angle to 105mm medium-telephoto shooting. In addition to achieving a broad zoom range, the optical system made up of 18 elements in 13 groups contains only environmentally-friendly lead-free glass. The various types of aberration are well

EF24-105mm f/4L IS USM·1/125sec.·f/10

EF24-105mm f/4L IS USM

● Focal length and maximum aperture: 24-105 mm 1:4
● Lens construction: 18 elements in 13 groups ● Diagonal angle of view: 84° - 23° 20'
● Focus adjustment: Ring-type USM, inner focusing system, full-time manual focus
● Closest focusing distance: 0.45 m/ 1.48 ft., 0.23 x magnification
● Zoom system: Rotating type ● Filter size: 77 mm
● Max. diameter x length, weight: ø 83.5 x 107 mm, 670 g/ 3.3" x 4.2", 1.5 lbs.

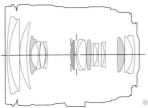

● Aspherical lens ● UD lens

compensated using one super UD lens and three aspherical lenses (replica and molded glass), and this enables high quality images befitting L-series lenses. In addition, optimization of lens positioning and coating minimizes the flare and ghosting to which digital cameras are susceptible, while an image stabilizer mechanism is incorporated to offer camera-shake compensation for approximately three shutter speed steps. Furthermore, the highly dust-proof and drip-proof* structure enabling shooting in harsh conditions, and full-time manual focusing make this a high-performance lens able to meet the high demands of professionals and highly skilled amateurs.

* Dust-proof and drip-proof models: EOS-1Ds Mark III, EOS-1Ds Mark II, EOS-1Ds, EOS-1D Mark IV, EOS-1D Mark III, EOS-1D Mark II N, EOS-1D Mark II, EOS-1D, EOS-1V/HS

A large-magnification zoom lens for freedom in framing.
Take photographs like a professional – from wide-angle to telephoto.

A standard zoom lens that achieves focusing distances of 28mm on the wide-angle side and 135mm and 200mm on the telephoto side, along with high magnification between 5x and 7x. This is a workhorse lens, great for traveling light, and great for times when you just don't have the space to haul a bunch of lenses all over creation. This single lens gives you three-in-one versatility – wide-angle, standard, and telephoto capabilities, and with magnification you just can't beat.

This lens can bring the player's quick movements right into the view-finder, put spatial perspective between a subject and the background, and do other things that telephoto lenses can do, while at the same time bringing you the close-up capabilities of wide-angle lenses for taking photos of flowers and other expressions of mother nature's beauty, all with the ability to decide the right framing in the flash of an eye. The 28-135mm/200mm can zoom from a wide angle to a

telephoto angle faster than the human eye, making this a lens that will help you discover new worlds of photographic and artistic expression.

■EF28-135mm f/3.5-5.6 IS USM

This standard zoom lens comes equipped with an Image Stabilizer mechanism that lets you drop down two shutter speeds* farther than you would normally be able to use during hand-held photography. Despite the roughly 5x large magnification zoom, the lens size itself is very compact, thanks to use of a compact EMD and a multi-group zoom system, which means this lens works well in fast-moving photographic situations. The optical system uses glass-mold aspherical lenses. Suppressing the curvature of field, spherical aberration, and other distortions common in long focal lengths over the whole zoom range and correcting for other aberrations makes for sharp picture quality. The autofocus is quick and quiet thanks to the ring-type USM and inner focusing system. The full-time manual focus, non-rotating

EF28-135mm f/3.5-5.6 IS USM·1/125sec.·f/8

front lens element, and wide zoom ring make the lens a dream to use. The hood for this lens is the petal-type EW-78BII.

* Based on a shutter speed of "1/focal length" seconds, said to be the limit for hand-held photography without image stabilization.

EF28-135mm f/3.5-5.6 IS USM

● Focal length and maximum aperture: 28-135 mm 1:3.5-5.6
● Lens construction: 16 elements in 12 groups ● Diagonal angle of view: 75° - 18°
● Focus adjustment: Ring-type USM, inner focusing system, full-time manual focus
● Closest focusing distance: 0.5 m/ 1.6 ft. (Macro), 0.19 x magnification
● Zoom system: Rotation type ● Filter size: 72 mm
● Max. diameter x length, weight: ø 78.4 x 96.8 mm, 540 g/ 3.1" x 3.8", 1.2 lbs.

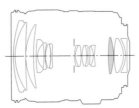

● Aspherical lens

EF70-200mm f/2.8L IS USM·1/1500sec.·f/4

Capturing natural perspective and dramatic scenes.
This lens is for serious telephoto work.

You survey the landscape before your eyes and find one spot that catches your attention. You frame it and it's yours. The satisfaction of moments like this is only possible when using a telephoto lens. These lenses cover the range from a 70mm or 80mm medium telephoto focal length with a natural perspective, to 200mm with its substantial telephoto effect. The visual effect changes a great deal, so if you are serious about your photography, this is the ideal lens for you to experience the feeling of working with a true telephoto lens.

Sports photography, with its fast action and rapidly changing distances, can only be captured accurately with fast autofocusing and zooming. The evanescent expression of the subject in a portrait demands to be set off from the background with a nice blur effect, up close. Finally, landscape photographs really put zoom lenses to the test, using the zoom at all positions to find just the right composition. The EF70-200mm telephoto zoom lenses are all L-type, which means you can count on all of them to deliver unequalled picture quality, despite individual differences in Image Stabilizing or maximum aperture.

■EF70-200mm f/2.8L IS USM

This large-aperture telephoto zoom lens has an Image Stabilizer that can compensate for approximately 3 shutter speeds[*1]. With thorough dust-proof and drip-proof[*2] treatment, this lens can be used under harsh conditions. The optical system uses four UD lens elements for high-contrast, sharp picture quality. The circular aperture diaphragm offers a beautiful blur effect. It is also equipped with a full-time manual focus that can be used in autofocus mode.

■EF70-200mm f/2.8L USM

This lens corrects color aberration with four low-refraction, low dispersion UD lens elements. It makes good use of available light for sharp, clear imaging performance. The ring-type USM and inner focusing system deliver quick and quiet autofocusing. Operability is enhanced by the full-time manual focus system as well as the possibility of autofocus at 98-280mm f/4 or 140-400mm f/5.6 when used together with the Extender EF1.4xⅡ or EF2xⅡ.

■EF70–200mm f/4L IS USM

This compact telephoto lens comes with an Image Stabilizer that compensates for camera shake so you can shoot at up to 4 shutter speed steps slower without blur. The lens's optical system uses one fluorite lens element and two UD lens elements to render high-resolution, high-contrast image quality at all zoom lengths. Another attraction of this lens is its circular aperture diaphragm, which creates beautiful blur. The dust-proof and drip-proof*² construction, along with fast and quiet AF and manual focus override, makes this lens an excellent performer in the field.

■EF70-200mm f/4L USM

With a low weight of 705g, this light and compact telephoto zoom lens is easy to carry around. It corrects for secondary spectrum with its one fluorite lens element and two UD lens elements, offering excellent imaging performance throughout the range of the zoom. With a closest focusing distance of 1.2m, close-up photography at a magnification of 0.21x is possible. And if used along with the EF17-40mm f/4L USM, you will be able to enjoy photography with a much higher efficiency than having to carry a dozen lenses around.

*1 Based on a shutter speed of 1/focal length x 1.6 seconds, which is considered the limit for handheld photography without image stabilization.
*2 Dust-proof and drip-proof models: EOS-1Ds Mark III, EOS-1Ds Mark II, EOS-1Ds, EOS-1D Mark IV, EOS-1D Mark III, EOS-1D Mark II N, EOS-1D Mark II, EOS-1D, EOS-1V/HS, Extender EF1.4x II, Extender EF2x II
* When the EF1.4x II or EF 2x II Extender is attached to the EF70-200mm f/2.8L USM, the AF function on multi-focus-point EOS cameras is limited to the center focus point only.

EF70-200mm f/2.8L IS USM

- Focal length and maximum aperture: 70-200 1:2.8
- Lens construction: 23 elements in 18 groups ● Diagonal angle of view: 34° - 12°
- Focus adjustment: Ring-type USM, inner focusing system, full-time manual focus
- Closest focusing distance: 1.4 m/ 4.6 ft., 0.17 x magnification
- Zoom system: Rotation type ● Filter size: 77 mm
- Max. diameter x length, weight: ø 86.2 x 197 mm, 1,470 g/ 3.4" x 7.8", 3.2 lbs.

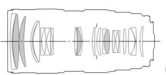

● UD lens

EF70-200mm f/2.8L USM

- Focal length and maximum aperture: 70-200 mm 1:2.8
- Lens construction: 18 elements in 15 groups ● Diagonal angle of view: 34° - 12°
- Focus adjustment: Ring-type USM, inner focusing system, full-time manual focus
- Closest focusing distance: 1.5 m/ 5.0 ft., 0.16 x magnification
- Zoom system: Rotation type ● Filter size: 77 mm
- Max. diameter x length, weight: ø 84.6 x 193.6 mm, 1,310 g/ 3.3" x 7.6", 2.9 lbs.

● UD lens

EF70-200mm f/4L USM

- Focal length and maximum aperture: 70-200 mm 1:4
- Lens construction: 16 elements in 13 groups ● Diagonal angle of view: 34° - 12°
- Focus adjustment: Ring-type USM, inner focusing system, full-time manual focus
- Closest focusing distance: 1.2 m/ 3.9 ft., 0.21 x magnification
- Zoom system: Rotation type ● Filter size: 67 mm
- Max. diameter x length, weight: ø 76 x 172 mm, 705 g/ 3" x 6.8", 1.6 lbs.

● UD lens ● Fluorite

EF70-200mm f/4L IS USM

- Focal length and maximum aperture: 70-200 mm 1:4
- Lens construction: 20 elements in 15 groups ● Diagonal angle of view: 34° - 12°
- Focus adjustment: Ring-type USM, inner focusing system, full-time manual focus
- Closest focusing distance: 1.2 m/ 3.94 ft., 0.21 x magnification
- Zoom system: Rotation type ● Filter size: 67 mm
- Max. diameter x length, weight: ø 76 x 172 mm, 760g/ 3" x 6.8", 1.7 lbs.

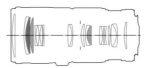

● UD lens ● Fluorite

EF70-300mm f/4.5-5.6 DO IS USM·1/400sec.·f/8

Newly developed triple-layered DO lens realizing a high-image-quality ultracompact telephoto zoom lens

Covering the 300mm telephoto range, this lens is a mere 99.9mm in length. By employing the newly developed triple-layered DO lens, this telephoto zoom lens realizes both high image quality comparable with an L lens and an ultracompact design. It covers the range from 70mm midrange telephoto, which offers natural perspective, to 300mm, providing full-scale telephoto effects. Its compact design makes it highly mobile, and it comes with an advanced image stabilization mechanism to greatly expand its suitability for hand-held telephoto zoom shooting. Whether you are shooting portraits or scenery, sporting events or birds in the wild, this lens ensures that you won't miss a single photo opportunity. With the sharp and clear imaging performance only a DO lens can provide, the lens also lets users enjoy highly mobile lens work.

■EF70-300mm f/4.5-5.6 DO IS USM

With the newly developed triple-layered DO lens and a glass-mold (GMo) aspherical lens, this telephoto zoom lens achieves high imaging quality comparable with L lenses in an ultracompact size, approximately two-thirds that of conventional lenses[*1]. The DO lens has a three-layer structure suited to zoom optics to resolve the problem of unwanted diffraction flares generated when zooming. While realizing a truly compact size, it compensates for chromatic and spherical aberration and offers the high-resolution and high-contrast imaging performance of an L lens. This lens also maximizes operability with an image stabilization mechanism with approximately 3 shutter speed[*2] correction capability, a zoom ring lock that maintains the lens at its shortest length when carried, and a full-time manual focus system. This lens employs environmentally friendly lead-free glass, and with an optimized lens coating and optical design, it minimizes flare and ghosts, which often occur with digital cameras.

Like the EF400mm f/4 DO IS USM, this lens bears a green line on the lens barrel, symbol of a revolutionary lens.

*1 Compared with the EF75-300mm f/4-5.6 IS USM, which has approximately the same focal length and f number value.
*2 Based on a shutter speed of "1/focal length" seconds, said to be the limit for hand-held photography without image stabilization.

EF70-300mm f/4.5-5.6 DO IS USM

- Focal length and maximum aperture: 70-300 mm 1:4.5-5.6
- Lens construction: 18 elements in 12 groups
- Diagonal angle of view: 34° - 8°15'
- Focus adjustment: Ring-type USM, rear focusing system, full-time manual focus
- Closest focusing distance: 1.4 m/4.6 ft., 0.19 x magnification
- Zoom system: Rotation type
- Filter size: 58 mm
- Max. diameter x length, weight: ø 82.4 x 99.9 mm, 720 g/3.2" x 3.9", 1.6 lbs.

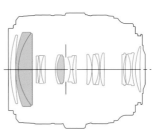

● Aspherical lens ● DO lens

A series of telephoto zoom lenses appropriate for covering a wide range of subject matter from portraits with natural perspective to impressive telephoto shots.

These lenses cover a zoom range of approximately four times spanning from medium telephoto focal lengths for portraiture with beautiful natural expression to full 300mm focal length capable of bringing distant subjects very close to provide an enhanced perspective compression effect. All forms of photographic expression are made possible, including impressive images that take full advantage of the perspective compression effect and also those that highlight sharply focused subjects by isolating them against beautifully blurred backgrounds.

The key point is how to effectively incorporate the variety of perspective and background blur effects resulting from changes in the angle of view. The high zoom ratio exhibits its real strength in photography from limited shooting positions, such as stage, sports, and wildlife photography. It fully covers the range from expansive scenic vistas to close-up shots, and offers the appeal of flexibility by enabling shooting at the optimal angle of view.

■EF70-300mm f/4-5.6 IS USM

This user-friendly telephoto zoom lens covers a broad zoom range from 70mm to 300mm. The built-in image stabilizer (IS) mechanism counteracts the effects of camera shake by approximately three shutter speed steps. In addition to "camera shake correction mode 1" suited for shooting stationary objects, this lens is also provided with "camera shake correction mode 2" that offers the easy enjoyment of panning filled with a sense of speed. Only environmentally-friendly lead-free glass is used in the optical system made up of 15 elements in 10 groups and a UD lens, which achieves high image quality at all focal lengths, is employed in the first lens of the third group. Furthermore, the optimization of lens positioning and coating minimizes the flare and ghosting that often occur in digital cameras. A zoom ring lock keeps the lens at its shortest length in the wide position and prevents the lens barrel from extending and striking any objects when the lens is being carried attached to a camera with a strap. The use of micro USM lens drive, a high-speed CPU and an optimized autofocus algorithm ensures autofocusing that is both quiet and fast. The image stabilizer mechanism and the optical

EF70-300mm EF75-300mm

Telephoto zoom lenses

EF70-300mm f/4-5.6 IS USM

● Focal length and maximum aperture: 70-300 mm 1:4-5.6
● Lens construction: 15 elements in 10 groups ● Diagonal angle of view: 34° - 8°15'
● Focus adjustment: Front group rotating extension system with micro USM
● Closest focusing distance: 1.5 m/ 4.9 ft., 0.26 x magnification
● Zoom system: Rotation type ● Filter size: 58 mm
● Max. diameter x length, weight: ø 76.5 x 142.8 mm, 630 g/ 3.0" x 5.6", 1.4 lbs.

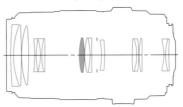

● UD lens

EF75-300mm f/4-5.6 III USM

● Focal length and maximum aperture: 75-300 mm 1:4-5.6
● Lens construction: 13 elements in 9 groups ● Diagonal angle of view: 32°11' - 8°15'
● Focus adjustment: Front group rotating extension system with micro USM
● Closest focusing distance: 1.5 m/ 4.9 ft., 0.25 x magnification
● Zoom system: Rotation type ● Filter size: 58 mm
● Max. diameter x length, weight: ø 71 x 122 mm, 480 g/ 2.8" x 4.8", 1.1 lbs.

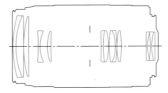

EF75-300mm f/4-5.6 III

● Focal length and maximum aperture: 75-300 mm 1:4-5.6
● Lens construction: 13 elements in 9 groups ● Diagonal angle of view: 32°11' - 8°15'
● Focus adjustment: Front group rotating extension system with micro USM
● Closest focusing distance: 1.5 m/ 4.9 ft., 0.25 x magnification
● Zoom system: Rotation type ● Filter size: 58 mm
● Max. diameter x length, weight: ø 71 x 122 mm, 480 g/ 2.8" x 4.8", 1.1 lbs.

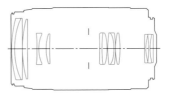

EF70-300mm f/4-5.6 IS USM·1/500sec.·f/11

system utilizing a UD lens, combined with other features such as the zoom ring lock function and relatively compact size and weight, make this a highly advanced and user-friendly lens.

■EF75-300mm f/4-5.6 III USM
This high-magnification zoom lens is the smallest and lightest in its class, offering ideal cost-performance. A lightweight glass material was used for the first element group - the heaviest group in the optical system - to reduce operational load during autofocus operation. Combined with the micro USM, the autofocus is quick and quiet. The slim exterior and smooth zooming makes this lens a delight to use.

■EF75-300mm f/4-5.6 III
With the same optical system as the EF75-300mm f/4-5.6 III USM, this lens is lightweight, compact, and has a high-magnification zoom. Able to cover the entire range from 75mm to 300mm (the most commonly used focal distances), it will let you stay on your feet looking for that perfect shot. The autofocus drive system has a micro motor.

Unsurpassed zoom of approximately 11x from 28mm to 300mm. Ultra-high-quality L zoom lens handles almost all photo scenes with one lens.

This single lens handles a variety of compositional needs from the 28mm wide-angle setting, with its broad linear perspective, to the powerful 300mm telephoto setting, which is extremely effective for pulling in faraway subjects and compressing perspective. Because it covers a zoom ratio of approximately 11x, users need only carry this one lens to shoot almost any subject. Capture magnificent landscape scenes at 28mm wide angle, and zoom in on distant subjects at 300mm. Track and capture the dexterous footwork of soccer players in a huge stadium. Take the photographs you want, of anything you can see, setting the frame for close-ups or pull-away shots to get just the framing you desire.

And the image stabilization mechanism lets you enjoy the full image quality of an L-series lens while taking active indoor shots.

■EF28-300mm f/3.5-5.6L IS USM

This ultra-high-quality zoom lens covers the entire zoom range from 28mm wide-angle to 300mm telephoto. With three UD lenses and three aspherical lenses, chromatic aberration and distortions are thoroughly suppressed, realizing an approximately 11x zoom range with image quality suited to an L lens. And because the lens comes with an image stabilization mechanism that can compensate for approximately 3 shutter speeds*1, users can take advantage of its full capabilities during handheld shooting at 300mm telephoto and in locations with insufficient lighting. The lens uses environmentally friendly lead-free glass,

EF28-300mm f/3.5-5.6L IS USM·1/320sec.·f/5.6

EF28-300mm f/3.5-5.6L IS USM

- Focal length and maximum aperture: 28-300mm 1:3.5-5.6
- Lens construction: 23 elements in 16 groups
- Diagonal angle of view: 75° - 8°15'
- Focus adjustment: Ring-type USM, inner focusing system, full-time manual focus
- Closest focusing distance: 0.7 m/2.3 ft., 0.3 x magnification
- Zoom system: Linear
- Filter size: 77 mm
- Max. diameter x length, weight: ø 92 x 184 mm, 1,670 g/3.6" x 7.2", 3.7 lbs.

and with an optimized lens coating and optical design, it minimizes flare and ghosts, which often occur with digital cameras. In addition, it features a zoom ring friction control mechanism, making it possible to freely set zoom operations, and enhanced dust-proof and drip-proof*2 design for shooting under severe conditions. The lens also comes with high-speed AF and full-time manual focus system. This ultrahigh-performance zoom lens meets the demands of all users from professionals to photo enthusiasts.

*1 Based on a shutter speed of "1/focal length" seconds, said to be the limit for hand-held photography without image stabilization.
*2 Dust-proof and drip-proof models: EOS-1Ds Mark III, EOS-1Ds Mark II, EOS-1Ds, EOS-1D Mark IV, EOS-1D Mark III, EOS-1D Mark II N, EOS-1D Mark II, EOS-1D, EOS-1V/HS

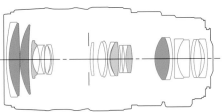

● Aspherical lens ● UD lens

Expanding the expressive region of telephoto lenses.
Telephoto lenses which can capture a moment and keep it from dying in captivity.

The tension of an image with the background encroaching on the subject, all perspective compressed. With an extraordinarily shallow depth of field, only the subject which has been captured using pinpoint focus is in focus – all else is blurred out. The effects created by telephoto lenses are actually quite profound. To bring out those depths, you need a telephoto zoom lens. Of course, to make sure these effects are brought out at their best, the lenses are designed so that the 400mm super telephoto regions are guaranteed to deliver fresh imaging and beautifully contrasted color reproduction. Light and compact, these lenses are mobile enough to be used for hand-held photography without a tripod.
In the field of journalistic photography, rapid-fire sports, free-moving stage production, and free-ranging wildlife, these zoom lenses show you their worth. These zoom lenses can be carried by the photographer when taking mountain photographs which are artistic, focusing on one small flower growing in a crevice on a distant unapproachable mountain.

■EF100-400mm f/4.5-5.6L IS USM
The EF100-400mm zoom lens is a telephoto zoom lens which also delivers very clear picture quality with an Image Stabilizing mechanism. With a 4x zoom ratio and high-contrast color reproduction, it has everything you could want from a telephoto zoom lens. The 6-group zoom system with 5 moving groups thoroughly eliminates secondary spectrum thanks to the fluorite and super UD lens elements. All aberrations are corrected in the middle focusing distances thanks to the rear focusing system and the floating system – a first for a zoom lens. The closest focusing distance is 1.8m, and the autofocus is quick and quiet thanks to

EF100-400mm f/4.5-5.6L IS USM·1/80sec.·f/14

the ring-type USM. A full-time manual focus, an adjustment ring which can adjust how the zoom ring feels, and much else besides combine to bring you outstanding operability.

EF100-400mm f/4.5-5.6L IS USM

- Focal length and maximum aperture: 100-400 mm 1:4.5-5.6
- Lens construction: 17 elements in 14 groups ● Diagonal angle of view: 24°- 6° 10'
- Focus adjustment: Ring-type USM, rear focusing system, full-time manual focus
- Closest focusing distance: 1.8 m/ 5.9 ft., 0.2 x magnification
- Zoom system: linear ● Filter size: 77 mm
- Max. diameter x length, weight: ø 92 x 189 mm, 1,380 g/ 3.6" x 7.4", 3.0 lbs.

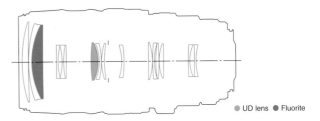

● UD lens ● Fluorite

The EF Lens World

The EF-S lenses can be used only with EOS 7D, EOS 50D, EOS 40D, EOS 30D, EOS 20D, EOS 20Da,
EOS Kiss X3/REBEL T1i/500D, EOS Kiss X2/DIGITAL REBEL XSi/450D,
EOS Kiss F/DIGITAL REBEL XS/1000D, EOS Kiss Digital X/DIGITAL REBEL XTi/400D DIGITAL,
EOS Kiss Digital N/DIGITAL REBEL XT/350D DIGITAL, EOS Kiss Digital/DIGITAL REBEL/300D DIGITAL.
(as of October 2009)

Portraying nature's tiny universe resplendent with plants and insects. A medium telephoto macro lens covering the range from life-size macro photography to distant scenic vistas.

The allure of a macro lens is being able to capture the drama of the beautiful forms and creatures of nature close-up, while also vividly and beautifully portraying their vibrant colors and diverse patterns brimming with life. With its generous working distance, i.e., the distance from the front the lens to the object being photographed, a medium telephoto macro lens is not only useful for macro shots, but also exhibits particular strength in shooting of fast-moving insects such as butterflies and dragonflies. At life-size (1:1), photographing flower pistils or water droplets in focus at maximum aperture reduces the depth of field, and the surrounding petals and leaves are wonderfully blurred in a way unique to life-size macro photography. In addition, since a medium telephoto macro lens has the same angle of view as a normal medium telephoto lens, it produces beautiful bokeh (blur effects) in portraits and snapshots with natural perspective, and can extract a particularly interesting area of a broader landscape.

■**EF-S60mm f/2.8 Macro USM** *[1]

This is a medium telephoto macro lens for EF-S lens-compatible EOS digital SLR cameras. It has an angle of view approximately equivalent to a 96mm lens in the 35mm format, and is capable of macro photography up to life size (1:1). With an optical design utilizing the advantages of the short back focus and smaller image circle of the Advanced Photo System C size imaging element, the lens achieves life-size macro photography together with lightweight compactness. Its lightweight, compact design makes it perfect for nature photography. The optical system of twelve elements in eight groups uses only environmentally friendly lead-free glass, and has inner focusing by the third group. It gives high image quality throughout the entire focusing range and a 90mm working distance, the longest in its class for life-size photography. Since the length of the lens does not change when focusing, there is no concern about the end of the lens touching the subject when focusing, allowing you to get even closer. The optical design and coating are optimized to reduce the flare and

EF-S60mm f/2.8 Macro USM ·1/60sec.·f/11

ghosts that are prone to occur with digital cameras. The quick and quiet inner focusing and ring-type USM autofocusing ensure that elusive photo opportunities are not missed when shooting insects and small animals. The lens mechanism is designed to ensure that it fits only EOS DIGITAL SLR cameras designed to take EF-S lenses. It is equipped with a special attachment indicator and protective rubber mount ring to prevent mistaken attempts to attach it to other EOS SLR cameras, and to prevent damage to the camera body.
(→ P.156 Special characteristics of EF-S lenses)

*1 Can be used only with EOS DIGITAL SLR cameras designed to take EF-S lenses.
* Compatible EOS DIGITAL SLR cameras: EOS 7D, EOS 50D, EOS 40D, EOS 30D, EOS 20D, EOS 20Da, EOS Kiss X3/REBEL T1i/500D, EOS Kiss X2/ DIGITAL REBEL XSi/450D, EOS Kiss F/DIGITAL REBEL XS/1000D, EOS Kiss Digital X/DIGITAL REBEL XTi/400D DIGITAL, EOS Kiss Digital N/DIGITAL REBEL XT/REBEL 350D DIGITAL, EOS Kiss Digital/DIGITAL REBEL/300D DIGITAL (as of October 2009)

EF-S60mm f/2.8 Macro USM

● Focal length and maximum aperture: 60mm 1:2.8
● Lens construction: 12 elements in 8 groups ● Diagonal angle of view: 24°30'
● Focus adjustment: Ring-type USM, inner focusing system, full-time manual focus
● Closest focusing distance: 0.2m/0.7ft., 1x magnification ● Filter size: 52mm
● Max. diameter x length, weight: ø 73 x 69.8mm, 335 g/2.9" x 2.7", 11.8 oz.

This macro lens can be used only with cameras designed to take EF-S lenses.
(It cannot be used with other EOS SLR cameras.)

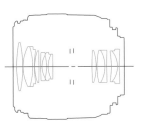

Ultra-wide angle EF-S zoom lens offers dramatic breadth and perspective.
Enabling truly creative composition of both portraits and scenery.
Created to meet strong demand for an ultra-wide-angle zoom in the EF-S lineup, this lens, which provides a focal length range equivalent to 16-35mm in 35mm format, is ideal for the whole range of wide-angle photography from compositions with the dramatic breadth and perspective offered by ultra-wide-angle to close-up portraits. The minimum zoom focal length of 10mm enables the shooting of images that exceed the capabilities of the human eye – breathtakingly broad vistas, and pan-focused cityscapes featuring striking juxtapositions of skyscrapers. At the maximum focal length of 22mm, the lens is a moderate wide angle, and is ideal for pictures like street snapshots or group shots at parties. The minimum focus of 0.24m enables you to crouch in a field of flowers to capture flowers in the foreground with the whole field spread out beyond in powerful perspective. Taking up little bag space, this lens is an ideal companion to standard zooms such

as the EF-S15-85mm f/3.5-5.6 IS USM or EF-S17-55mm f/2.8 IS USM, considerably expanding your vision.

■EF-S10-22mm f/3.5-4.5 USM *[1]
This lightweight, compact EF-S series ultra-wide-angle zoom lens is designed to take advantage of the short back focus and smaller image circle of the Advanced Photo System C size imaging element. It meets all the demands of both ultra-wide-angle zoom photography, and lightweight compactness. The optical system of thirteen elements in ten groups uses only environmentally friendly lead-free glass. Use of three aspherical lenses of two types (replica and molded glass), and one Super UD lens ensures outstanding picture quality over the entire zoom range, while the optical design and coatings have been optimized to reduce the flare and ghosts that are prone to occur with digital cameras, resulting in sharp images with excellent color balance. Minimum focus is a constant 0.24m over the zoom range, and the round

EF-S10-22mm f/3.5-4.5 USM ·1/180sec.·f/11

diaphragm provides exquisite bokeh (blur effects). The internal focusing system with its ring-type USM is quick and quiet, while the full-time manual focus enables manual focusing even in autofocus mode. The lens mechanism is designed to ensure that it fits only EOS DIGITAL SLR cameras designed to take EF-S lenses, and it is equipped with a special attachment indicator and protective rubber mount ring to prevent mistaken attempts to attach it to other EOS SLR cameras, and to prevent damage to the camera body.
(→ P.156 Special characteristics of EF-S lenses)

*1 Can be used only with EOS DIGITAL SLR cameras designed to take EF-S lenses.
* Compatible EOS DIGITAL SLR cameras: EOS 7D, EOS 50D, EOS 40D, EOS 30D, EOS 20D, EOS 20Da, EOS Kiss X3/REBEL T1i/500D, EOS Kiss X2/DIGITAL REBEL XSi/450D, EOS Kiss F/DIGITAL REBEL XS/1000D, EOS Kiss Digital X/DIGITAL REBEL XTi/400D DIGITAL, EOS Kiss Digital N/DIGITAL REBEL XT/REBEL 350D DIGITAL, EOS Kiss Digital/DIGITAL REBEL/300D DIGITAL (as of October 2009)

EF-S10-22mm f/3.5-4.5 USM

● Focal length and maximum aperture: 10-22mm 1:3.5-4.5
● Lens construction: 13 elements in 10 groups ● Diagonal angle of view: 107°30'-63°30'
● Focus adjustment: Ring-type USM, inner focusing system, full-time manual focus
● Closest focusing distance: 0.24 m/0.8 ft., 0.17 x magnification
● Zoom system: Rotation type ● Filter size: 77 mm
● Max. diameter x length, weight: ø 83.5 x 89.8 mm, 385 g/3.3" x 3.5", 13.6 oz.

This macro lens can be used only with cameras designed to take EF-S lenses.
(It cannot be used with other EOS SLR cameras.)

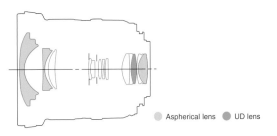

Aspherical lens   UD lens

A spectacular all-around performer.
Enjoy the best of both worlds — wide-angle and telephoto coverage.
Covering focal lengths quivalent to 24mm through 135mm in 35mm format, this 5.7x zoom lens is an excellent choice as a "standard" lens for any photographer. The wide angle of view at its shortest focal length provides outstanding coverage inside small rooms or when shooting nearby subjects, such as people sitting across a table. This attribute can also be employed to obtain breathtaking landscapes that display exceptional depth, or to dramatically emphasize perspective — a technique that is only possible with wide-angle lenses for which a change of a few millimeters in focal length produces markedly different results. At the other end of the zoom range, medium telephoto capability allows you to easily capture natural expressions from a comfortable distance, making the lens ideal for shooting indoor sports, children at play or portraits.

■**EF-S15-85mm f/3.5-5.6 IS USM*[1]**
Superb image quality, easy operation and optical IS (Image Stabilizer) assure that this well-crafted lens will please any camera enthusiast. With an optical system that includes two high-precision glass-molded aspherical elements, one replica aspherical element and one UD element, the EF-S15-85mm f/3.5-5.6 IS USM efficiently corrects aberrations common to zoom lenses in order to achieve clear, sharp images over the entire zoom range. It incorporates a circular aperture for creating beautiful background blur as well as an IS that allows shooting at shutter speeds up to four shutter speeds* slower than with non-IS lenses. The intelligent IS system also distinguishes between normal shooting and panning, automatically selecting the appropriate mode and thereby freeing you to concentrate on the action without having to make additional settings. This high-magnification IS zoom lens is designed specifically for Canon digital cameras that are compatible with EF-S lenses.

EF-S15-85mm

EF-S15-85mm f/3.5-5.6 IS USM ·1/250sec.·f/8

(→ P.156 Special characteristics of EF-S lenses)

*1 Can be used only with EOS DIGITAL SLR cameras designed to take EF-S lenses.
* Compatible EOS DIGITAL SLR cameras: EOS 7D, EOS 50D, EOS 40D, EOS 30D, EOS 20D, EOS 20Da, EOS Kiss X3/REBEL T1i/500D, EOS Kiss X2/ DIGITAL REBEL XSi/450D, EOS Kiss F/DIGITAL REBEL XS/1000D, EOS Kiss Digital X/DIGITAL REBEL XTi/400D DIGITAL, EOS Kiss Digital N/DIGITAL REBEL XT/REBEL 350D DIGITAL, EOS Kiss Digital/DIGITAL REBEL/300D DIGITAL (as of October 2009)
*2 Based on a shutter speed of "1/focal length x 1.6" second, which is considered the limit for handheld photography without image stabilization.

EF-S15-85mm f/3.5-5.6 IS USM

- Focal length and maximum aperture: 15-85mm 1:3.5-5.6
- Lens construction: 17 elements in 12 groups ● Diagonal angle of view: 84°30'-18°25'
- Focus adjustment: Ring-type USM, inner focusing system, full-time manual focus
- Closest focusing distance: 0.35 m/1.1 ft., 0.21 x magnification
- Zoom system: Rotation type ● Filter size: 72 mm
- Max. diameter x length, weight: ø 81.6 x 87.5 mm, 575 g/ 3.2" x 3.4", 1.3 lbs.

This macro lens can be used only with cameras designed to take EF-S lenses.
(It cannot be used with other EOS SLR cameras.)

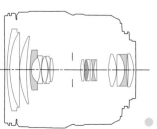

● Aspherical lens　● UD lens

EF-S17-55mm f/2.8 IS USM ·1/15sec.·f/2.8

f/2.8 aperture brightness and IS flexibility.
This EF-S large-diameter standard zoom lens satisfies the most demanding professionals.

With its Image Stabilizer and large diameter, this lens dramatically expands the scope of what can be photographed, as well as how it is expressed. Fleeting moments of natural beauty at dawn, for example, or views of city skylines at night can be beautifully captured with handheld shots. In portrait photography, the large diameter can create a shallow depth of field that sets your subject apart from the background for expressive results that are truly impressive. By freeing you from camera-shake blur and empowering you with a large maximum aperture, this flexible, high-quality standard zoom lens lets you explore infinite photographic possibilities.

■EF-S 17-55mm f/2.8 IS USM *1

This large-aperture EF-S Series standard zoom lens features an optical system consisting of 19 lens elements in 12 groups. Three aspherical lens elements (one glass-molded and two replica surfaces) efficiently compensate for aberration fluctuations over the entire zoom range while enabling a large f/2.8 aperture and high image quality. Two UD lenses also reduce secondary chromatic aberrations to produce high-resolution, high-contrast images without color bleeding around subject edges. The inner focus and a ring-type USM achieve silent, high-speed autofocusing, while full-time manual focus override offers excellent operability by enabling users to tweak focusing without exiting the autofocusing mode. Now it's easier to determine the ideal focus when shooting portrait and close-up photos with a large aperture setting. A circular aperture diaphragm contributes to beautiful background blur, and the optimized lens configuration and coating reduce the flare and ghost so common with digital cameras. This outstanding optical performance and operability is further enhanced by an Image Stabilizer that reduces the amount of camera-shake blur to roughly that of a 3 f-stop faster shutter speed.*2 Clearly, this standard zoom lens meets the stringent requirements of professionals. The lens mechanism is designed to ensure that it fits only EOS DIGITAL SLR cameras designed to take EF-S lenses, and it is equipped with a special attachment indicator and protective rubber mount ring to prevent mistaken attempts to attach it to other EOS SLR cameras, and to prevent damage to the camera body.
(→ P.156 Special characteristics of EF-S lenses)

*1 Can be used only with EOS DIGITAL SLR cameras designed to take EF-S lenses.
* Compatible EOS DIGITAL SLR cameras: EOS 7D, EOS 50D, EOS 40D, EOS 30D, EOS 20D, EOS 20Da, EOS Kiss X3/REBEL T1i/500D, EOS Kiss X2/ DIGITAL REBEL XSi/450D, EOS Kiss F/DIGITAL REBEL XS/1000D, EOS Kiss Digital X/DIGITAL REBEL XTi/400D DIGITAL, EOS Kiss Digital N/DIGITAL REBEL XT/REBEL 350D DIGITAL, EOS Kiss Digital/DIGITAL REBEL/300D DIGITAL (as of October 2009)
*2 Based on a shutter speed of "1/focal length x 1.6" second, which is considered the limit for handheld photography without image stabilization.

EF-S17-55mm f/2.8 IS USM

● Focal length and maximum aperture: 17-55mm 1:2.8
● Lens construction: 19 elements in 12 groups ● Diagonal angle of view: 78°30'-27°50'
● Focus adjustment: Ring-type USM, inner focusing system, full-time manual focus
● Closest focusing distance: 0.35 m/1.5 ft., 0.17 x magnification
● Zoom system: Rotation type ● Filter size: 77 mm
● Max. diameter x length, weight: ø 83.5 x 110.6 mm, 645 g/3.3" x 4.4", 1.4 lbs.

This lens can be used only with cameras designed to take EF-S lenses
(Cannot be used with other EOS SLR cameras)

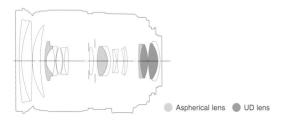

● Aspherical lens ● UD lens

EF-S17-85mm f/4-5.6 IS USM ·1/8sec.·f/5.6

A 5x zoom covering wide-angle to medium telephoto.
The ideal lens for traveling light while still packing a lot of punch.

This is a highly versatile standard zoom lens for EF-S lens compatible EOS digital SLR cameras. Covering a focal length range equivalent to 27-136mm in 35mm format, and providing 5x zoom, it is the ideal lens for trips, being not only light and compact, but also serving almost all shooting needs from wide-angle scenics and groups through standard snapshots to medium telephoto portraits and action photography. You can make full use of the versatility offered by the 5x zoom to capture magnificent mountain ranges or dramatically angled shots of huge trees at the wide-angle end, or zoom to the end to put spatial perspective between subject and background and use the beautiful bokeh (blur effects) to advantage in capturing facial expressions and gestures. The image stabilizer system counters camera shake, enabling the use of available light to take naturally lit shots in many indoor and other low light conditions that would otherwise require use of flash. You can also of course use the camera's slow sync flash function and a small aperture to boost depth of field for crisp handheld wide-angle shots of family and friends that also capture sunsets or other background scenery. Combining this lens with the EF-S10-22mm f/3.5-4.5 USM ultra wide-angle zoom lens will provide even greater versatility in subject and method of expression.

■EF-S17-85mm f/4-5.6 IS USM *1

This lightweight, compact EF-S series standard zoom lens is equipped with an image stabilizer, and takes advantage of the small image circle of the EF-S format to deliver 5x zooming in an amazingly compact form. The seventeen element, twelve group optical system uses only environmentally friendly lead-free glass, with a double aspherical molded glass lens as the 15th element to ensure high picture quality over the whole zoom range. The image stabilizer gives stability equivalent to about three shutter speeds*2, substantially improving handheld steadiness, and together with the high-speed ring-type USM internal autofocus, ensures that you won't miss that once-in-a-lifetime shot. The optical design and coating have been optimized to reduce the flare and ghosts that are prone to occur with digital cameras. Exquisite bokeh (blur effects) enabled by the round diaphragm, and the full-time manual focus function further expand expressive possibilities. The lens mechanism is designed to ensure that it fits only EOS DIGITAL SLR cameras designed to take EF-S lenses, and it is equipped with a special attachment indicator and protective rubber mount ring to prevent mistaken attempts to attach it to other EOS SLR cameras, and to prevent damage to the camera body.
(→ P.156 Special characteristics of EF-S lenses)

*1 Can be used only with EOS DIGITAL SLR cameras designed to take EF-S lenses.
*2 Based on a shutter speed of "1/focal length x 1.6" second, which is considered the limit for handheld photography without image stabilization.
* Compatible EOS DIGITAL SLR cameras: EOS 7D, EOS 50D, EOS 40D, EOS 30D, EOS 20D, EOS 20Da, EOS Kiss X3/REBEL T1i/500D, EOS Kiss X2/DIGITAL REBEL XSi/450D, EOS Kiss F/DIGITAL REBEL XS/1000D, EOS Kiss Digital X/DIGITAL REBEL XTi/400D DIGITAL, EOS Kiss Digital N/DIGITAL REBEL XT/REBEL 350D DIGITAL, EOS Kiss Digital/DIGITAL REBEL/300D DIGITAL (as of October 2009)

EF-S17-85mm f/4-5.6 IS USM

- Focal length and maximum aperture: 17-85mm 1:4-5.6
- Lens construction: 17 elements in 12 groups ● Diagonal angle of view: 78°30'-18°25'
- Focus adjustment: Ring-type USM, inner focusing system, full-time manual focus
- Closest focusing distance: 0.35 m/1.2 ft., 0.2 x magnification
- Zoom system: Rotation type ● Filter size: 67 mm
- Max. diameter x length, weight: ø 78.5 x 92 mm, 475 g/3.1" x 3.6", 1 lb.

This lens can be used only with cameras designed to take EF-S lenses
(Cannot be used with other EOS SLR cameras)

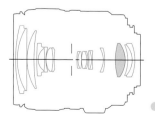

● Aspherical lens

EF-S18-55mm f/3.5-5.6 IS ·1/40sec.·f/6.3

Standard zoom lenses

Exclusively for EF-S compatible SLR cameras

Standard zoom lenses effortlessly capture both smiles and scenery.
Explore different compositional possibilities in each scene with these two compact zoom lenses. Designed specifically to support Canon digital SLR cameras using EF-S lenses, the 3x zoom ratio provides wide-angle to medium-telephoto coverage, equivalent to a zoom range of 29-88mm for 35mm cameras.

Shooting at the 18mm wide-angle focal length maintains background focus while emphasizing foreground subjects. At the 55mm medium-telephoto setting, they exhibit a natural perspective closely resembling that of the human eye when staring at a fixed point. In addition, this focal length provides the ability to blur backgrounds — ideal for creating half-length portraits. These lenses are aptly suited to a wide variety of photographic situations, from snapshots and ceremonial photos to scenics and portraits. Photographers equipped with one of these lenses along with either (or both) the EF-S10-22mm f/3.5-4.5 USM or EF-S55-250mm f/4-5.6 IS will be assured of having the proper focal length for nearly any photo opportunity.

■EF-S18-55mm f/3.5-5.6 IS *¹

Despite a compact, lightweight design that makes it highly portable, this lens includes a newly developed image stabilization mechanism. The IS provides camera shake compensation up to an equivalent of approximately four full shutter speed steps*², enabling natural looking photos in dim environments under existing light. Tack-sharp images and a 0.25m/9.8 inch minimum shooting distance are maintained over the entire zoom range. Flare and ghost are minimal, and the circular aperture produces beautiful background blur effects. Also featuring high-speed autofocus, this IS zoom lens is an excellent choice as a "standard" lens.
(→ P.156 Special characteristics of EF-S lenses)

■EF-S18-55mm f/3.5-5.6 Ⅱ *¹

The standard zoom lens offers great value in a compact, lightweight design. Its aspherical 10th element ensures excellent image quality over the entire zoom range. The arrangement of lens elements along with a superior lens coating are optimized to reduce flare and ghost, problems often associated with digital SLR photography. Additionally, this lens exhibits outstanding color balance and sharpness. Other features include superb high-speed autofocusing, a 0.28m/11 inch minimum shooting distance, and a circular aperture for beautiful background blurring.
(→ P.156 Special characteristics of EF-S lenses)

*1 Can only be used with digital SLR cameras that support EF-S lenses.
*2 Based on a shutter speed of "1/focal length x1.6" second, which is considered the limit for handheld photography without image stabilization.
* Compatible EOS DIGITAL SLR cameras: EOS 7D, EOS 50D, EOS 40D, EOS 30D, EOS 20D, EOS 20Da, EOS Kiss X3/REBEL T1i/500D, EOS Kiss X2/ DIGITAL REBEL XSi/450D, EOS Kiss F/DIGITAL REBEL XS/1000D, EOS Kiss Digital X/DIGITAL REBEL XTi/400D DIGITAL, EOS Kiss Digital N/DIGITAL REBEL XT/REBEL 350D DIGITAL, EOS Kiss Digital/DIGITAL REBEL/300D DIGITAL (as of October 2009)

EF-S18-55mm f/3.5-5.6 IS

● Focal length and maximum aperture: 18-55 mm 1:3.5-5.6 ● Lens construction: 11 elements in 9 groups ● Diagonal angle of view: 74°20'-27°50' ● Focus adjustment distance: Front group rotating extension system with micro motor ● Closest focusing distance: 0.25 m/0.82 ft., 0.34 x magnification ● Zoom system: Rotation type ● Filter size: 58 mm ● Max. diameter x length, weight: ø 68.5 x 70 mm, 200 g/2.7" x 2.8", 7.1 oz.

This lens can be used only with cameras designed to take EF-S lenses
(Cannot be used with other EOS SLR cameras)

● Aspherical lens

EF-S18-55mm f/3.5-5.6 Ⅱ

● Focal length and maximum aperture: 18-55 mm 1:3.5-5.6 ● Lens construction: 11 elements in 9 groups ● Diagonal angle of view: 74°20'-27°50' ● Focus adjustment: Front group rotating extension system with micro motor ● Closest focusing distance: 0.28 m/0.92 ft., 0.28 x magnification ● Zoom system: Rotation type ● Filter size: 58 mm ● Max. diameter x length, weight: ø 68.5 x 66 mm, 190 g/2.7" x 2.6", 6.7 oz.

This lens can be used only with cameras designed to take EF-S lenses
(Cannot be used with other EOS SLR cameras)

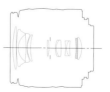

● Aspherical lens

An exceptional "starter" lens.
Discover the joy of artistic expression with this 7.5x zoom lens.
Expand your creative horizons with this superb zoom lens. Covering focal lengths equivalent to 29mm through 215mm in 35mm format, this 7.5x zoom makes a great "starter" lens. The wide zoom range allows you to handle a variety of shooting situations, from indoor parties and majestic landscapes to tight portraits and sports.

The key to shooting with high-magnification zoom lenses is awareness of the different visual effects produced at each focal length. For example, when using a wide-angle setting to photograph a person up close, the background seems to recede from the subject, resulting in a dynamic image with a dramatic feel. Conversely, photographing a person using a telephoto setting compresses the scene, with the background appearing to envelop the subject. Rich visual effects such as these are available only with high-magnification zoom lenses like the EF-S18-135mm

f/3.5-5.6 IS − the perfect tool to expand your repertoire of photographic techniques and explore new avenues of artistic expression.

■EF-S18-135mm f/3.5-5.6 IS [1]
This high-magnification, IS (Image Stabilizer) zoom lens is designed specifically for Canon digital cameras that are compatible with EF-S lenses. The lens incorporates high-precision glass-molded aspherical and UD lens elements to help reduce aberrations and achieve excellent image quality over the entire zoom range despite a high magnification ratio. Because it employs an inner focusing system, the length of the lens never changes and consistent image quality is always assured. For extended handheld shooting capability, the lens incorporates an IS, which allows shooting at shutter speeds up to four steps* slower than with non-IS lenses − ideal for shooting without a tripod or flash in dimly lit environments or when using longer

EF-S18-135mm f/3.5-5.6 IS·0.6sec.·f/8

focal lengths. The intelligent IS system also distinguishes between normal shooting and panning, then automatically selects the appropriate mode for you. Furthermore, Canon technology minimizes flare and ghosting common to digital SLRs, enabling you to shoot casually without being overly concerned with the location of the light source. Complementing the excellent optical performance of the EF-S18-135mm f/3.5-5.6 is its trim, powerful appearance stylishly accented with a leather-tone finish.
(→ P.156 Special characteristics of EF-S lenses)

*1 Can be used only with EOS DIGITAL SLR cameras designed to take EF-S lenses.
*2 Based on a shutter speed of "1/focal length x1.6" second, which is considered the limit for handheld photography without image stabilization.
* Compatible EOS DIGITAL SLR cameras: EOS 7D, EOS 50D, EOS 40D, EOS 30D, EOS 20D, EOS 20Da, EOS Kiss X3/REBEL T1i/500D, EOS Kiss X2/ DIGITAL REBEL XSi/450D, EOS Kiss F/DIGITAL REBEL XS/1000D, EOS Kiss Digital X/DIGITAL REBEL XTi/400D DIGITAL, EOS Kiss Digital N/DIGITAL REBEL XT/REBEL 350D DIGITAL, EOS Kiss Digital/DIGITAL REBEL/300D DIGITAL (as of October 2009)

EF-S18-135mm f/3.5-5.6 IS

● Focal length and maximum aperture: 18-135mm 1:3.5-5.6
● Lens construction: 16 elements in 12 groups ● Diagonal angle of view: 74°20'-11°30'
● Focus adjustment: Micro motor, inner focusing system
● Closest focusing distance: 0.45 m/1.5 ft., 0.21 x magnification (at 135mm)
● Zoom system: Rotation type ● Filter size: 67 mm
● Max. diameter x length, weight: ø 75.4 x 101 mm, 455 g/ 2.7" x 4.0", 1.0 lbs.

This macro lens can be used only with cameras designed to take EF-S lenses.
(It cannot be used with other EOS SLR cameras.)

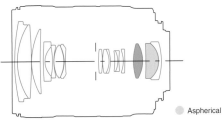

● Aspherical lens ● UD lens

Wide-angle to telephoto coverage at a high zoom ratio of approximately 11x.

An ultra high-power zoom with excellent mobility — the ideal solution for photographing a wide range of subjects with just one lens.

This ultra high-power zoom lens boasts a wide zoom range of approximately 11x. With a focal length equivalent to 29 to 320mm in 35mm format, it allows quick, accurate composition of a wide range of subjects, including landscapes and group shots taken in small rooms as well as naturally expressive portraits shot at medium telephoto focal lengths. It is also well suited for photographing distant subjects from a restricted shooting position such as sporting and theatrical events, mountains, railroads, and wild animals. In addition, changes in visual effects due to the angle of view are dynamic. Perspective can be exaggerated or constricted, and backgrounds deeply focused or fully blurred to emphasize the subject. The ability to use just one lens to take photos with completely different looks is an attractive quality unique to ultra high-power zoom lenses. The lens also provides

extremely high functionality, saving time by doing away with the need to change lenses and enabling use in a variety of different situations such as traveling, mountain climbing, or any other activity where it is desirable to keep equipment to a minimum.

■ EF-S18-200mm f/3.5-5.6 IS [1]

The EF-S18-200mm f/3.5-5.6 IS is a zoom lens designed exclusively for use with digital SLR cameras compatible with EF-S lenses. It has a zoom ratio of approximately 11x and is equipped with an Image Stabilizer. Two molded glass aspheric lenses and two UD lenses correct various anomalies such as chromatic aberration, resulting in a lens with a high zoom ratio that produces superior quality photos with superb sharpness over the entire image area. Camera shake correction is equivalent to approximately 4 steps[2] in terms of shutter speed. For telephoto photography, during which camera shake tends to more easily occur, agile operation is possible even when shooting handheld.

EF-S18-200mm f/3.5-5.6 IS·1/500sec.·f/5.6

EF-S18-200mm f/3.5-5.6 IS

● Focal length and maximum aperture: 18-200mm 1:3.5-5.6
● Lens construction: 16 elements in 12 groups ● Diagonal angle of view: 74°20'-7°50'
● Focus adjustment: Micro moter, inner focusing system, full-time manual focus
● Closest focusing distance: 0.45 m/1.5 ft., 0.24 x magnification
● Zoom system: Rotation type ● Filter size: 72 mm
● Max. diameter x length, weight: ø 78.6 x 102 mm, 595 g/3.1" x 4.0", 1.3 lbs.

This macro lens can be used only with cameras designed to take EF-S lenses.
(It cannot be used with other EOS SLR cameras.)

In addition, automatic switching between regular and panning modes assures capturing unexpected photo opportunities at the press of the shutter. A minimum focus distance of approximately 0.45m throughout the entire zoom range makes the lens useful for close-up photography, adding to its all-around usability and outstanding versatility. The lens also features a zoom ring lock that prevents the barrel from extending and striking objects while being carried. Other performance features include high-speed AF and a circular aperture for producing nicely rounded blurs while at the same time controlling flaring and ghosting.
(→ P.156 Special characteristics of EF-S lenses)

*1 Can be used only with EOS DIGITAL SLR cameras designed to take EF-S lenses.
*2 Based on a shutter speed of "1/focal length x1.6" second, which is considered the limit for handheld photography without image stabilization.
* Compatible EOS DIGITAL SLR cameras: EOS 7D, EOS 50D, EOS 40D, EOS 30D, EOS 20D, EOS 20Da, EOS Kiss X3/REBEL T1i/500D, EOS Kiss X2/DIGITAL REBEL XSi/450D, EOS Kiss F/DIGITAL REBEL XS/1000D, EOS Kiss Digital X/DIGITAL REBEL XTi/400D DIGITAL, EOS Kiss Digital N/DIGITAL REBEL XT/REBEL 350D DIGITAL, EOS Kiss Digital/DIGITAL REBEL/300D DIGITAL (as of October 2009)

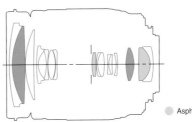

Aspherical lens   UD lens

Image stabilization in a small, lightweight telephoto zoom lens assures crystal clear photos.

A surprisingly compact design makes it easy to explore the many photographic possibilities of telephoto zooms. Select a portion of landscape to create a breathtaking scenic, or zoom in on a fast moving subject from afar. Wide coverage (equivalent to a zoom range of 88-400mm in 35mm format) offers a great deal of freedom in framing to obtain just the right composition. At 55mm, the natural perspective and soft background blur combine to produce pleasing portraits. Zooming to 250mm reveals a world unique to super-telephoto lenses with effects such as perspective compression — a great technique for creating dramatic, eye-catching photos and ideally suited for sports and nature photography. Built-in image stabilization expands the range for hand-held shooting and is especially useful at longer focal lengths. This lens is an excellent complement to the EF-S18-55mm f/3.5-5.6 IS.

■**EF-S55-250mm f/4-5.6 IS***[1]

Equipped with image stabilization, this telephoto zoom lens is designed specifically for digital SLR cameras that support the EF-S series. Thanks to an optical system that maximizes the potential of a small image circle, it boasts a high zoom ratio while maintaining a wonderfully compact and lightweight design. Superb ease-of-handling assures effortless shooting of fast moving subjects and the super compact IS unit reduces camera shake by up to approximately four full shutter speed steps*[2] — a must at long focal lengths and helpful when focusing and framing. Because the IS unit automatically distinguishes between normal shooting and panning, it ensures appropriate camera shake compensation without the need for manual adjustments. This brings peace of mind in situations containing both static and dynamic activity, as well as when shooting erratically moving subjects such as children and animals.

Featuring a UD lens element to greatly minimize color bleeding,

EF-S55-250mm

Telephoto zoom lenses

Exclusively for EF-S compatible SLR cameras

EF-S55-250mm f/4-5.6 IS ·1/125sec.·f/7.1

this lens delivers sharp, clean images that exhibit high resolution and superb contrast. Both the lens element array and lens coating are optimized to reduce flare and ghost, problems often associated with digital SLR photography. A minimum shooting distance of approximately 1.1m/3.6 feet applies over the entire zoom range and combines with a circular aperture to produce extraordinary close-ups with beautiful background blurs.
(→ P.156 Special characteristics of EF-S lenses)

*1 Can only be used with digital SLR cameras that support EF-S lenses.
*2 Based on a shutter speed of "1/focal length x1.6" second, which is considered the limit for handheld photography without image stabilization.
*   Compatible EOS DIGITAL SLR cameras: EOS 7D, EOS 50D, EOS 40D, EOS 30D, EOS 20D, EOS 20Da, EOS Kiss X3/REBEL T1i/500D, EOS Kiss X2/DIGITAL REBEL XSi/450D, EOS Kiss F/DIGITAL REBEL XS/1000D, EOS Kiss Digital X/DIGITAL REBEL XTi/400D DIGITAL, EOS Kiss Digital N/DIGITAL REBEL XT/350D DIGITAL, EOS Kiss Digital/DIGITAL REBEL/300D DIGITAL (As of October 2009.)

EF-S55-250mm f/4-5.6 IS

● Focal length and maximum aperture: 55-250mm 1:4-5.6
● Lens construction: 12 elements in 10 groups ● Diagonal angle of view: 27°50'-6°15'
● Focus adjustment distance: Front group rotating extension system with micro motor
● Closest focusing distance: 1.1 m/3.6 ft., 0.31 x magnification ● Filter size: 58 mm
● Max. diameter x length, weight: ø 70 x 108 mm, 390 g/2.8" x 4.3", 15.4 oz.

This macro lens can be used only with cameras designed to take EF-S lenses.
(It cannot be used with other EOS SLR cameras.)

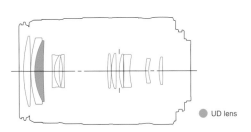

● UD lens

Filters that can adjust light to further optimize shooting performance.

FILTER

PROTECT   SKYLIGHT   UV

PROTECT
52mm 58mm 67mm 72mm 77mm 82mm

This neutral filter protects your valuable lens while maintaining perfect color balance. Its Super Spectra Coating prevents harmful light reflections. It can be used for general shooting.

SKYLIGHT
52mm 58mm 72mm

This light amber skylight filter is for use with both black-and-white and color film for daylight exposures on sunny days. This filter reduces the blue cast that occurs due to sky and water reflections and when photographing subjects in shadows. The filter has minimal effect on exposure and color temperature.

UV
52mm 58mm 72mm

This colorless filter is for use with black-and-white film, and absorbs ultraviolet light without cutting visible light. Its use is most effective on sunny days for cutting haze out of the shot. This filter has no effect on exposure and minimal effect on color temperature.

ND4X-L   ND8X-L

ND4X-L·8X-L
52mm 58mm 72mm

These filters are used with both black-and-white and color film to reduce the light entering the lens to one-fourth the original level (two f/steps) and one-eighth the original level (three f/steps) respectively. These filters are invaluable for large-aperture and slow shutter-speed photography.

Softmat No. 1   Softmat No. 2

Softmat No.1 & No.2
52mm 58mm

Softmat filters mildly soften the focus for flattering portraits and dreamy landscapes. These filters utilize the effect of diffraction, which occurs between light passing through the transparent part and light passing through the coated part. Use Softmat No. 1 filter for a gentle soft focus effect, and Softmat No. 2 for a stronger effect.

52mm Drop-in Screw Filter Holder

52mm Drop-in Screw Filter Holder (with protect filter)

A holder for the 52mm screw-type filters available on the market. Use by replacing the filter with the protect filter provided.

Compatible with the EF200mm f/2L IS USM, EF300mm f/2.8L IS USM, EF400mm f/2.8L IS USM, EF400mm f/4 DO IS USM, EF500mm f/4L IS USM, EF600mm f/4L IS USM, EF800mm f/5.6L IS USM.

GELATIN FILTER HOLDER SYSTEM

Gelatin Filter Holder Hood III   Gelatin Filter Holder III   Gelatin Filter Holder Adapter III

Gelatin Filter Holder Hood IV   Gelatin Filter Holder IV   Gelatin Filter Holder Adapter IV

This convenient holder system allows the use of commercially available square filters without the need for cutting. The holder attaches to the lens through an adapter that fits the filter diameter. A special hood is available for use with the system. Use with 3-inch square type III and 4-inch square type IV gelatin filters. Gelatin filters can be used with most EF lenses.

Refer to the Specifications Chart in the back for lens compatibility and the number of hoods that can be used with each holder.

POLARIZING FILTER

Circular Polarizing Filter PL-C B

Circular Polarizing Filter PL-C B
52mm 58mm 67mm 72mm 77mm 82mm

Circular polarizing filters suppress light reflecting off glass and water and intensify the blue in skies. Theses filters are easy to use because they do not interfere with autofocus or light metering. In addition, they can be fitted with a lens cap to protect against scratches that adversely affect performance.

Drop-in Circular Polarizing Filter PL-C52

Drop-in Circular Polarizing Filter PL-C52

A drop-in filter for use with lenses equipped with large aperture Image Stabilization in the super telephoto series. It can be rotated from the outside without removing it from the lens, enabling precise control.

Compatible with the EF200mm f/2L IS USM, EF300mm f/2.8L IS USM, EF400mm f/2.8L IS USM, EF400mm f/4 DO IS USM, EF500mm f/4L IS USM, EF600mm f/4L IS USM, EF800mm f/5.6L IS USM.

GELATIN FILTER HOLDER

52mm Drop-in Gelatin Filter Holder

52mm Drop-in Gelatin Filter Holder

Up to three gelatin filters can be placed in this holder. To use, insert a cut piece of gelatin film between the holder's filter frame and pressure clip, and screw on to the lens.

Available for both 48mm-compatible and 52mm-compatible lenses.

Compatible lenses: EF200mm f/2L IS USM, EF300mm f/2.8L IS USM, EF400mm f/2.8L IS USM, EF400mm f/4 DO IS USM, EF500mm f/4L IS USM, EF600mm f/4L IS USM, EF800mm f/5.6L IS USM.

Circular PL Filter Effects

Without Circular PL Filter

With Circular PL Filter

Emphasizes the blue of the sky

Suppresses the reflection of the glass surface

Suppresses the reflection from the surface of the leaves and the
surface of the water

CLOSE-UP LENS

250D   500D   500

52mm 58mm 72mm*¹ 77mm*¹

These screw-in lenses are an easy way to provide enhanced close-up photography. The 250D/500D series incorporates double-element achromatic design for maximum optical performance while the 500 series features single-element construction for maximum economy. An excellent way to further improve close-up shooting skills.

*¹ For the 500D only.
* The working distance from the end of the lens is 25cm for the 250D, and 50cm for the 500D-500. (At ∞) In addition, the magnification is higher for the 250D than for the 500D-500.

EXTENSION TUBE

EF12 II   EF25 II

These close-up accessories, placed between the camera body and lens, can be used with most EF lenses, including EF-S lenses. Through eight electronic contact points, electronic function is the same as during normal photography. The magnification differs according to the lens, but for standard zoom lenses it is about 0.3 to 0.5 for the EF12 II and 0.7 or over for the EF25 II. By using both tubes together effectively, the choice of magnifications can be greatly extended. Manual focusing is recommended.

Extension Tube EF25 II is not compatible with: EF15mm f/2.8 Fisheye, EF14mm f/2.8L II USM, EF20mm f/2.8 USM, EF24mm f/1.4L II USM, MP-E65mm f/2.8 1-5x Macro Photo, TS-E17mm f/4L, TS-E45mm f/2.8, EF16-35mm f/2.8L II USM (at wide angles), EF17-40mm f/4L USM (at wide angles), EF24-70mm f/2.8L USM (at wide angles), EF24-105mm f/4L USM (at wide angles), EF28-300mm f/3.5-5.6 L IS USM (at wide angles), EF-S10-22mm f/3.5-4.5 USM (at wide angles), EF-S15-85mm f/3.5-5.6 IS USM, EF-S17-85mm f/4-5.6 IS USM (at wide angles), EF-S18-55mm f/3.5-5.6 IS (at wide angles), EF-S18-55mm f/3.5-5.6 II (at wide angles), EF-S18-135mm f/3.5-5.6 IS (at wide angles), EF-S18-200mm f/3.5-5.6 IS (at wide angles). (We do not recommend use of the Extension Tube EF12 II with TS-E24mm f/3.5L II, EF-S10-22mm f/3.5-4.5 USM at near the tele end, EF-S17-55mm f/2.8 IS USM at near the tele end, since it radically reduces working distance.) Extension Tube EF12 II is not compatible with: EF15mm f/2.8 Fisheye, EF14mm f/2.8L II USM, MP-E65mm f/2.8 1-5x Macro Photo, TS-E17mm f/4L, EF16-35mm f/2.8L II USM (at wide angles), EF-S10-22mm f/3.5-4.5 USM (at wide angles), EF-S15-85mm f/3.5-6.5 IS USM (at wide angles), EF-S17-55mm f/2.8 IS USM, EF-S17-85mm f/4-5.6 IS USM (at wide angles), EF-S18-55mm f/3.5-5.6 IS (at wide angles), EF-S18-135mm f/3.5-5.6 IS (at wide angles), EF-S18-200mm f/3.5-5.6 IS (at wide angles).
* Refer to the Specifications Chart for the magnification rate for each lens.

TRIPOD MOUNT

Tripod Mount Ring A II (B)

This is a separately sold black ring-type tripod mount for the EF200mm f/2.8L II USM. It provides stable mount-ing and smooth rotation with excellent operability.

Tripod Mount Ring A II (W)

This is a separately sold white ring-type tripod mount for the EF70-200mm f/4L IS USM. It provides stable mounting and promises smooth rotation with comfortable operation.

* Can also be used for the EF400mm f/5.6L USM and EF70-200mm f/4L USM.

Tripod Mount Ring B (B)
With EF100mm f/2.8
Macro USM adapter

This makes it possible to quickly and easily change the setup between vertical and horizontal positions with-out disturbing the optical axis.

* Can also be used without an adapter for the EF180mm f/3.5L Macro USM and MP-E65mm f/2.8 1-5x Macro Photo.

Tripod Mount Ring D (B)

This optional black, ring-type tripod mount for the EF100mm f/2.8L Macro IS USM allows you to quickly and easily switch between vertical and horizontal orientations without changing the optical axis.

TS-E Lens Tripod Adapter

This tripod adapter improves the operability when using a TS-E lens. This adapter prevents the lens from striking the tripod or ball-head mounting plate when tilting or shifting.

MACROLITE ADAPTER

Macrolite Adapter 67

Macrolite Adapter 67

This adapter is required to use Macro Ring Lite MR-14EX or Macro Twin Lite MT-24EX when the EF100mm f/2.8L Macro IS USM lens is mounted on the camera.

Macrolite Adapter 72C

This adapter is required to use Macro Ring Lite MR-14EX or Macro Twin Lite MT-24EX when the EF180mm f/3.5L Macro USM lens is mounted on the camera.

Hoods

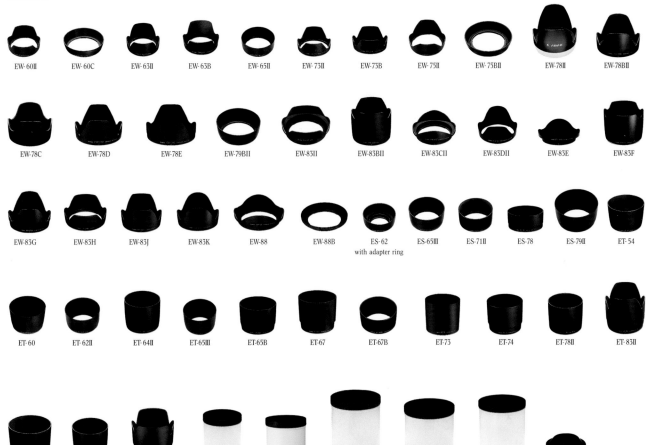

EW-60II   EW-60C   EW-63II   EW-63B   EW-65II   EW-73II   EW-73B   EW-75II   EW-75BII   EW-78II   EW-78BII

EW-78C   EW-78D   EW-78E   EW-79BII   EW-83II   EW-83BII   EW-83CII   EW-83DII   EW-83E   EW-83F

EW-83G   EW-83H   EW-83J   EW-83K   EW-88   EW-88B   ES-62 (with adapter ring)   ES-65III   ES-71II   ES-78   ES-79II   ET-54

ET-60   ET-62II   ET-64II   ET-65III   ET-65B   ET-67   ET-67B   ET-73   ET-74   ET-78II   ET-83II

ET-83BII   ET-83C   ET-86   ET-120   ET-120B   ET-138   ET-155   ET-160   MP-E65 Hood

Cases

There are functional, strong and well-designed cases available for each lens. The cases protect the valuable lenses while they are being moved.

Lens Pouch
LP811, LP814, LP1011, LP1016, LP1019, LP1022, LP1116, LP1214, LP1216, LP1219, LP1222, LP1224, LP1319

Zipper Case
LZ1128, LZ1132, LZ1324

Lens Case
Lens Case 200, Lens Case 300, Lens Case 400, Lens Case 400B, Lens Case 500, Lens Case 600, Lens Case 800

Lens Pouch (LP type)

Zipper Case (LZ type)

Lens Case

Variety in the Canon Lens World

Although Canon's precision optical technology is readily visible
in Canon cameras and lenses, most people might not know that its existence actually extends much
further into a wide variety of high-technology fields, supporting the steady progress of society.
This section provides a brief introduction to the various fields other than conventional photography
where Canon lenses are playing an ever-expanding role.

Fine Optical Components

Catching the Light from Distant Stars: The Subaru Observatory Optics

At an altitude of 4200m above sea level, the Japanese "Subaru" large optical-infrared telescope atop Mauna Kea on the island of Hawaii is home to Canon ultra-high performance lens technology.

With an 8.2-meter diameter, the telescope's main mirror is the largest in the world, and is equipped with an optical system that creates an image at the principal focus — an unheard-of feature in large reflecting telescopes. And it is Canon lens technology which made the principal focus correction optical system possible. Canon developed this system using the concept of "smaller and lighter" in order to solve the problem of how to fit it onto the principal focus of the telescope — a feat otherwise impossible using conventional optical design. Indeed, compared to the original design specifications, Canon succeeded in making the system 70% smaller and 50% lighter than it would have turned out otherwise.

This principal focus correction optical system possesses a field of view of 30 arc-minutes, which is overwhelmingly wider than that of other large telescopes, and it is also equipped with a mechanism that uses a shift method to deliver high-precision optical correction of atmospheric dispersion, a phenomenon that causes light entering the earth's atmosphere to turn different colors due to the varying index of refraction of each wavelength. Astronomy – observing distant celestial bodies to find out how the universe was created. Here, too, Canon's optical technology is hard at work.

Subaru's principal focus correction optical system

The Subaru Observatory

Digital Cameras and Digital Video Camcorders

Canon High-Performance Lens Technology also at Work in the Field of Digital Imaging

Digital imaging devices are now mainstream and continue to advance by leaps and bounds in terms of image quality and operability. Recognizing that lens performance significantly influences the image quality and desirability of digital cameras and video camcorders, Canon incorporates leading lens technology developed originally for EF lenses to meet the most demanding expectations of users. For example, Canon's IXY DIGITAL/PowerShot DIGITAL ELPH/DIGITAL IXUS series cameras, renowned for their wealth of functions and ease of use, offer superb image quality and surprisingly high zoom ratios thanks to UA aspherical lens elements boasting a super-high refractive index and UD lens elements that efficiently reduce color aberrations. Moreover, most models feature a lens-shift Image Stabilizer mechanism that greatly reduces the incidence of camera-shake blur. Canon's interchangeable lenses for XL series digital video camcorders and advanced lens technology in High Definition consumer-level compact cameras like the HF21 have also received widespread acclaim.

Broadcasting Equipment

Canon TV Zoom Lenses Play a Key Role Worldwide

Just turn on the television to reveal the world as seen by Canon. With a vast lineup of feature-rich lenses ideally suited for covering sports, studio productions, and news broadcasts, Canon's professional TV zoom lenses can be found in television stations just about anywhere in the world.

The growing popularity of HDTV requires lenses capable of superior image quality and increasingly higher standards of performance. Widely diverse TV programming also creates a strong demand for lenses with wider angle of view, greater zoom ratios, and other technological enhancements. These changes are continually driving the need for optical image stabilizer, autofocus, and other new functions for smoother, easier operation.

By developing products to satisfy the needs of professionals, Canon has become a major supplier to the broadcasting industry. In 2002, we released the world's first broadcast-use zoom lens with a triple-digit zoom ratio. This 100x zoom lens includes optical image stabilizer and HDTV support, as well as an expanded angle of view of 38mm to 7600mm (35mm SLR camera standards). Later, in 2007, precision autofocus was added, making this revolutionary lens fully capable of meeting the exacting standards of HDTV.

PowerShot G11

IXY DIGITAL 930 IS
PowerShot SD980 IS DIGITAL ELPH
DIGITAL IXUS 200 IS

HJ14ex4.3B
(HDTV portable type 14x zoom lens)

HJ40x10B
(HDTV portable type 40x zoom lens)

HD 20x zoom lens XL 5.4-108mm L IS Ⅲ attached to XL H1S digital video camcorder

DIGISUPER 100AF (HDTV autofocus 100x zoom lens with optical image stabilizer)

Semiconductor Manufacturing Equipment

Supporting the Progress of Electronic Technology: Ultra-High-Resolution Canon Lenses

CPUs, LSIs, memory, and other high-precision electronic components are essential to the operation of computers and other electronic equipment. Behind the manufacturing of such components is semiconductor exposure equipment which projects intricate electronic circuit patterns over and over onto silicon wafers during the manufacturing process for large integrated semiconductor chips. The development and manufacture of semiconductor exposure equipment requires positioning and control technologies which make it possible to move superior optics and silicon wafers at high speeds and with ultra-high precision. Canon is one of the few makers of semiconductor exposure equipment in the world, and has always contributed as a leading company in the field.

In response to the growing demand for semiconductor miniaturization, Canon is honing its liquid filtering exposure technologies to enable their eventual practical application. In response to the growing demand for semiconductor miniaturization, Canon has developed liquid immersion exposure technology. This employs an ArF (argon fluoride) excimer laser as the light source and ultra-pure water in the gap between the water and the semiconductor exposure device projection optics. The technology enables ultra miniaturization of circuit line width down to 45 nanometers (1 nanometers = 1/1,000,000mm), a significant improvement over 65 nanometers, which was previously assumed to be the smallest width possible due to technological limitations.

Office Automation Equipment

High-Precision Optical Technology: The Heart of Laser Beam Printers

Canon holds an overwhelming world market share for laser beam printers. At the heart of the laser beam printer is the laser scanner unit. The laser is reflected by a four- to six-sided polygon mirror rotating at 10,000 to 20,000 rpm and then scanned onto a photosensitive drum.

To print an image with a resolution of about 560 dots per square millimeter, the drum scanning must be ultra-precise. Canon laser beam printers feature state-of-the-art electronics, precision optics, and manufacturing technologies. They include a polygon mirror with a finish smoother than one-fifth of the wavelength (780nm) of the laser used, a motor which spins this mirror at high speed, and a special optical system which uses an aspherical element. Canon precision optics technology is a traditional stronghold and continues to play an important role in a variety of fields.

The photograph below shows the laser scanner unit for an economy-priced laser beam printer designed for small and home offices. Use of a special aspherical element to which plastic molded lens technology has been applied permits the printer to achieve high performance and low cost.

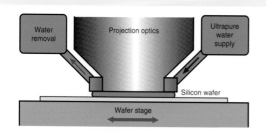

Liquid film filtering method using ultrapure water

FPA-7000AS7

LBP laser scanner lens optics

Medical Equipment

Contributing to Human Health:
Another Type of Canon Lens

Advances in modern medical equipment lead to healthier, more productive lives. Canon's contributions in this field are well appreciated, especially in the development of retinal cameras — invaluable for diagnosing different types of eye disorders as well as helpful in the early detection of adult diseases that may cause loss of vision, such as diabetes and glaucoma. Our retinal cameras are world renowned for superbly detailed images of the retina. Non-mydriatic retinal cameras from Canon, which show the retina at the back of the eye without the need for pupil dilation, are widely used for early patient screening. Additionally, our mydriatic retinal cameras are highly useful for detailed examination of diseased eyes. We also offer Myd/Non-myd Hybrid retinal cameras with Fundus Auto Fluorescence for capturing images. These precision instruments are widely used in the medical field and have contributed greatly to improved eye care worldwide.

Canon also produces the Auto-Ref. Keratometer, a device which simultaneously measures eye refraction and cornea shape for optometric and contact lens applications.

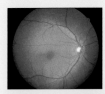

Retinal Image

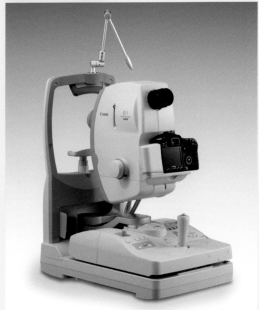

Digital Retinal Camera CX-1

The Basics of Interchangeable Lenses

Relationship between SLR Camera Structure and Lens

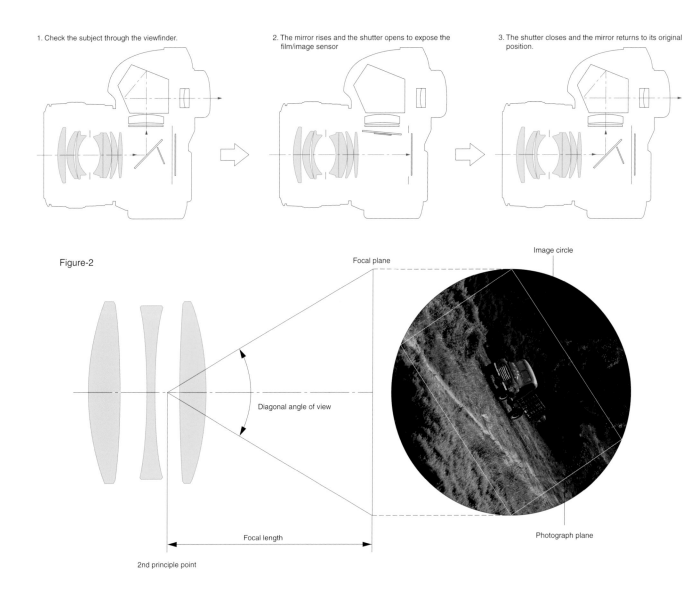

Figure-1

1. Check the subject through the viewfinder.

2. The mirror rises and the shutter opens to expose the film/image sensor

3. The shutter closes and the mirror returns to its original position.

Figure-2

Image circle

Focal plane

Diagonal angle of view

Photograph plane

Focal length

2nd principle point

What does the world look like through a lens?
Construction and characteristics of the SLR camera.

The single-lens reflex (SLR) camera construction makes it possible to use a wide variety of interchangeable lenses to build the optimum system for photography. This is the attraction of the SLR camera. The major characteristic of this camera is the viewfinder system. Because the image that actually reaches the focal plane is displayed in the viewfinder, the image that will be captured digitally or on film can be checked in advance.

The light rays that pass through the lens are deflected upward by a mirror in front of the lens to show the image in a focusing screen that is equidistant with the focal plane. A pentaprism is then used to correctly orient and project the image before it is seen through the eyepiece. When the shutter button is pressed, the mirror rises up and the shutter opens to expose the film or image sensor. When the shutter closes, the mirror returns to its original position (Figure-1).

This makes it possible to accurately frame images without being affected by parallax, a problem with compact cameras, which have different light paths for the shooting lens and the viewfinder.

How different focal lengths can change your shots.

The impression given by a photograph can be greatly changed by using a variety of different lenses for different purposes. In particular, differences in lens focal length greatly change the range (angle of view), perspective, and depth of field of the

Figure-3

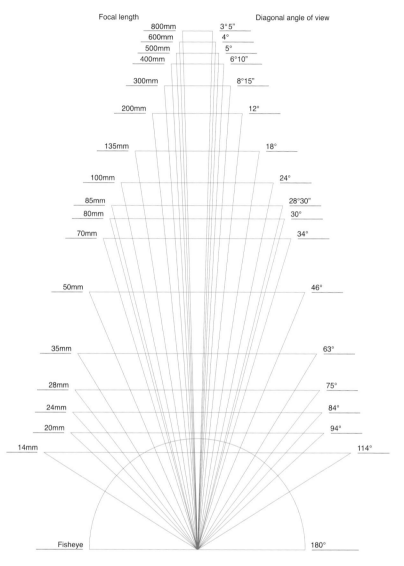

Focal length — Diagonal angle of view

Focal length	Diagonal angle of view
800mm	3°5"
600mm	4°
500mm	5°
400mm	6°10"
300mm	8°15"
200mm	12°
135mm	18°
100mm	24°
85mm	28°30"
80mm	30°
70mm	34°
50mm	46°
35mm	63°
28mm	75°
24mm	84°
20mm	94°
14mm	114°
Fisheye	180°

Photo 1
Photographed using an EF28-135mm f/3.5-5.6 IS USM

28mm

50mm

135mm

subject being photographed.

The angle of view is expressed as the angle of the range being photographed, so it is generally shown as the angle of the diagonal direction. Naturally, the image captured by the lens is circular — not a rectangle the size of the focal plane — and this image is called an "image circle." The image that is actually photographed is taken from the center of the image circle (Figure-2).

In the case of a 35mm camera, the angle of view (diagonal view angle) is 180° using a 15mm fisheye lens, 46° using a 50mm lens, 24° for a 100mm lens, 12° for a 200mm lens, and about 3.5° for a 800mm telephoto lens, so the longer the focal length, the narrower the angle of view (Figure-3). The angle of view becomes approximately 1/2 when the focal length is x2

and the photographed area becomes 1/4.

Photo 1 shows photographs taken using 28mm, 50mm, and 135mm focal lengths. The composition changes dramatically from a wide view showing the table and surrounding area to a close-up of the subject.

Screen change in accordance with focal length

15mm (fisheye)

14mm

28mm

35mm

100mm

135mm

400mm

600mm

20mm

24mm

50mm

85mm

200mm

300mm

800mm

Understanding focal length allows you to select the appropriate lens.

This series of photographs shows how lenses with different focal lengths photograph the same location.

The shorter the focal length of the lens, the wider the scene coverage, and the longer the focal length, the narrower the scene coverage.

As was mentioned on the previous page, when the focal length is 2x, the area of the photographed image is 1/4, so it is useful to remember the degree of change, especially for the lenses you normally use. For example, being able to imagine that the dome, which is the main subject using 50mm, gradually appears closer when using 100mm, 200mm, and 300mm without looking in the viewfinder is useful when selecting lenses.

Perspective/Depth of field

f/1.4

f/22

f/2.8

f/5.6

f/11

The depth of field is the range that is in focus.
The smaller the aperture, the deeper the depth of field.

The depth of field is the range in front of and behind the subject that is in focus. The depth of field is greatly changed in accordance with various conditions that include the lens' focal length, aperture setting, position in focus, photographing distance, and the difference in distance between the main subject and the background.

Photo 5 shows that under the same shooting conditions, the smaller the aperture is made, the wider the depth of field becomes. In addition, the range in focus is a ratio of approximately 1:2 with the range being shallower in front and deeper behind the actual focusing distance.

Further, the "blurring" of the area away from the depth of field produces different photographic effects depending on the lens that is used, so it is important to use this effect skillfully to produce works that have a sense of perspective.

In addition, at the same aperture setting, the depth of field can be made shallower by decreasing the photographing distance or deeper by increasing it. Also, shortening the lens focal length makes the depth of field deeper, and increasing the focal length makes the depth of field shallower at any given distance. The distance between the subject and the background also greatly affects the depth of field. For example, even when a wide aperture telephoto lens is used to shoot a portrait, if there is no distance between the person and the background, the background cannot be blurred, and even when a wide-angle lens with a deep depth of field is used, blurred backgrounds can be created during close-up photography.

16mm

24mm

50mm

200mm

135mm

Perspective is the visual effect of the photographic world.
Effectively using perspective, such as for creating dynamic wide-angle photos and compressed effects with telephoto lenses, makes it possible to produce expressive photographs with impact. Perspective is the visual effect that determines how close or far away the background appears to be from the subject. The shorter the focal length of the lens, the more this effect is expressed, and the longer the focal length of the lens, the less this effect is expressed and the more compressed the photograph looks.

Looking at a series of images photographed by changing the shooting distance while keeping the subject the same size makes this effect readily apparent. It is easy to see how the perspective is greatly changed depending on the focal length.

Compare the above 16mm and 200mm photographs, with the wide angle lens, it looks like the background is stretching out far behind the subject. Conversely, using a telephoto lens there appears to be very little distance between the two, which gives the photograph a compressed feeling.

In other words, comparing the apparent distance between the subject and the background as the focusing distance and the focal length of the lens are varied shows how perspective is created. For this reason, even when you want to keep the person the same size, use a wide-angle lens when you want to have a panoramic background, and a telephoto lens when you want to adjust the background to emphasize the subject. This is why it is important to differentiate between which lenses to use depending on the desired photographic effect.

Special characteristics of EF-S lenses

EF-S60mm
f/2.8 Macro USM

EF-S10-22mm
f/3.5-4.5 USM

EF-S15-85mm
f/3.5-5.6 IS USM

EF-S17-55mm
f/2.8 IS USM

EF-S17-85mm
f/4-5.6 IS USM

EF-S18-55mm
f/3.5-5.6 IS

EF-S18-55mm
f/3.5-5.6 II

EF-S18-135mm
f/3.5-5.6 IS

EF-S18-200mm
f/3.5-5.6 IS

EF-S55-250mm
f/4-5.6 IS

Optical System of the EF-S Lenses

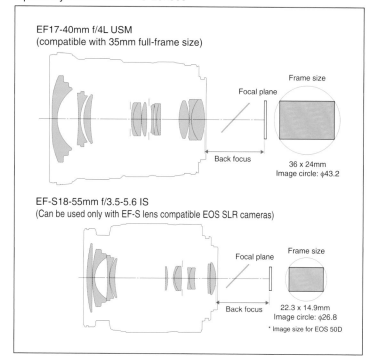

EF17-40mm f/4L USM
(compatible with 35mm full-frame size)

Focal plane

Frame size

Back focus

36 x 24mm
Image circle: φ43.2

EF-S18-55mm f/3.5-5.6 IS
(Can be used only with EF-S lens compatible EOS SLR cameras)

Focal plane

Frame size

Back focus

22.3 x 14.9mm
Image circle: φ26.8
* Image size for EOS 50D

Comparison of Rear Portions of Lenses

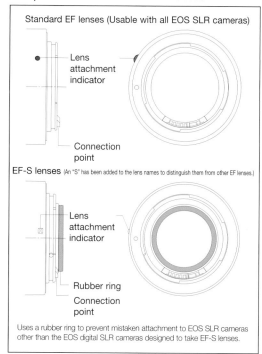

Standard EF lenses (Usable with all EOS SLR cameras)

Lens
attachment
indicator

Connection
point

EF-S lenses (An "S" has been added to the lens names to distinguish them from other EF lenses.)

Lens
attachment
indicator

Rubber ring

Connection
point

Uses a rubber ring to prevent mistaken attachment to EOS SLR cameras
other than the EOS digital SLR cameras designed to take EF-S lenses.

EF-S lenses redefine "compact and lightweight."

Our EF-S lenses feature optical systems and lens mechanisms designed specifically for digital SLR cameras employing sensors of the APS-C frame size, which is smaller than that of the 35mm format. In addition to possessing a smaller image circle than other EF lenses to match the smaller frame size, they also allow adoption of short back focus (distance from the rear of the lens to the focal plane) made possible by the compact quick return mirrors in the camera bodies.*

The APS-C sized sensor gives the camera a 1.6x focal length conversion factor over the 35mm film format, resulting in an angle of view biased towards telephoto.

Currently, EF-S lenses are available in focal lengths between 10mm and 250mm. From super wide-angle to telephoto and macro, these superb optics fulfill nearly any photographic requirement.

* Some EF-S lenses do not employ a short back focus optical system.
Note: EF-S lens compatible cameras: EOS DIGITAL SLR cameras: EOS 7D, EOS 50D, EOS 40D, EOS 30D, EOS 20D, EOS 20Da, EOS Kiss X3/REBEL T1i/500D, EOS Kiss X2/DIGITAL REBEL XSi/450D, EOS Kiss F/DIGITAL REBEL XS/1000D, EOS Kiss Digital X/DIGITAL REBEL XTi/400D DIGITAL, EOS Kiss Digital N/DIGITAL REBEL XT/350D DIGITAL, EOS Kiss Digital/DIGITAL REBEL/300D DIGITAL (As of October 2009.)

Measures to prevent EF-S lenses from being mistakenly mounted on incompatible EOS cameras.

The EF-S lenses are designed in such a way that their mechanism fits completely only into the bodies of EOS SLR cameras that support EF-S lenses, and are fitted with a rubber ring at the rear of the lens to prevent damage to the camera body in the event of mistaken attempts to attach them to incompatible EOS SLR cameras. EF-S lenses also feature both a different attachment position and a white rectangular lens mounting index that differs in shape and color from other EF lenses to help prevent inadvertent attempts to attach these lenses to incompatible EOS SLR cameras.

A complete lineup of lenses is available, from wide-angle and telephoto to macro and large diameter, as well as lenses for special applications.

■EF-S60mm f/2.8 Macro USM

With a focal length equivalent to approximately 96mm in 35mm format, this medium telephoto macro lens is able to cover in-focus shooting from life-size macro photography to infinity. It can handle a broad range of subjects including not only macro shots of flowers, insects and small animals, but also scenery, portraits and snapshots.

■EF-S10-22mm f/3.5-4.5 USM

Featuring a 35mm-equivalent focal-length coverage of 16-35mm, this ultra wide-angle zoom lens dramatically expands the field of view beyond the range of human eyes. This capability makes it perfect for shooting expansive seascapes or zooming in on large fields of flowers.

■EF-S15-85mm f/3.5-5.6 IS USM

This compact, standard zoom lens covers focal lengths equivalent to 24mm through 136mm in 35mm format and delivers outstanding image quality. It offers a wide angle of view, approximately 5.7x magnification and IS (image stabilizer) as well as supreme ease of use. These and other features make the EF-S15-85mm f/3.5-5.6 IS USM an excellent choice as a "standard" lens.

■EF-S17-55mm f/2.8 IS USM

This large-diameter zoom lens covers a focal length range equivalent to 27-88mm in the 35mm format. Its f/2.8 maximum aperture with circular diaphragm achieves beautiful background blur, and a mechanism for camera-shake blur compensation makes it ideal for use in a wide variety of shooting conditions, including portrait shots in natural lighting.

■EF-S17-85mm f/4-5.6 IS USM

This 5x zoom lens with a focal length range equivalent to 27-136mm in 35mm format covers from wide angle to telephoto photography. Its high zoom range makes it a highly versatile lens for almost all shooting needs — from landscape and group photos to snapshots and portraits.

■EF-S18-55mm f/3.5-5.6 IS/EF-S18-55mm f/3.5-5.6 II

These standard zoom lenses are lightweight and compact with a focal length range equivalent to 29 to 88mm in 35mm format. Highly mobile, the lenses enable shooting a wide range of subjects, from group shots and city streets to portraits with superb background blur. Additionally, the Image Stabilizer of the EF-S18-55mm f/3.5-5.6 IS assists in obtaining blur-free photos even when shooting in dim natural light.

■EF-S18-135mm f/3.5-5.6 IS

Explore a wide variety of artistic effects provided by this 7.5x magnification IS telephoto lens with focal lengths equivalent to 29-216mm in 35mm format.

■EF-S18-200mm f/3.5-5.6 IS

This ultra high-power zoom lens has a focal length range equivalent to 29 to 320mm in 35mm format. A wide zoom ratio of approximately 11x and built-in Image Stabilizer make it ideal for nearly any subject. Owing to its high mobility, it is also an excellent choice when you want to carry as little equipment as possible, such as when traveling or mountain climbing.

■EF-S55-250mm f/4-5.6 IS

This telephoto zoom lens has a focal length range equivalent to 88-400mm in 35mm format. Equipped with an IS unit that prevents camera shake — a major concern when shooting with a long lens — this addition to the EF-S lineup enhances creative expression via a variety of photographic techniques, including background blurring and perspective compression.

10mm (equivalent to 16mm in 35mm format)

EF-S10-22mm f/3.5-4.5 USM

85mm (equivalent to 136mm in 35mm format)

EF-S17-85mm f/4-5.6 IS USM

250mm (equivalent to 400mm in 35mm format)

EF-S55-250mm f/4-5.6 IS

Benefits of In-lens image stabilization

Viewfinder image with IS on

Viewfinder image with IS off

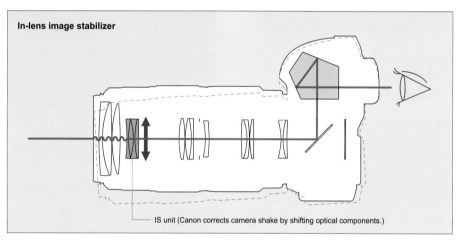

In-lens image stabilizer

IS unit (Canon corrects camera shake by shifting optical components.)

IS lenses greatly expand the joy of photography.

Camera shake becomes more noticeable as the shutter speed decreases or the focal length increases. As a rule of thumb, the slowest shutter speed at which hand-held photos can be taken without causing camera shake is generally accepted to be the inverse of the focal length (e.g. 1/300 sec. for a 300mm lens). For digital SLR cameras equipped with an APS-C sensor, this changes to the inverse of the focal length multiplied by 1.6. For example, in order to prevent camera shake for hand-held shots when using a 100mm lens with an APS-C digital camera, the slowest shutter speed would be 1/160 sec. or faster (i.e. 1/100 x 1.6).

In low light situations, flash or tripods essentially eliminate concerns for camera shake, but are not always suitable solutions. Flash may ruin the atmosphere of a naturally lit scene such as a sunset or interior, and tripods lack mobility and flexibility so vital to sports photographers. Canon IS lenses, however, compensate for camera shake, allowing shutter speeds that are considerably slower than generally thought acceptable for hand-held shooting. These lenses have an Image Stabilizer unit, which precisely shifts the optical system perpendicular to the optical axis in order to stabilize incoming light rays.

Look through the viewfinder and see the difference in-lens image stabilization makes.

Basic to shooting with an SLR camera is using the viewfinder to frame and focus. Since images are formed by light passing through the lens and reflected up to the viewfinder, camera shake must be minimized in the lens or else the viewfinder image will also suffer. Using an IS lens solves this problem, not only for the final photo, but also for the image seen through the viewfinder. A steady image facilitates precise framing and focusing with the end result being better photographs. For example, when shooting portraits, subtle changes in facial expressions can be noticed, making it easier to choose the right moment to press the shutter. This is why Canon is committed to providing SLR camera users with precise, accurate in-lens image stabilization.

Canon in-lens stabilization allows you to obtain a sharply focused image even when shooting at longer focal lengths.

Optical correction systems placement

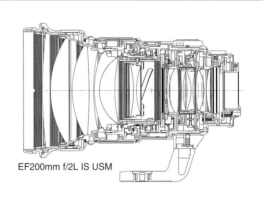

EF200mm f/2L IS USM

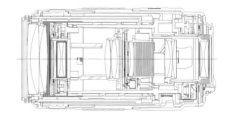

EF70-300mm f/4-5.6 IS USM

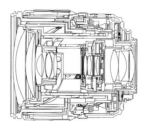

EF-S15-85mm f/3.5-5.6 IS USM

☐ : OPTICAL CORRECTION SYSTEMS

Image stabilization designed to fit the specific characteristics of each Canon lens results in highly accurate camera shake compensation.

Each Canon lens has its own unique optical design. By taking into account the different characteristics of each lens, the Image Stabilizer unit can be precisely located to better correct camera shake. This is one reason why Canon has been able to achieve such a high level of camera shake compensation over the entire range of IS lenses, from wide-angle to super telephoto lenses.

Correspondence of EF Lens to Digital Photography

Image size and lens selection

35mm full size and digital shooting range image size (picture dimensions) and lens selection

EOS-1D Mark Ⅳ

EOS 7D*

— **EOS-1Ds Mark Ⅲ / EOS 5D Mark Ⅱ**   — **EOS-1D Mark Ⅳ**   — **EOS 7D***

Differences in image size

Digital SLR cameras contain CMOS or CCD image sensors instead of film. The size of the sensor determines the size of the image (picture dimensions), which varies depending on the camera body. Canon digital SLR cameras have images in the following three sizes.

36.0 x 24.0mm (EOS-1Ds Mark Ⅲ, EOS 5D Mark Ⅱ)

27.9 x 18.6mm (EOS-1D Mark Ⅳ)

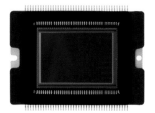

22.3 x 14.9mm (EOS 7D)

Image size and effective angle of view

Differences in image size affect the actual area that appears in the photograph, or, put another way, the effective angle of view. The EOS-1Ds Mark Ⅲ/EOS 5D Mark Ⅱ has an image size equivalent to that of 35mm film, while the EOS-1D Mark Ⅳ has a smaller image size, and the image size of the EOS 7D* is even smaller. The smaller the image size, the smaller the effective angle of view becomes at any given focal length. As the above image size comparisons show, using a 100mm lens with the EOS-1D Mark Ⅳ and EOS 7D will produce photographs with effective angles of view approximately equivalent to photos taken with a 130mm lens and a 160mm lens, respectively, on the EOS-1Ds Mark Ⅲ/EOS 5D Mark Ⅱ. In other words, the focal length conversion factor for the EOS-1D Mark Ⅳ is about 1.3 times that of regular 35mm film image, and about 1.6 times for the EOS 7D.

This effect can be used to your advantage to increase the effect of using a telephoto or macro lens in order to bring the subject in even closer. On the other hand, wide-angle photography will require an even wider lens.

* EOS 50D, EOS Kiss X3/REBEL T1i/500D, EOS Kiss F/DIGITAL REBEL XS/1000D SLR camera have similar image size as the EOS 7D.

Selecting a wide-angle lens

For the EOS 7D, for example, shooting in the focal length range of 16mm can obtain the same angle of view as that shot with a 25mm focal length range by a 35mm full-size camera. The perspective is determined by the shooting distance, so Photo 1 and Photo 2 will have the same perspective. In other

35mm full-size camera with 16mm focal length

— **EOS-1Ds Mark Ⅲ / EOS 5D Mark Ⅱ** — **EOS 7D***

Photo 1

35mm full-size camera with 25mm focal length

Photo 2 || Equivalent angle of view

EOS 7D* with 16mm focal length

words, to obtain the same angle of view as when shooting at 35mm full size with an EOS 7D, a wider lens must be selected. The EF lens series contains a full line of wide-angle zoom lenses and wide-angle single focal-length lenses, including the EF16-35mm f/2.8L II USM, EF17-40mm f/4L USM, EF24-70mm f/2.8L USM, and EF-S10-22mm f/3.5-4.5 USM to allow you to select the lens that matches the camera body's screen size.

Depth of field and perspective

The EF85mm f/1.8 USM lens is effectively a 136mm f/1.8 lens in terms of angle of view when attached to the EOS 7D. Looking at these specs, it would seem possible to take a photograph with a shallower depth of field than if the EF135mm f/2L USM were used with 35mm film, but this is not the case. Since the focal length does not actually change, the depth of field in terms of the sensors and the blurred image in the out-of-focus area remain the same for the EF85mm f/1.8 USM. And if the image is enlarged to the size of an A3 print (approx. 11 x 14 inches), the amount of enlargement required by the EOS 7D is greater than that for 35mm film size, because its screen size is smaller. Nevertheless the depth of field on the print will be shallower for the latter combination, creating greater blur in the background. This means that if you want to achieve more blur in the background using the EOS 7D, you will have to shoot at a larger aperture. Furthermore, perspective is related to angle of view, so even if the focal length is different for each particular lens, if the resulting angle is the same due to the difference in image size, as in the photographs shown above, the perspective will remain

unchanged, too.

Selecting a lens from our broad line-up

The differences in angle of view for each screen size might cause confusion when you first use a digital SLR camera. However, once you get used to this new aspect, you will be able to use these differences to your advantage in creating new angles of view and depths of field for each lens. Part of the appeal of the EF lens series lies in the wide range of selection they offer you with a line-up of over 60 lenses, allowing you find just the right lens for your needs.

Full lineup of EF lenses

163

How to deal with flaring and ghosting particular to digital photography

For flat protective glass

In lenses employing flat protective glass, a reflection occurs between the image sensor and the protective glass, which causes the subject to be photographed in a position different from the actual position.

For a meniscus lens

In lenses employing a meniscus lens, no reflection like that seen to the left occurs.

Protective glass (flat glass)

Light ray reflected by the protective glass

Image sensor

Entering light ray

Light ray reflected by the image sensor surface

Spherical protective glass (meniscus lens)

Light ray reflected by the protective glass

Entering light ray

Light ray reflected by the image sensor surface

Reflective characteristics of image sensors

The reflective characteristics of the image sensors in a digital camera differ from those of film in that they possess a higher reflectivity as well as a characteristic known as regular or "mirror" reflection, which has the effect of creating flaring and ghosting inside the lens when light from a bright source enters the lens and reflects back to the image sensor. In order to resolve this problem particular to digital cameras, a new approach to optical design has already been adopted, with the goal of bringing the outstanding imaging performance of EF lenses to digital photography. This is, after all, the mission of EF lenses in the digital age, because they occupy the core of the EOS system, whether film or digital.

Use of meniscus lenses

Players in a stadium or racecars whizzing round the circuit. All are lit up by the bright lighting in the stands, or the headlights on the cars, creating numerous bright light sources. Ordinary super-telephoto lenses have protective glass in front of the first lens unit. If this glass is flat, any light entering the lens from a bright light source will be reflected off the image sensor and back onto the inside of the protective element, causing spot-shaped ghosting.* To prevent this, meniscus lenses are used as the protective glass on all of Canon's large-aperture IS super-telephoto lenses. Meniscus lenses are spherical lenses which have the same curvature on both sides of the lens. By using these lenses as the protective glass, the light reflected off the image sensor forms an image in front of the image sensor and then disperse. Since almost all the light

Many telephoto lenses, including the EF300mm f/2.8L IS USM employ a meniscus lens to suppress internal reflection of the image that occurs in digital cameras.

Lens for which the lens shape and coating have not been optimized

Flaring and ghosting occurs with lens for which the lens shape and coating have not been optimized.

Lens for which the lens shape and coating have been optimized

Flaring and ghosting are suppressed with lens for which the lens shape and coating have been optimized.

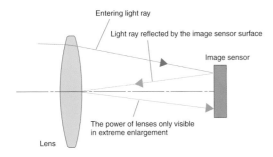

Entering light ray

Light ray reflected by the image sensor surface

Image sensor

The power of lenses only visible in extreme enlargement

Lens

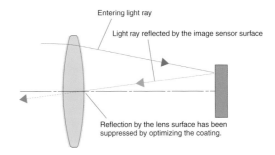

Entering light ray

Light ray reflected by the image sensor surface

Reflection by the lens surface has been suppressed by optimizing the coating.

which is dispersed does not hit the reflective elements, this prevents ghosting while at the same time achieving high contrast for the resulting image.

Large-aperture IS super-telephoto lenses used in sports stadiums and racing circuits can now deliver the expressiveness needed by professional photographers using digital SLR cameras thanks to their outstanding imaging performance.

* When a filter is mounted on a regular lens, ghosting can occur above the same spot where there is a strong light source inside the frame. When this occurs, remove the filter to photograph.

Super-telephoto lenses using meniscus lenses
- EF300mm f/2.8L IS USM
- EF400mm f/4 DO IS USM
- EF600mm f/4L IS USM
- EF400mm f/2.8L IS USM
- EF500mm f/4L IS USM
- EF800mm f/5.6L IS USM

Optimum lens shape and coating
Even when using lenses without built-in protective glass, the particular photographic conditions might mean that using a digital camera will result in more flaring and ghosting than if a film camera were used. If a strong light source is present inside the frame, the light reflected off the image sensor can create complex reflective patterns inside the lens, resulting in flaring and ghosting. To prevent this effect particular to digital photography, we have optimized the shape and coating of

f/2.8L zoom series, including the EF16-35mm f/2.8L II USM, and other models such as the EF17-40mm f/4L USM. Specifically, each lens element has a different design, in order to reduce the amount of repeated reflection inside the lens. Further, the lens surface, which has a large effect on reflectivity, is treated with a special multi-layer coating with high transmittance. This allows any light reflected off the image sensor to escape out of the lens in the direction of the subject, thus reducing flaring and ghosting. And Canon's legendary color balance is not compromised, thanks to an exact balance between multi-layer and single-layer coatings.

An optimized coating is used for the EF16-35mm f/2.8L II USM and other lenses to suppress the flaring and ghosting that occurs easily with digital cameras.

The power of lenses only visible in extreme enlargements

When the lens has high resolution

When the lens has low resolution

Even when combined with a digital camera, an EF lens has high potential. In this photo of a harbor crowded with yachts, high resolution reveals the fine detail in individual boats. Photographing images with detailed subject matter, such as landscapes, is possible without having to differentiate between a digital camera and a 35mm film camera.

The fun of extreme digital enlargements

Thanks to the improved performance of ink-jet printers, some models can achieve quality equal to that of gelatin silver prints. Add to this the lower cost of printing afforded by a printer and the ability to manipulate the image on a computer, and you are close to realizing an ideal in image reproduction. It is for these and other reasons that there will likely be more and more chances to experience the fun of enlarging digital images to sizes of up to A4 and A3 (approximately 8.5 x 11 and 11 x 14 inches, respectively).

Choosing a lens with high resolution

While the same can be said about gelatin silver prints for film cameras, when enlarging a digital photograph many times, the power of the work is largely determined by the sharpness of the image. Shooting with a high-resolution lens produces more impressive shots when enlarging digital images to sizes of up to A4 and A3. The EF lens series contains a broad line-up of high-resolution lenses, including the L-type lenses, which deliver an extremely sharp result for enlargements of digital photographs.

Choosing a lens with little color aberration

Axial color aberration often found in telephoto lenses and the chromatic difference in magnification often caused by wide-angle lenses appear in photographs as colors which run over dividing lines in the subject. This type of color running is more noticeable the larger the size of the print, causing a deterioration in the overall quality of the image.

The L-type lenses in the EF lens series employ fluorite, UD, and super UD lens elements to correct the aberrations mentioned for telephoto and wide-angle lenses. The EF400mm f/4 DO IS USM and EF70-300mm f/4.5-5.6 DO IS USM have DO lens elements, which are very effective in suppressing strong color aberration. The effects of these special optical materials and the DO lenses are most evident when a photograph is extremely enlarged. And since less color aberration means greater overall image sharpness, the result is very good even for very big enlargements.

Image stabilizing IS lenses

Another factor that increases in visibility with larger print sizes is blur caused by hand movement when taking the photograph. This is a small factor, but can ruin an otherwise excellent photograph.

The effects of hand movement can appear more pronounced depending on the size of the image in the digital camera. For example, since the image in the EOS 7D is smaller than in a 35mm film camera, making a print of the same size involves enlarging the original image to a greater degree. And since the more a photograph is enlarged, the more blur becomes evident, a similar amount of hand movement will be more

When the lens corrects the magnification color aberration

When the lens does not correct the magnification color aberration

Axial chromatic aberration (also called "chromatic difference of magnification") occurs because of variations in the wavelength or frequency of light reflected from the subject. This phenomenon not only reduces photo sharpness, but it can also create borders of color, which should not be present, at the edges of subjects in the image. EF lenses designed to counter chromatic aberration make it possible to achieve uniform sharpness and correct color reproduction from the center of a photo to its edges.

noticeable with the EOS 7D.

The current EF lens series contains a line-up of 24 IS lenses, covering the spectrum from wide-angle to super-telephoto. Using the right IS lens for the scene can allow you to achieve sharp image performance with little evident blur even when making large prints.

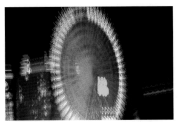

IS OFF

IS ON

IS Lens Series Line-up
- EF100mm f/2.8L Macro IS USM
- EF200mm f/2L IS USM
- EF300mm f/2.8L IS USM
- EF300mm f/4L IS USM
- EF400mm f/2.8L IS USM
- EF400mm f/4 DO IS USM
- EF500mm f/4L IS USM
- EF600mm f/4L IS USM
- EF800mm f/5.6L IS USM
- EF24-105mm f/4L IS USM
- EF28-135mm f/3.5-5.6 IS USM
- EF28-300mm f/3.5-5.6L IS USM
- EF70-200mm f/2.8L IS USM
- EF70-200mm f/4L IS USM
- EF70-300mm f/4-5.6 IS USM
- EF70-300mm f/4.5-5.6 DO IS USM
- EF100-400mm f/4.5-5.6L IS USM
- EF-S15-85mm f/3.5-5.6 IS USM
- EF-S17-55mm f/2.8 IS USM
- EF-S17-85mm f/4-5.6 IS USM
- EF-S18-55mm f/3.5-5.6 IS
- EF-S18-135mm f/3.5-5.6 IS
- EF-S18-200mm f/3.5-5.6 IS
- EF-S55-250mm f/4-5.6 IS

Color reproduction in digital cameras

When photographing subjects under fluorescent light using AWB (Auto White Balance)

The true color can be reproduced even when under fluorescent lighting.

When photographing subjects under fluorescent light using the white balance mode (sunlight)

The correct color cannot be recreated such as when using "daylight type" color film.

Factors involved in color reproduction

In the case of gelatin silver photographic prints, it is generally believed to be the lens and film which determine the color reproduction. However, in the case of digital cameras, it is not only the lens, but rather the process of how the light received by the image sensor is turned into an image that makes the difference in color reproduction. It is also possible to fine-tune the color reproduction, the white balance setting and the Picture Style selection.

White balance setting

There are two types of general silver halide color film. One is the "daylight type," which provides the correct color balance under sunlight, and the other is the "tungsten type," which provides the correct color balance under tungsten lamp light. In addition, under fluorescent light, the correct color cannot be obtained without using a gelatin filter, etc., to correct the color tones.

Digital cameras, however, do not require such methods. Instead of choosing film types for different light sources and filters for color compensation and color warmth, the white balance is set beforehand to match the lighting conditions. The digital EOS series offers preset white balance modes which can be selected for natural light, shade, cloudy conditions, incandescent lighting, fluorescent lighting, and flash photography. Not only that, but the white balance can be adjusted manually or automatically. The blue shadow-like effect seen in portraits taken in the shade using daylight-type color film is no longer a problem, thanks to the white balance adjustment offered by digital photography.

Picture Style (Landscape)

This photograph was taken using Picture Style (Landscape) with a high saturation setting.

Picture Style (Standard)

This was photographed using Picture Style (Standard).

Versatile Picture Styles

Different types of film exhibit distinct characteristics — even film of the same type such as daylight color film. For example, one brand of film may be well suited for portraiture owing to the natural skin colors that can be obtained while another may be more desirable for nature photography due to its highly saturated colors. Because of these differences, photographers have their favorites depending on subject and shooting environment.

Canon EOS Picture Styles act in much the same way as film. Each Picture Style embeds key image attributes such as sharpness, contrast, color density and hue in order to give photos a particular look and feel. By selecting the Picture Style that best suits a specific purpose, photographers can control the look of photos when shooting in order to decrease post-shooting operations.

Picture Styles can be applied to RAW image data while performing post-shooting operations on a PC using Canon's bundled Digital Photo Professional software. You can also create custom Picture Styles, which can be likened to designing your own film. Furthermore, additional Picture Styles can be downloaded from Canon's website onto a PC, then uploaded to an EOS digital camera. Canon offers a wide variety of Picture Styles, including ones that enhance emerald green and other hard-to-reproduce colors such as yellow leaves in autumn scenes. Take advantage of the versatility provided by Picture Styles to obtain just the right look for a variety of subjects.

Lens color balance

It is often thought that if you can adjust the settings on a digital camera and check the result, you can adjust the color balance of the lens. However, SLR cameras are founded on the assumption of being able to change the lens. Whether you are using a film or digital camera, it is very important that the color reproduction (color balance) of all the lenses be standardized. The traditional standardized color balance that Canon lenses are renowned for is also a vital element in providing an exceptionally convenient photographic environment — even for digital cameras.

xy chromaticity diagram

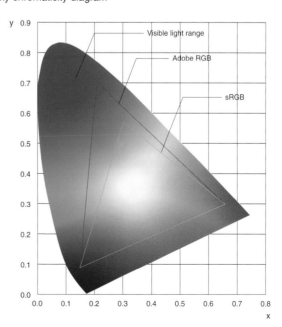

Precautions when using digital cameras

When printed to A3 size

If there is dust on the image sensor, it will be recorded in the photograph. This will especially stand out in large prints.

Do not depend on your computer to fix your images

Images taken using a digital camera can be adjusted for sharpness, brightness, contrast, and other factors using a computer. However, avoid becoming over-dependent on your computer to fix the shortcomings of your photography. The reason is that most image processing is accompanied by a drop in the quality of the image. The basics of good photography are the same for digital cameras as they are for film cameras. If your goal is to take a good photograph, it is of vital importance that you check the exposure and focus and prevent the camera from shaking. It will be safest if you only rely on computer touch ups as a final, complementary aspect of your photography, if you wish to get the most out of your EF lens's image performance.

It is often difficult to achieve better results than the actual photograph by touching up the image afterwards on your computer, especially with JPEG format images, since a standardized type of "developing" (actually a type of digital image processing) takes place inside the camera right when the photograph is taken. If you use a RAW format, you have to process the image on your computer using the bundled software (including Digital Photo Professionals). This process allows you to manipulate the image as you like without causing a drop in image quality — even if the same data is treated over and over. But again, no amount of treatment later can fix a picture that was taken at a wrong exposure, out of focus, or if the camera shook when the picture was being taken.

Preventing dirt and dust from getting in the camera body or onto the lens when changing lenses

Changing lenses in windy places can cause dirt and dust to enter the camera through the lens mount. Any dust that gets on the image sensor may appear as black specks or smudges on the image. To avoid this, we recommend doing the following:

● Change lenses quickly in places where there is no wind
● Always attach the body cap to the camera body when no lens is attached
● Change lenses with the camera mount facing down
● Do not place the camera face down
● Watch out for dust getting inside the body cap on the camera or the lens's dust cap

Image sensors are very delicate. If dirt or dust ever needs to be cleaned off the sensor surface, either do it as described in the camera manual or take the camera to a Canon service center.

Photo Techniques

Portraits

This was photographed using the EF85mm f/1.2L Ⅱ USM medium telephoto zoom lens, which is the standard portrait lens. The objective is to focus on the eyes and adjust the image using a blur effect to transmit a feeling of the surroundings.

Photography that takes advantage of the superiority of large-aperture lenses

Communication between the photographer and the model in portrait photography is very important. For this reason among others, lenses between 50mm and 135mm are often used, in order to maintain a certain distance from the model. The standard zoom lenses which are often sold together with camera bodies cover this focal length range, and are therefore generally suitable for this type of photography. Sometimes, however, it is necessary in portrait photography to use a large-aperture lens with a larger maximum aperture than is offered with such zoom lenses. It goes without saying that getting the most out of the lenses you already have is a good thing, but the powerful effect afforded by a large-aperture lens is the *ne plus ultra* of interchangeable lenses in SLR photography.

The first element is the beauty of the blur. The wider the aperture, the shallower the depth of field becomes, increasing the blur in the out-of-focus areas. 85mm lenses, which are often used for portrait photography, can deliver an impressionistic background blur effect since they are much brighter than zoom lenses. Single focal length lenses generally have a brighter maximum aperture than zoom lenses, making them ideal for photography using a shallower depth of field. And of course if you want to reduce the blur a bit all you have to do is close the aperture the required amount, which gives large-aperture lenses a broader range of expressiveness.

Using f/1.2

When shooting with a large-aparture lens with the aperture open, only the main object clearly stands out.

Using f/4.5

When using a standard zoom lens, the background might not sufficiently blur even when photographing with the aperture open.

IS OFF

This is a hand-held photograph of a city corner at nightfall using an EF28-135mm f/3.5-5.6 IS USM. The shutter speed was slow and the image is not clear due to shaking.

IS ON

The images of the person in the front and the background appear crisp. The images of the people walking in the background are blurred showing that this photograph was taken with a slow shutter speed.

Canon has a large line-up of large-aperture lenses with outstanding optical characteristics. Not only do they allow you to emphasize the subject with their shallow depth of field, but they also deliver excellent image quality compared to zoom lenses.

The extremely shallow depth of field offered by large-aperture lenses when used at maximum aperture means that you have to be extra careful with focusing. Most USM lenses are equipped with full-time manual focusing, making it possible to make small adjustments to the focus even when in autofocus mode, which can be a great help when you have to get the right focus rapidly in difficult focusing conditions.

IS lenses which make shake-free handheld photography possible even in dark places

Portrait photography is not always done outside on sunny days or in a studio with professional lighting equipment. Often the greatest photo ops come outside at dusk or in a poorly lit interior. And there are many places that don't allow the use of tripods. All of these difficult lighting situations are ideal for IS lenses to show off their capabilities.

No matter how beautiful the model's smile or the location, any hand movement during the shot will ruin the photograph. This type of shaking requires the utmost caution and attention especially when blowing up photographs taken with digital cameras.

Methods for preventing the shaking effect of hand movement include using a flash, high sensitivity film for film cameras, and a high ISO sensitivity setting for digital cameras. However, flashes can destroy the lighting atmosphere of a location, high-sensitivity film is grainy, and a high-sensitivity setting on a digital camera will cause noise to be generated in

Soft value 1

This portrait was photographed using an EF135mm f/2.8 lens with a built-in soft focus mechanism. The soft value was set to 1. This image has a soft tone while keeping the facial outline crisp.

the resulting image. With an IS lens, not only does handheld photography become possible in these situations, but image quality is maintained because the effects of hand movement can be suppressed even when using low-sensitivity film.

Using soft-focus lenses

Soft focus is sometimes used when taking portraits of women. This can be done by using either a special soft-focus lens or a soft-focus filter.

Soft-focus filters are inexpensive, but they require care when being used. Many of them achieve the soft focus effect through a clear pattern on the surface of the glass, which can often cause the blurred areas of a photograph to appear

Soft value 0

Setting the soft value to 0 produces a sharp image.

Soft value 2

Setting the soft value to 2 produces a softer image.

splotchy or become too evident and ruin the photographic image. In contrast, specially designed soft-focus lenses deliver a natural, beautiful softening effect that envelops the subject in a soft light, throughout the whole image, and the effect can be adjusted. The EF lens series includes a 135mm soft-focus lens that is easy to use in portrait photography, allowing you to achieve expressive and beautiful soft-focus effects.

Shorten the closest focusing distance with an extension tube

Using medium telephoto and super-telephoto lenses allows you to bring a model's face completely into the frame when using a 35mm or digital SLR held horizontally. However, when you want to get that one step closer for a shot with greater impact, an extension tube can be useful. Although using one will cause distant objects to go out of focus, it will reduce the closest focusing distance of the master lens.

Extension tubes are attached between the lens and the camera body and can be used with most EF lenses, including the EF-S series lenses. They come in two types, the EF12 II and EF25 II, with different thicknesses (approximately 12mm and 25mm respectively), and the EF25 II can be used at closer distances. The amount you can get closer depends on the master lens being used.

Photographed at the EF70-200mm f/2.8L IS USM's closest focusing distance (1.4m)

When shooting portrait photography, a child's face can be made to fill the entire screen.

Photographed using an extension tube

Using an extension tube brings the subject even closer. This is effective when you want to further emphasize impressive areas, such as the eyes or smile.

Macro photography

Capturing a young mantis polishing its forelegs in the shade with pleasingly bright and sharp results. EF100mm f/2.8L Macro IS USM

The Beautiful World of Macro Lenses

Within the EF Lens Series, including EF-S Lenses, there are several macro lenses with different focal lengths and maximum photographic magnification to match all subjects and situations. There is always something new to discover when you glimpse into the world of macro lenses.

Many people think they can photograph flowers and the like with their standard zoom lens, making it unnecessary to buy a macro lens. True enough, many common standard zoom lenses come with a macro function, and are designed to allow a certain level of close-up photography. But using a macro lens which is specifically designed for close-up photography makes it a completely different experience thanks to its much higher photographic magnification. And not just with flowers either — attach a macro lens to your camera and take a look at some of the things around the house for some fun. It's just like when you were a kid and went around looking at things through a magnifying glass. Macro lenses maintain high image quality during the high magnification photography of life-size, 0.5× size, and even 5× magnification. EF50mm f/2.5

Canon macro lens series

Focusing at a winter bud and adjusting the lens opening to make leaves blurred nicely, I captured a mysterious breath of new life.
EF-S60mm f/2.8 Macro USM·1/50 sec.·f/3.2

Compact Macro, EF100mm f/2.8L Macro IS USM, EF100mm f/2.8 Macro USM, EF180mm f/3.5L Macro USM and EF-S60 f/2.8 Macro USM can focus up to infinity, and not just to close distances, so they can be used like normal lenses for landscape and portrait photography. In addition, the brighter maximum aperture of macro lenses provides a greater blur effect for backgrounds. Macro lenses are no longer just for close-up anymore, and can even be used for subjects which are far away. Your photographic enjoyment will grow by adding a macro lens to your standard zoom lens.

Being able to show the subject close up and beautifully blur the background to produce a mysterious effect is the major characteristic of the macro lens. EF-S 60mm f/2.8 Macro USM·1/80 sec.·f/8.0 (1 x magnification)

Photographed at the EF28-135mm f/3.5-5.6 IS USM's 0.19 magnification. 1/250 sec.·f/8.0

●Choosing by focal length

Choosing macro lenses according to focal length actually means choosing according to the desired focusing distance and depth of field. Photographing still-life compositions (which by definition don't move) poses no particular problems, but it is always best to use a telephoto macro lens in order to maintain reasonable distance from the subject when taking pictures of insects and other living creatures that are likely to flee at the sight of a photographer. However, using a telephoto macro lens often makes it difficult to fit the entire subject inside the depth of field because it becomes too shallow. In such cases, a standard macro lens with a shorter focal length can be handy. Of course, if you want to emphasize the subject by blurring the background, a telephoto macro lens is a good option. The medium telephoto EF100mm f/2.8L Macro IS USM and EF-S60mm f/2.8 Macro USM lenses are halfway between standard macro lens and long telephoto macro lens, making them popular, easy-to-use choices for beginners and pros alike.

Difference in how the background appears depending on the focal length

EF50mm

EF100mm

EF180mm

Working distance at an image magnification of 0.5x (Distance from the end of the lens to the subject)

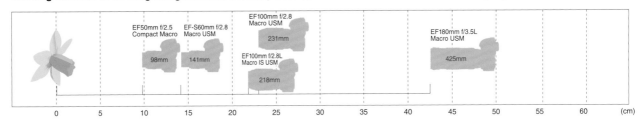

●Choosing a Magnification

Another factor is photographic magnification. Photographic magnification is how much larger the subject appears on the film or the photographic elements than in real life. Maximum photographic magnification is a lens's magnification when it photographs a subject as large as it can. The EF50mm f/2.5 Compact Macro used by itself has a magnification of 0.5×, the EF100mm f/2.8L Macro IS USM and more have life size magnification, and the MP-E65mm f/2.8 1-5× Macro Photo specially designed for close-up photography has a magnification of 5×. Choose a lens which best suits your subject size and purpose.

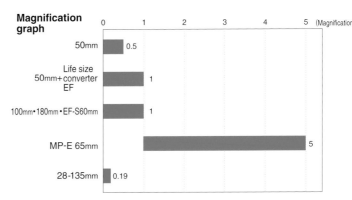
Magnification graph

Difference in how the subject appears depending on the image magnification

0.5×

1× (life-size)

5×

Points to keep in mind when doing macro photography

When taking photographs with a macro lens, controlling the depth of field and preventing the camera from shaking are very important. Compared with ordinary photography, the depth of field with a macro lens which has a short focusing distance is extremely shallow. 1:1 photography with a 180mm macro lens offers a depth of field of less than 1mm at maximum aperture. By blurring the area before and behind the subject taking advantage of the shallow depth of field, it is possible to emphasize the subject. That said, when you are taking a photograph of merchandise for an advertisement and want to make sure the entire subject is in focus, close the aperture and position the camera so that the subject is as parallel as possible to the camera's focal plane.

When the depth of field becomes this shallow, you need to pay careful attention to focusing, as it can be thrown off by even the smallest adjustments in the position of the focus ring, resulting in an out-of-focus photograph. Basic rules of thumb include focusing on the center of a flower when photographing flowers and on the eyes of an animal when photographing animals. If the location which you want to put in focus is small, the autofocus may latch onto a different location depending on how the photograph is framed. However, the full-time manual focus function on macro lenses such as the EF100mm f/2.8L Macro IS USM can fix this by allowing you to make minute adjustments to the focus even after the autofocus lamp comes on indicating focus has been achieved.

In addition to focusing, camera shake is also a major consideration since the higher the image magnification, the higher the risk of hand or camera shaking with lenses that have a long focal length. For this reason, a tripod and remote shutter release switch are indispensable for preventing camera shake.

Using Hybrid IS

The Hybrid IS incorporated in the EF100mm f/2.8L Macro IS USM is the most effective countermeasure for camera shake except other than a tripod. It is the world's first*[1] IS that simultaneously compensates for both angle camera shake and the type of shake that affects macro photography, shift camera shake.

A general rule of thumb for avoiding the effects of camera shake is to use a shutter speed that is as fast or faster than the reciprocal of the lens focal length. For macro photography, however, the shutter speed should be an additional one or two steps faster. The Hybrid IS incorporated in the EF100mm f/2.8L Macro IS USM provides outstanding camera shake compensation for macro photography. It allows use of shutter speeds approximately three steps*[2] slower at 0.5x magnification, and approximately two steps*[2] slower at 1x, providing an excellent solution when a tripod is either impractical or prohibited. This makes high magnification macro shooting as easy as normal photo shooting.

*1 For interchangeable SLR camera lenses.
*2 Effects of camera shake compensation vary depending on the type of photography. In non-macro shooting situations, it allows use of shutter speeds approximately four steps slower than 1/focal length of the lens in seconds.

Photographed using EF100mm f/2.8L Macro IS USM lens with Hybrid IS, which enables sharp results without camera-shake blur even during handheld macro shooting.

Hybrid IS On (compensates for angle and shift camera shake)

IS On (compensates only for angle camera shake)

IS Off

Landscape

A wide-angle lens is the best for capturing the grandeur of nature. Here an EF28mm f/1.8 USM is used to capture the composure of the distant mountains.
EF28mm f/2.8·1/180sec.·f/11

Selecting a lens for its mobility

Landscape photography is done with a broad array of lenses, from ultra wide-angle to ultra telephoto. Driving around in a car is useful for getting shots of everyday life around town, but if you're looking for scenes in nature, you'll find yourself climbing mountains and trekking along snowy trails, using a lot of energy, so you won't want a lot of heavy equipment dragging you down. For these situations, selecting zoom lenses for their mobility and ease of carrying is the most effective answer.

The EF lens lineup includes the high-performance EF16-35mm f/2.8L II USM, EF24-70mm f/2.8L USM, and the EF70-200mm f/2.8L IS USM and EF70-200mm f/2.8L USM. While they may not rival a single focal length lens in terms of brightness, they are nevertheless a large-aperture zoom lens set with a bright maximum aperture of f/2.8 covering the whole range from a very wide 16mm to a telephoto 200mm. If it's light weight you're looking for, there are also the EF17-40mm f/4L USM, EF24-105mm f/4L IS USM, EF70-200mm f/4L IS USM and

EF70-200mm f/4L USM, which have a maximum aperture which is a bit smaller at f/4. None of these high-performance zoom lenses will let you down no matter what conditions or scenes you come across in the field.

When traveling, this is a lightweight and compact combination of zoom lenses. A three-lens set with an F value of 2.8 is optimum for photography utilizing a large aperture. In addition, the three-lens f/4 set is lightweight and compact while allowing you to enjoy shooting with an L lens.

Photographed using an aspherical lens

The evening sky with beautiful light sources is an attractive subject. Using an aspherical lens you can clearly capture the various points of light.

Photographed using a spherical lens

The power of the aspherical lens

Taking photographs of scenes that include many pinpoints of light, such as night scenes, often causes those points to appear blurry due to the effects of spherical aberration in the lens. Spherical aberration also causes wide-angle lenses to produce images which appear distorted. To eliminate these effects, the EF lens series has benefited from the development of four types of aspherical lenses, (ground aspherical lens, replica aspherical lens, glass molded aspherical lens, plastic molded aspherical lens) which correct this aberration. The L series, in particular, delivers images with little or no blurring or distortion even at wide angles and large apertures.

Here you can see that lights at the edge of the frame are blurred.

Photographed using tilt

A tulip field that stretches as far as the eye can see. A TS-E45mm f/2.8 lens's tilt mechanism is used to achieve a pan focus effect that allows focusing all the way to the back.

Photographed using reverse tilt

Reverse tilt greatly reduces the range in which focusing is possible. This allows you to enjoy the composition of the color tones.

Tilt and shift photography using TS-E lenses

Capturing the image you see without changing it. This is the goal of all photographers, but it is often hampered by the optical characteristics of the lens. For example, tall buildings and trees often seem to taper annoyingly when photographed with a wide-angle lens due to the low angle from which they are inevitably shot. Not only that, it is often difficult to keep the entire subject in focus from top to bottom.

To solve this, we use what is known as tilt and shift. Tilt and shift functions exist as a standard feature on large-format cameras, in which the lens, the film, and the focusing adjustment are each designed independently of each other.

Photographed using shift

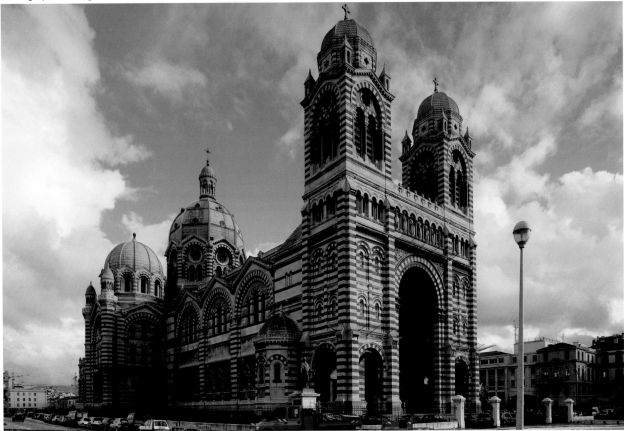

Shift was used to adjust the image to keep the building perpendicular all the way to the top.

For 35mm and digital SLR cameras, only Canon's TS-E lens series offers tilt and shift with automatic aperture control.

Tapering and other types of perspective distortion are corrected using shift. Also, you can make sure the entire length of a receding subject is in focus by using tilt. With ordinary lenses, it is often impossible to fit the entire subject into the depth of field, even when the aperture is closed to the smallest size. The tilt function overcomes this obstacle by changing the normally perpendicular relationship between the optical axis and the camera's focal plane. As an added plus, you can use shift and tilt in situations where it is not required, to achieve surreal effects. This is known as reverse tilt and shift.

Photographed without shift

Photograph of the same building as above taken without using shift. The intrinsic wide-angle perspective causes the image of the building to lean in at the top.

Underwater photography

Even the nimble amphiprion ocellaris can be captured in focus using autofocus. Location: Ishigaki Island, Okinawa Prefecture (Japan)·water depth: approximately 8m/26ft.·EF180mm f/3.5L Macro USM·1/125sec.·f/8·ISO/200·white balance/auto white balance·underwater housing·2 underwater flashes·autofocus

Using wide-angle lenses and macro lenses when each is most appropriate

The undersea world is filled with bright colors and strange shapes that do not exist on land. To take photographs underwater, however, you need to put your camera and lens in a waterproof, pressure-proof case known as an underwater housing, or a blimp. These are often sold in diving shops.

The switch to digital photography has been a boon to underwater photography because photographers are no longer restricted to a measly 36 exposures per roll and also because they can now check each shot as it is taken. The only problem that remains is the impossibility of switching lenses underwater, forcing photographers to choose between a wide-angle lens or a macro lens.

Before you start shooting, take some time to find out what creatures inhabit the area you will be visiting and imagine the types of photographs you want to take. For example, a 20mm, 14mm, or 15mm fisheye lens would be good if you were going to be taking photographs of manta rays, which can

reach up to 4m/13.2ft. in size. If you are going to be taking shots of small creatures, or you want close-ups of the expressions on the different creatures' faces, use a 100mm macro. And if you are dealing with timid little fish like gobies, a 180mm telephoto macro would be best.

The underwater housing is vital for underwater photography. Dome ports (for wide-angle lenses) and macro ports (for macro lenses) are available depending on the lens being used.

An ecsenius yaeyamaensis with a cute, slightly bewildered expression, caught by waiting for the creature to peek out from the coral. Location: Iriomote-jima, Okinawa Prefecture (Japan)·water depth: approximately 9m/30ft.·EF180mm f/3.5L Macro USM·1/125sec.·f/8·ISO/200·white balance/auto white balance·underwater housing·2 underwater flashes·autofocus

A female cocktail wrasse peeking out from behind some undersea vegetation, showing the beautiful nuptial coloration indicating spawning season. Location: Atami, Shizuoka Prefecture (Japan)·water depth: approximately 17m/56ft.·EF100mm f/2.8 Macro USM·1/125sec.·f/11·ISO/200·white balance/auto white balance·flash underwater housing·2 underwater flashes·autofocus

Getting as close as you can to the subject

The trick to taking good underwater photographs is to get as close as possible to the subject, in order to reduce the amount of water between the lens and the subject, as the water is filled with plankton and other flotsam and jetsam, which reduce the clarity of the photograph.

You have to decide whether you are looking for dynamic photographs of the subject taken with a wide-angle lens at very close distances, or shots of the subject only, using a macro lens. In order to develop your own sense of what you want, you should become very familiar with one kind of lens. The most appropriate lenses for this purpose are the EF20mm f/2.8 USM, EF28mm f/1.8 USM, EF50mm f/2.5 Compact Macro, EF100mm f/2.8L Macro IS USM and EF100mm f/2.8 Macro USM. The lens ports on the housing (the part of the housing that holds the lens) come in two different shapes: a dome port for wide-lenses and a macro port for macro lenses.

When selecting one of these, you should think about how to approach the subject, and how to frame it. It is probably better if you choose a slow subject at first. Look through the finder and try different shots at different angles. If you are using a digital camera, you can see the image as you aim, so the results of your experimentation can be applied right away.

Note: regarding captions with underwater housings: dome port housings (for wide-angle lenses) and macro port housings (for macro lenses) are available. WB: white balance. AWB: auto white balance.

This excellent example of a sea fan is 3m wide by 3m high. I waited until the sun was in just the right position in the background to take this silhouette. Location: Iriomote Island, Okinawa Prefecture (Japan)·water depth: approximately 18m/59ft.·EF15mm f/2.8 Fisheye·shutter speed priority AE·1/125 sec.·ISO/200·white balance/electric bulb·underwater housing·autofocus

Securing your body

Because the sea is filled with currents, eddies, and tides, which can all cause your body to move around, the most common shooting problems are focusing errors and camera movement. Focusing errors can occur because the lens may have been aimed at something other than the subject when the picture was taken, and unwanted blurring can occur if the camera moves during the exposure.

In order to prevent this, you must take steps to prevent your body from moving – usually by standing, kneeling or lying down on the sea bottom. Another way is to add weight to the weight belt, removing some of the air in the BCD (the diving equipment which helps to adjust your float as well as keep the air tank on your back).

You can also hold your body still by straddling rocks, pinioning yourself between rocks, or gripping with your elbows. If you are dealing with a sandy bottom, you can simply lie down on it commando-style, with one of your legs out and bent at the knee (making the shape of a "4") to stabilize yourself. None of this should ever be done on a coral reef, however, since this will destroy the coral, so choose a place without coral.

The ultimate way of stabilizing your body is a breathing method. When you are underwater, inhaling fills your lungs with air, making them act like flotation devices, while exhaling has the opposite effect, making you sink. Floating up and down as you breath is one factor in camera movement, so you should try to breathe as slowly as possible, especially when you press the shutter button.

Using autofocus underwater

It used to be that using autofocus underwater was pointless because of the low precision, but now with all the advances that have been made in autofocus sensors on the camera, almost all underwater photography employs autofocus, especially when using wide-angle lenses. The autofocus is in fact more accurate than manual focus when you are dealing with a backlit situation, so depending on how you choose the area for autofocus, you should definitely take advantage of elements which allow you to focus on a spot which will let you take the photographs you have in mind.

With macro lenses — especially the EF100mm f/2.8 Macro USM — preferences regarding autofocus and manual vary. Once you get used to it, manual focusing delivers more in-focus photographs, but at the same time, if the autofocus is used correctly, it can give you some pretty sharp shots. The trick is to set the camera to one-shot autofocus and use the autofocus lock by pressing the shutter button halfway. Then, move the camera forward or backward until the shot is in focus, and press the shutter button the rest of the way.

If you are using the EF180mm f/3.5L Macro USM, it is better to use autofocus. Coastal waters tend to be murky, presenting many problems, but the focus can be accurate in very interesting ways in Okinawa (Japan) or other locations where the sea is very clear. One thing you should keep in mind, however, is that overusing the autofocus will consume electrical power, so you should have extra batteries handy.

The 4m/13ft.-long manta ray – the star of the diver's world. White balance manipulated using tungsten film under natural light in order to bring out the mysteriousness of the creature. Ishigaki Island, Okinawa Prefecture (Japan)·water depth: approximately 8m/26ft.·EF15mm f/2.8 Fisheye·1/125sec.·f/8·ISO/200·white balance/auto white balance·incandescent lighting·natural light·underwater housing·autofocus

The Serranocirrhius latus in deep seas with its beautiful coloring. Ishigaki Island, Okinawa Prefecture (Japan)·water depth: approximately 30m/98 ft·EF180mm f/3.5L Macro USM·1/125sec.·f/6.7·ISO/200·white balance/auto white balance·underwater housing·2 underwater flashes·autofocus

Wildlife

Amboseli National Park is home to many African elephants. When an elephant calf is born to the herd, the herd encircles it like a wagon train to protect it from predators. If you try to approach it, one of the adult elephants will always block your view, but if you keep your distance, you are able to see the elephant family in their natural habitat.
African elephant·Amboseli National Park, Kenya·EF500mm f/4L IS USM·aperture priority AE·f/4

Keep your distance with a telephoto lens.

Wild animals are very cautious, and run away at the slightest whiff of danger – you can only get so close to them. To overcome this obstacle, photographers use telephoto lenses. One technique is to lie in wait for the animal, with the distance predetermined, but if you are new to the location or the animal, you might want to test your stealth and get as close as you can. Some animals require distance, so you will need a lens with a long focal length, which you can then use to get closer and closer until the animal fills the frame.

African elephants and other large, powerful animals do not tend to run at the sight of a car, although they might get excited and approach the car. If a baby elephant is with its mother, she won't take any chances and will generally get in the way between the camera and her offspring. In this type of situation, a 500mm super-telephoto lens should allow you sufficient distance to capture photos of the elephants without alarming them.

Of course, you may not necessarily want close-ups of wild animals. Placing them in their surroundings is another way of achieving beautiful wildlife photographs. You won't have the freedom to walk around and position the camera at any angle you want, since you are dealing with untamed animals, which require delicate handling. Even if you are including the surrounding scenery in the photograph, a telephoto zoom lens

like the EF70-200mm f/2.8L IS USM or the EF100-400mm f/4.5-5.6L IS USM may come in handy to allow you to keep the animal as the central emphasis of the shot. Let the zoom do the walking, as it were.

Sometimes, if you are lucky, you can get an otherwise unapproachable animal to approach you if you keep your distance and don't move. If you succeed in making the animal

Amboseli National Park at the foot of Kilimanjaro is a marshland formed by the ground water from the mountain. For this reason there are few roads, making it difficult to position yourself as you might want to, to get the pictures you want. A lot of triangulating is needed if you want to include the looming form of Kilimanjaro as the backdrop to a photograph. So let your zoom do the walking.
African elephants and Mt. Kilimanjaro·Amboseli National Park, Kenya·EF70-200mm f/2.8L IS USM·aperture priority AE·f/4.5

understand that you do not intend to hurt it, then it might come really close. Examples are the Japanese macaque, which tends to converge in groups on natural hot springs in the mountains, and baby seals. If you're in a wildlife park in Africa, families of elephants may pass by your safari car, so an EF16-35mm f/2.8L II USM will be useful in letting you achieve the wide angle needed to capture such a large animal from a relatively close distance, while including the surrounding savannah too.

If you're after something a bit more pastoral than that, then you probably won't need a telephoto lens to capture images from afar. For instance, a standard or moderate telephoto lens can be handy to capture horses and cows on a ranch, taking close-ups with the background slightly blurry, emphasizing the subject and giving the image that much more impact. The relatively wide angle of view gives you more freedom to experiment with the background, such as capturing the vastness of the open plains, being careful to exclude unnecessary elements.

A shallow depth of field only possible with a telephoto lens.

Wild animals don't always go where you want or expect them to go. They often hide in dense undergrowth, in the tops of trees, or in deep grasses, which can get in the way of a good shot. You want a clean, clear shot, but you've got branches and leaves and all sorts of other things in the way. What to do? You can take advantage of the shallow depth of field of a telephoto lens to put everything but the subject of the photograph out of focus, thereby drawing the viewer's attention to the animal and not the surroundings. The longer the focal length, or the larger the aperture, the shallower the depth of field becomes. The grass that was in the way of the animal's face as seen with the naked eye is no longer so

August is the best time to see gnus crossing the Mara River, often in herds of thousands at one time. I was training my 500mm on the activity, when suddenly those gnus were right before my eyes. An alligator had approached, spooking the gnus in their crossing and making them run up the river. I was able to capture the moment with the 70-200mm zoom I had on another camera.
Gnus·Maasai National Reserve, Kenya·EF70-200mm f/2.8L IS USM·aperture priority AE·f/4

Lions lie in wait for their prey, hiding in the tall savannah grasses. The grass and the lion's protective coloring, in addition to the grass in front of its face makes the lion hard to make out with the naked eye, but if you use a 500mm super-telephoto lens and its unrivalled shallow depth of field, you can put everything but the lion's face out of focus. Be careful to make the lion's eyes your focal point.
Lion·Buffalo Spring National Reserve, Kenya·EF500mm f/4L IS USM·aperture priority AE·f/4

visible through the viewfinder at maximum aperture.

This method can be used at zoos, too, to keep obstructions like cage bars and fences out of the photograph. The shallow depth of field of a telephoto lens lets you blur them out of the shot, leaving only the pacing panther as the center of attention. Bring the camera as close to a shaded part of the fence as possible and photograph the animal when it is some ways from the fence. Telephoto lenses – they're not just for mountaintops and sporting events anymore.

One thing you have to be careful to do, however, is to focus on the animal's eyes. This is a generally applicable rule. When taking a picture with a telephoto lens at maximum aperture, the depth of field becomes very shallow, and if your focal point is the animal's nose or mouth, the eyes will be out of focus.

Getting closer to the sun with the Extender EF2xII

Wildlife photography involves capturing the environment surrounding the animals, and not just close-ups of lions, bears, and gazelles. One element that no photographer can even hope to get close to is the sun. The focal length of a lens must be very long to produce a photograph in which the sun fills a sizable area of the frame. The sun takes up an area about 1% of the focal length in the frame, so its diameter will be 2mm if the lens used is a 200mm lens, or 5mm for a 500mm lens. So if you want it to fill half the viewfinder, you will have to use the

Birds are more cautious than other animals, making it hard to get close to them. If you get too close, they simply turn their backs and fly off. One evening a flock of pelicans were all facing the same direction waiting for the wind to rise, when they started taking off one at a time. The image was a bit too small even when I used the 500mm, so I attached the Extender EF1.4x Ⅱ. I followed the pelican with the camera as it took off, leaving the focus up to the AI servo.
Pelican·Lake Nakuru National Park, Kenya·EF500mm f/4L IS USM + Extender EF1.4x Ⅱ ·aperture priority AE·f5.6

Extender EF2xⅡ in combination with a 800mm lens, resulting in a focal length of 1600mm, and giving you a sun 16mm in diameter. And if you're using a digital camera, which has a smaller image size than a 35mm film camera, the sun will appear even larger, so there may be times when the Extender EF1.4xⅡ might be the better choice. You have to place the camera at just the right distance for an animal – say a goat on top of a hill or a bird in a tree – to capture it in combination with the sun at the available focal length. The sun seen through a super-telephoto lens does not stay still, either, so there is but a moment when it will form the right composition with the animal. As a reminder, these recommendations are only appropriate when the sun is very low in the sky, such as at dawn or dusk. Staring at the sun at other times, whether it's with the naked eye or through the viewfinder of your camera, is extremely dangerous unless proper precautions are taken to prevent eye damage or blindness, not to mention possible damage to your camera.

Rapid response to unexpected situations

You have to guess where animals are going and choose a focal length to suit. There are many unknowns, though, and you never know what they will do from one moment to the next. That's where a zoom lens can come in very handy, because you won't have to miss any shots while switching lenses. The EF70-200mm f/2.8L IS USM is great anywhere. If 200mm doesn't give you enough distance, attach an extender. The bright maximum aperture lets you use the lens as though the extender weren't there. And with the EF100-400mm f/4.5-5.6L IS USM, you won't have any problem finding the right angle of view when you need it thanks to the 8x magnification it offers. Speed is often of the essence when photographing in the wild.

A super-telephoto focal length and IS function – an invaluable combination for bird photography

There are more birds out there than you could count in a lifetime, and some of them are pretty small – so small, in fact, that you will probably need a lens with a long focal length if you want to get a reasonably sized shot of one. Even larger birds, like cranes, white herons, and eagles, tend to be cautious, and will fly away at the first click of a shutter, so getting close-ups of them is difficult. Photographers often turn to a combination of super-telephoto lens plus extender, which is unfortunately accompanied by the drawback of making the lens even harder to keep still than usual. Even more care is needed to keep the subject inside the viewfinder, requiring care with focusing and avoiding shaking the camera.

It is no easy task to keep a bird in the frame when it is in a tree whose branches are swaying in the wind. The shallow depth of field means that with each gust of wind the bird goes out of focus. This problem was resolved by using an Extender EF1.4xII with the EF500mm f/4L IS USM, taking advantage of its autofocus and IS functions to keep the bird's head right in the focus frame. I placed the lens on the window frame of the car to maintain more sharpness, in a halfway hand-held type of situation.
Long-created eagle·Buffalo Spring national Reserve, Kenya·EF500mm f/4L IS USM + Extender EF 1.4x II ·aperture priority AE·f/5.6

Use the EF300mm f/2.8L IS USM with the Extender EF2xII or the EF500mm f/4L IS USM with the Extender EF1.4xII and you can still use the autofocus. When used in combination with the IS function, you can reduce the risk of blurry pictures even more, allowing you to move the lens to capture a bird suddenly taking off or a flock in flight.
If you want to take a slow-shutter moving shot of the flapping wings of a swan taking off, the IS function's mode 2 is effective. Keep the bird in the viewfinder as it flies past you and use a shutter speed of 1/15 sec. to take multiple shots. Of the shots you take, one or two are bound to be keepers.
All the L-type super-telephoto EF lenses have outstanding optical characteristics, yet their true worth (as well as that of the IS function) can only truly be understood when you make large prints of a photograph taken with a digital SLR camera.

Switching between auto and manual focus using the full-time manual focus

Animals don't keep still for very often, which means you'll find yourself relying on the autofocus more than you normally would - even at times when it really isn't appropriate, such as when a fox gets behind a fern in the undergrowth, and the lens refuses to focus on the fox, or when the wind kicks up a cloud of dust partially hiding a herd of giraffes. At times like these, you can use the full-time manual focus (a standard feature on many USM lenses) to make slight adjustments to the autofocus without having to switch into manual focus mode, allowing you to concentrate on the photograph instead of the camera.

EF Lens Technology

1 Constantly Pursuing the Best: Canon's Lens Design Concept

The primary task of a photographic lens is to reproduce an image of a subject as clearly and accurately as possible on film or via digital capture. This is not, however, an easy task, because lens elements invariably have properties and imperfections which prevent them from accurately converging light rays into a single point and which tend to disperse light near the edges. These properties, which prevent a group of light rays from a single subject point from reconverging at the ideal image point or cause dispersion when the light rays pass through the lens, are called aberrations.

Put simply, the main objective of lens design is "to determine lens construction data for minimizing aberrations." However, although there is no single ideal solution for the design of a certain type of lens, there are countless solutions which approach the ideal. The problem becomes which solution to select, and how that selection is made greatly determines the performance of the lens.

A method of lens design used since the 19th century is a method of calculation called ray tracing. Although this method makes it possible to determine aberrations, it only allows calculations in one direction (i.e., the calculation of aberrations for a predetermined lens design) and thus does not allow lens construction data to be determined from aberration specifications.

In the mid-1960's, Canon became the first company to successfully develop practical computer software for analytically determining detailed lens construction data of near-optimum lens configurations achieving minimal aberrations (target values), together with computer software for automatically directing the analysis procedure.

Since then, Canon has continued to develop many other original computer programs for use in lens design. At present, use of this software enables Canon to consistently produce precision lenses with the original product concept virtually unchanged in the final product. Equating the act of designing a lens to climbing a mountain at night, Canon's advancement from conventional lens design techniques to its current computerized lens design methods is equivalent to leaping from a state where a flashlight illuminates only the feet in pitch black darkness and nothing can be done except to keep walking, to a state where not only the road but

also the objective point can be clearly seen, allowing sure and steady progress to the desired goal.

(Canon's idea of an ideal lens)

There are three general image formation requirements of an ideal photographic lens:
① The light rays from a single subject point should converge at a single point after passing through the lens.
② The image of a flat subject perpendicular to the optical axis should be contained in a plane behind the lens,
③ The shape of a flat subject perpendicular to the optical axis should be accurately reproduced without distortion in the image. In addition to these three general requirements, Canon adds one more:
④ The colors in the subject should be accurately reproduced in the image.
Although the above four requirements are "ideal" and can therefore never be perfectly satisfied, it is always possible to make improvements which come closer to those ideals. Canon's constant goal is to produce lenses which are in the market's top class in terms of every facet of performance and quality. To accomplish this, lofty objectives are set. The latest technology combined with years of accumulated experience and knowledge are used to realize lenses having the best possible picture quality with the simplest possible lens construction.

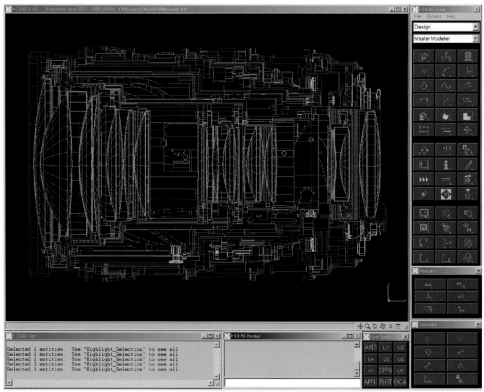

Photo-1 CAD-facilitated lens design

(Canon EF lens design fundamentals)

To be able to offer EF lenses which satisfy the needs of all kinds of users, Canon has set the six basic design goals described below. For Canon EF lenses, all of these conditions are of absolute importance and must be satisfied before lenses can be approved for production.

High picture quality over the entire image area

A lens cannot be said to have high picture quality if it provides only high resolution or high contrast. It must provide both. However, depending on the lens type, resolution and contrast generally have a mutually opposing relationship where improvement of one results in degradation of the other. To achieve both of these goals simultaneously, Canon makes liberal use of materials such as aspherical lenses, fluorite, UD glass, super UD glass, and high-refraction glass, which have outstanding optical characteristics, delivering sharpness, clarity, and unrivaled imaging performance (high picture quality).

True color reproduction characteristics uniform among all lenses

Color reproduction (color balance) is a Canon tradition and one of the most important features of EF lenses. Not only is each lens designed for optimum color balance, but color balance must be made uniform among all interchangeable lenses. Canon established many highly reliable single and special multi-coating techniques early on, and has undertaken scrupulous control of color balance ever since development of the FD lens series. For the EF lens series, the latest computer simulation techniques are used to determine the optimum type of coating for each lens element in order to both eliminate ghost images and achieve superior color reproduction, as well as ensuring true color balance uniform among all lenses.

Natural blur effect

While photographic lenses record three-dimensional subjects as a flat image on film or image sensor, in order to achieve a three-dimensional effect, not only must the image which is in focus appear sharp, but the out-of-focus, or "blurred," image in front of and behind the focused image must be natural. While it is of top priority to maximize the picture quality of the in-focus image plane, Canon also analyzes the effects of aberration correction and other considerations in the lens design stage to ensure that the out of focus portion of the image appears natural and pleasing to the eye. Attention is also paid to factors unrelated to optical design in the pursuit of a natural blur effect, including development of a circular diaphragm which achieves apertures with a high degree of roundness.

Superior operability

No matter how great a lens's optical performance is, it must always be kept in mind that a lens is a tool used for taking pictures and it must therefore exhibit good operability. All EF lenses are designed to deliver sensitive manual focus, smooth zooming, and outstanding operability in general. From the optical lens design stage, Canon lens designers are actively involved in the development of optical systems (such as rear and inner focusing systems) for achieving faster autofocusing, better manual focusing performance, quieter operation, and multi-group zoom systems for more compact lenses.

Silent operation

Cameras and lenses have become increasingly noisy in recent years, influencing the photographic subject and often causing the photographer to miss valuable picture-taking opportunities. In EF lenses, Canon has worked actively from the start to develop new technologies to minimize the AF drive sound with the goal of producing lenses similar in silence and performance to manual focus lenses. Since then, Canon has independently developed two types and four models of Ultrasonic motors (USM), and is quickly nearing its goal of incorporating quiet-operation USM in all EF lenses.

Reliability

To ensure total reliability — quality, precision, strength, shock resistance, vibration resistance, weather resistance and operation durability — of every lens in each EF lens group, the various operating conditions each lens is likely to be subjected to are surmised and consideration of these operating conditions is made during the design stage. Not only this, but each successive prototype is subjected to strict tests until a final product is generated. Thorough quality control based on original Canon standards is carried out during production. Further, new autofocus and digital factors are constantly being added to the list of considerations for the Canon standards, based on Canon's highly reputed FD lens standards.

These six design fundamentals are the backbone of modern EF lens development. Supporting them is the "Canon spirit" which has produced a constant stream of new technologies since the company's founding, and which continues to pulsate in Canon's never-ending effort to realize unrivaled lens quality approaching the ideal.

2 Development of High-Performance EF Lenses

1 Challenge to Create the Ideal Lens:
— Development of High-Performance EF lenses —

The development of an EF lens starts with careful listening to the opinions and requests of actual EF lens users.

While the requests of professional users are very important, the types of users that Canon designs its products for also include amateurs, advanced amateurs and semi-professionals of all ages, sexes and walks of life. In short, Canon products are designed for "people who love photography." Thus, requests from all types of users are gathered through various routes and collected at Canon headquarters. The product planning division and development division cooperate to closely analyze the requests and carefully study the marketability of the desired lenses. If sufficient demand is deemed to exist for a particular lens, a clear concept of a product which will appeal to a wide variety of users is determined. This concept is then carefully studied from both the standpoint of the user-i.e., focal length, zoom range, aperture ratio, closest shooting distance, required imaging performance, size, weight, cost, etc.-and the standpoint of the developer and manufacturer, and thus further refined into a concrete plan. Once this stage is completed, design of the actual lens optics begins. Since EF lenses combine optical, mechanical and electronic technologies, designers in charge of various areas such as lens barrel design, lens drive design, electronic control circuit design and industrial design work closely together from the initial design stage through the entire development process to produce an optimum lens based on the initial design concept.

(Actual EF lens design and development processes)

Optical lens design

Figure-1 shows the lens optical design process used by Canon. Once basic specifications such as focal length and maximum aperture are set, the "lens type" is determined. This is where the so-called structure of the lens is decided. The structure selected here is for all intents and purposes a general conjecture of what structure the lens will likely have, but since it has a large influence on the subsequent process flow, special software is used to search every possible lens type with an original evaluation algorithm used to select the optimum solution. Next, the process proceeds to the initial design stage where the optimum solution is analyzed based on Canon's own near-axis theory and aberration algorithms, and the initial shape of each lens element is determined. Since this initial design stage is the most important part of the design process flow, Canon utilizes analytic solutions based on theory, a rich databank of accumulated data and years of accumulated design experience to establish a system which can determine the ideal final configuration in a short amount of time.

Once the initial lens configuration is determined, a super-high-speed large scale computer is used to repeatedly perform the following design cycle: ray tracing → evaluation → automated design → type/shape change → ray tracing. In this process, as shown in Figure-2, the computer methodically varies each parameter such as the curvature of each lens surface, the surface interval (thickness) of each lens, each lens interval, and the material characteristics of each lens to

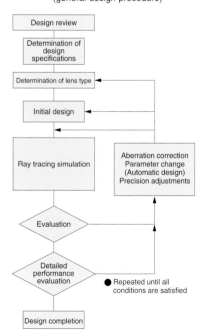

Figure-1 Lens Design Process Flow
(general design procedure)

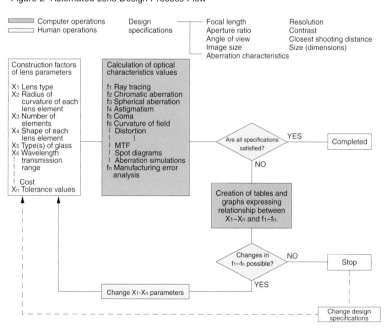

Figure-2 Automated Lens Design Process Flow

Figure-3 Computer Simulation of Aberration Characteristics

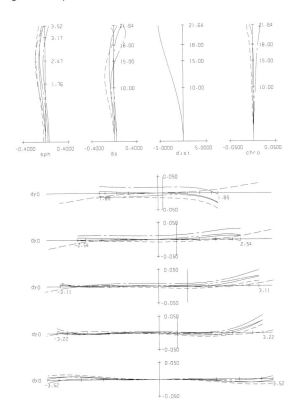

gradually progress toward the optimum design configuration in which every type of aberration is reduced to a minimum. This part of the process requires the most complicated and largest volume of calculations in the entire design process. With Canon's original optical design software, however, an environment is available in which design procedures can be carried out interactively and with great efficiency.

The automated design software used in this process was developed independently by Canon based on Canon's own automated design theories. By simply inputting the target values, the optimum solution for those values can be obtained in a short period of time.

Without having their train of thought constantly interrupted by mundane procedures, our designers can smoothly pursue the optimum final design values by setting the starting data and target values for input to the automatic design system, evaluating the simulation results, and setting the optimum re-input values for minimizing aberrations. In this way, our designers interact with the computer to repeatedly make accurate judgments which eventually lead to near-ideal design values. The effect of using aspherical lenses or special material such as fluorite or UD glass can also be thoroughly considered during this process, enabling designers to determine whether their use is necessary or not.

Next, taking an ultra-compact 28-105mm zoom lens as an example, we will describe the actual design process flow.

Figure-4 shows the zoom type structure of this lens. The lens has a 4-group convex-concave-convex-convex construction,

with the movement of all groups linked to the zooming action and the 2nd group used for focusing. The optimum lens type and power distribution for an ultra-compact zoom lens are determined by the software which determines power distribution. At this stage it is possible to estimate various specifications such as the track of the zoom cam, the focus extension amount, the total length of the lens, the diameter of the front lens element and the back focus distance.

The next diagram, Figure-5, shows a minimum-element construction using thick lenses. The shape of each lens was selected from the optimum solution determined from the specified conditions. At this stage, a simulation of light passing through the lens is performed and the minimum number of elements required for each group is estimated from the way the light rays bend and from the various aberration algorithms.

Ray tracing by computer

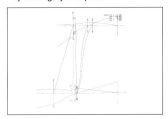

Figure-4

Spot diagram

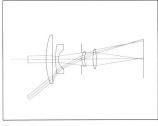

Figure-5

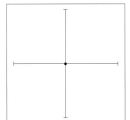

Figure-8

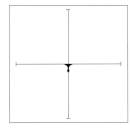

Figure-6

Figure-9

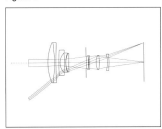

Figure-7

Figure-10

Photo-2 Actual Lens Barrel Design Example (Structure)

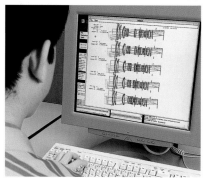

Photo-3 Actual Computer-aided Lens Design Example (Optical)

length are added into the equation and the automated design cycle is repeated many times while slightly varying design factors such as glass material and power distribution. Looking at the final result in Figure-7 and Figure-10, it can be seen that the light ray groups converge extremely well.

Lens barrel design

Now that design of the optical system is completed, the process moves to the design of the lens barrel which must hold the lens elements in precise position according to the optical design values and must move the various lens groups with high precision during zooming and focusing. Several basic conditions are required of a lens barrel, as follows:

① The lens barrel must, in every conceivable situation, hold the lens elements in precise position according to the optical design values in order to maintain optimum optical performance at all times.

② Mechanisms must be positioned for superior operability.

③ The size and weight should be appropriate for superior portability.

④ The construction should be designed to ensure maximum mass production stability.

⑤ The inner walls of the lens barrel should prevent harmful reflections.

⑥ The barrel should be provided with sufficient mechanical strength, durability and weatherability.

The factors listed below must be taken into consideration when designing the lens barrels for EF lenses, which have been made completely electronic.

● An electronic mount and various electrical circuitry must be built into the lens.

● A construction which achieves both high-speed auto focus

Next, with this lens it is necessary to eliminate the aberration fluctuations caused by the focusing movement of the 1st group. To do this, one element is added to the 1st group. Since the 2nd group shoulders most of the burden of magnification, it must be powerful and since it is also the focusing group, aberration fluctuation caused by zooming and focusing must be thoroughly eliminated. Two elements — one positive, one negative — are added to make it a three-element group. The 3rd group absorbs the dispersed light from the 2nd group, so a negative lens is added to correct axial color aberration and spherical aberration, making it a 2-element group. In this manner, the minimum number of lens elements is determined and the result of several repeated automated design cycles can be seen in Figure-6. From this it can be seen that the convergence of the light rays has improved greatly. Finally, to better correct the comatic astigmatic aberration at wide angles, an aspherical element is added to the imaging surface side of the 4th group, where the light ray groups are relatively far outside the light axis.

Once the final lens construction is determined, all desired specifications such as shooting distance, aperture and focal

Figure-11
Cross-Section of the EF24-70mm f/2.8L USM

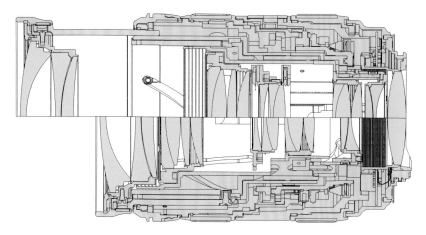

Photo-4 Precision Zoom Cam Lens Barrel

and outstanding manual focus operation.
● Incorporation of new actuators such as USM, EMD, and IS.
● Multi-group zoom design and rear and inner focusing lens designs.
● Light weight, compact size, and low cost.
Incorporating these factors has made lens barrel design more complex and more precise with each passing year, but even with the increased complexity, however, optimum designs are obtained using CAD (computer-aided design), which allows us to make designs with a thorough three-dimensional understanding of the lens construction, and various computer simulation techniques which let us analyze and optimize the design. To make compact and lightweight lenses, engineering plastic materials are liberally used. Such use of engineering plastics was made possible only after many years of analysis of the material characteristics, the establishment of ultra-high-precision molding technology, and countless rigorous product tests designed to ensure ample durability and reliability.

Thorough prototype performance checks and reliability evaluations

After a prototype is made based on the design drawings, the lens is rigorously tested to see if its performance actually satisfies the design goals. Many different tests are carried out, including comparison with existing products of the same class; precision measurement of specifications such as focal length, aperture ratio, aberration correction level, aperture efficiency, resolving power, MTF performance and color balance; field tests under various shooting conditions; ghost/flare spot tests; operability tests; temperature and humidity weather resistance tests; vibration resistance tests; operation durability tests and shock tests. That information is fed back to the design group and the lens is redesigned until all the results from these tests satisfy Canon's standards.

At present, even lenses in the highly-reputed EF lens group have to be tested to ensure they meet initial goals during prototype process before mass production begins and the lens hits the market as a Canon product. To maintain stable product quality at the mass production stage, analysis of manufacturing errors and the setting of appropriate tolerance levels obtained from the analysis results using computer simulations starting from initial development are extremely important factors. In this way, the high performance and quality of Canon EF lenses is ensured through a fusion of sophisticated technologies including aberration correction algorithms and their application, advanced automated design technology employing high-performance computers and specialized software, high-level measurement and performance evaluation technologies, manufacturing error analysis and tolerance setting technologies, and precision molding technologies. Then, and only then, are the lenses sent out into the world proudly bearing the name Canon.

2 Eyes Fixed On the Future: Advanced Electronic Control System Design

Selection of a new system with a view to the future

In the EOS system, why is rangefinding carried out in the camera body and lens drive carried out by a motor built into each lens?
The answer goes back to 1985, when in order to respond to the new trend in SLRs towards full-fledged autofocusing, most AF SLR camera makers other than Canon opted for a body rangefinding/body drive system (a system where the AF drive motor is built into the camera body and lens drive is carried out through a mechanical coupler). This system works well with standard zoom lenses and lenses of standard focal lengths; however, when considering the biggest feature of an SLR — the ability to interchange all types of lenses from fisheyes to super-telephotos — Canon decided not to use it for the following reasons:
① Since one motor must be able to handle the load of all types of interchangeable lenses (which can vary in focus torque by as much as a factor of 10), system efficiency is poor.
② Inserting an extender between the lens and body breaks the mechanical linkage used for transmitting AF drive power, impeding future system expansions.
③ For a camera which must provide constant performance in all types of environments from Arctic cold to tropical heat, relying on one motor for all lenses is undesirable in terms of environment resistance and operation durability.
In addition to these basic technological weak points, the in-body motor system does not conform to Canon's basic concept of mechatronics camera system design, which emphasizes system efficiency and flexibility by allowing the ideal actuator for each task to be located close to the corresponding drive unit and enabling electronic control of all data transmission and drive operations.
Moreover, Canon also judged that this trend toward automation not only concerned the simple addition of an autofocusing function to SLR cameras, but signaled the arrival of an innovative period which would not mature until sometime later in the future. Canon looked at the advanced technologies it was developing at the time, such as USM, BASIS (Base-stored Image Sensor) and EMD component technologies, and carefully studied them from the viewpoints of the fusion of innovative technologies and new functions (autofocus) and the future potential for technological development, and decided that for both users and Canon to take a bold leap forward, the best course would be to shake off old, impeding technologies and build a new system which will eventually surpass all other systems. Thus, Canon decided to develop the EOS system based on Canon's original body focusing/in-lens motor drive system and fully-electronic mount system.
Proving that Canon's decision was correct, other camera companies began incorporating in-lens motor drive systems and eliminating mechanically-mounted data communication systems.

Figure-12 Control System Basic Structure

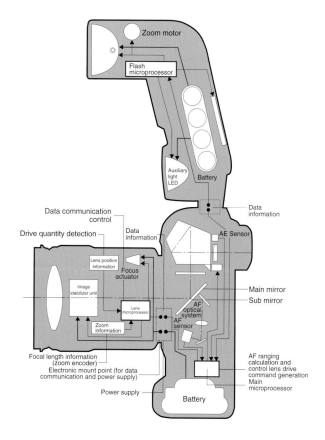

Zoom motor

Flash microprocessor

Auxiliary light LED

Battery

Data communication control

Data information

Drive quantity detection

Data information

AE Sensor

Lens position information

Focus actuator

Image stabilizer unit

Lens microprocessor

Zoom information

AF optical system

AF sensor

Main mirror

Sub mirror

Focal length information (zoom encoder)

Electronic mount point (for data communication and power supply)

Power supply

Battery

AF ranging calculation and control lens drive command generation Main microprocessor

③ Fully-electronic interfaces
All transfer of data between the body, lens, and flash is carried out electronically without a single mechanical linkage. This not only increases the functionality of the present system but also forms a network ready to accept future system developments.

Fully electronic mount system and data communications
The key to the realization of fully electronic data transfer between the body and lens is the EF mount. This is a large mount having an attachment rotation angle of 60° and a flange-back distance (distance from the mount reference surface to the focal plane) of 44.00mm.
Information transfer between the body and lens is carried out instantaneously via 8-bit bidirectional digital communications using three pairs of pins and contacts from the eight pins on the body mount and the seven contacts (which include common contacts) on the lens mount. Four types of commands are sent from the camera's high speed super-microcomputer to the lens:
① Send the specified lens data.
② Drive the lens as specified.
③ Close the diaphragm by the specified number of steps.
④ Open the diaphragm to the full-open position.
Primary data sent from the lens in response to command ① is shown in Table-1. Data communications are carried out immediately after the lens is mounted on the body and thereafter whenever some type of operation is carried out. Transfer of approximately 50 types of data is performed in real-time according to the situation.

Basic EOS system control structure
The EOS system is centered around regular and digital camera bodies and consists of various components such as a full line of EF lenses and flashes. From an overall system control standpoint, the various sensors, microprocessors, actuators, light emitters, electronic dials, input switches and power sources are skillfully intertwined, and the various functions of all the different components work together to operate systematically as an image expression tool for recording and expressing selected instants in the flow of time. The three main features of this system are as follows:
① Multi-processor system control
The high-speed super-microcomputer in the camera body interfaces with the microcomputers in the lens and flash (for high-speed data processing, calculation and data communication) to carry out high-level system operation control.
② Multi-actuator system
The ideal actuator for each drive unit is located in the vicinity of the drive unit, forming an integrated multi-actuator system which realizes high-level automation, high efficiency and high performance.

Table-1 Data Communication Content

Type of information	Purpose		
	AF precision	AF control	AE control
① Lens type (ID-code)			
② Lens status		●	
③ Metering information			
1.Full aperture F No.		●	●
2.Minimum aperture			●
④ Focal length information	●	●	●
⑤ AF drive information			
1.Focusing ring drive quantity (lens position)	●	●	
2.Lens extension response factor		●	
3.Lens extension response correction factor		●	
4.Focusing ring drive constant		●	
5.Maximum defocus quantity		●	
6.Best focus compensation amount	●		

Advantages of the fully electronic mount system

Features of the large-diameter, fully electronic mount include the following:

① Realization of quiet, high-speed, high-precision AF. Since the optimum actuator can be selected and incorporated in each lens, silent, fast and accurate autofocusing can be realized for all lenses from fisheyes to super-telephotos.

② Realization of quiet, high-precision aperture control. By incorporating the ideal EMD in each lens, high-precision digital diaphragm control is realized.

③ Built-in EMD allows the aperture to be closed down for checking the depth of field at the touch of a button. Moreover, the built-in EMD improves sequence control freedom by allowing the aperture to remain stopped down during continuous shooting to increase shooting speed.

④ The fully electronic aperture control system has permitted the development of TS-E lenses — the world's first lenses which tilt and shift with fully automatic diaphragm operation.

⑤ Achievement of the large-aperture EF50mm f/1.0L USM lens. (A feat only physically possible thanks to the large-diameter EOS mount.)

⑥ Realization of full-frame viewfinder coverage. (Virtually 100% coverage is realized in EOS-1 series cameras.)

⑦ Elimination of viewfinder and mirror blockage with super-telephoto lenses.

⑧ When using a zoom lens which varies the maximum aperture according to the focal length, aperture values which are calculated by the camera or set manually (except for maximum aperture) are automatically compensated so that the aperture setting does not change during zooming. For example, when using the EF28-300mm f/3.5-5.6L IS USM with a manually set aperture of f/5.6 or smaller, the aperture setting does not change when the lens is zoomed even though the lens' maximum aperture value changes. This means that when using a handheld exposure meter or flash meter to determine the appropriate camera settings for a certain scene, you can simply set the aperture value manually according to the meter reading without worrying about the zoom position.

⑨ Since it automatically compensates and displays the change in the lens' effective F-number when an extender is mounted, even when using a handheld meter no additional compensation is needed when you set the camera according to the metering reading.

⑩ Being able to make the rear aperture of the lens larger than before is beneficial for improving marginal illumination in the optical system. Advantages are also gained in terms of optical performance improvement when an extender is used with a super telephoto lens.

⑪ Since the fully-electronic mount system has none of the shock, operation noise, abrasion, play, lubrication requirements, poor response, reductions in precision caused by lever operation or design restrictions related to linkage mechanisms present in systems which use mechanical linkages to transfer data, operation reliability is significantly improved.

⑫ There is no need for the mechanical auto diaphragm linkage mechanism or aperture control mechanism in the camera body, making possible a lighter and more compact body design together with improved system operation reliability.

⑬ A lens operation self-test system using the lens' built-in microcomputer (which displays a warning in the camera's LCD (Liquid Crystal Display) panel in the event of a malfunction) ensures high reliability.

⑭ Since all control is carried out electronically, designers have great flexibility with regard to incorporating future new technologies such as image stabilization and improving camera performance.

Compatibility with new technologies and future system upgrades has already been proven with increased AF functionality (higher speeds, better predictive autofocus for moving subjects, multi-point autofocusing compatibility), the achievement of auto-aperture TS-E lenses mentioned above, the use of USMs in most EF lenses, the development of the first image stabilizer lens in the world, and the creation of a digital SLR camera system that can work with all EF lenses.

Photo-5 Electronic Mount — Body Side

Photo-6 Electronic Mount — Lens Side

Photo-7 Mounted Lens Electronic PCB

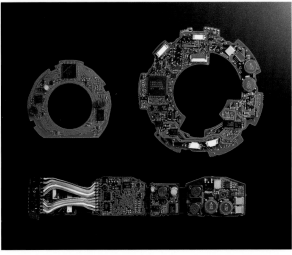

3 Seventeen Technologies Used in High-Performance EF Lenses

1 Transcending the Theoretical Limit of Spherical Lenses: Super-Precision Aspherical Lenses

Most lenses used for photographic purposes are made by combining several spherical lens elements. The radius of curvature and type of optical glass used for each element and the amount of air space between the elements are designed in such a way that the final lens combination eliminates the various lens aberrations to a degree large enough to achieve the desired performance. Today, computers provide us with automatic design and simulation techniques which enable development of high-performance lenses in a short period of time. Use of only spherical lenses, however, presents a basic problem in which parallel light rays entering a spherical lens theoretically do not perfectly converge at a single point, introducing restrictions with regard to:

● performance of large aperture lenses,
● distortion compensation in super-wide-angle lenses, and
● minimum size of compact lenses.

To remove these restrictions and realize lenses with even higher performance, less distortion and smaller size, the only way is to utilize aspherical lens technology.

Canon started developing aspherical lens technology in the mid-1960s and established design theories and precision processing and measurement technologies in the early 1970s. In 1971, Canon succeeded in commercially releasing an SLR lens incorporating an aspherical lens element — the FD55mm f/1.2AL. This success can be attributed to the following two points:

① Establishment of ultra-precision measurement technology

For measuring aspherical lens surfaces, Canon independently developed the "polar coordinate conversion measurement system," in which the object to be measured is placed on a rotating table and rotated around its center of curvature while a gauge interferometer is used to measure the difference between the object surface and a reference spherical surface. Measurement results are then processed by a computer to determine the surface shape. With this technique, an ultra-high precision of 1/32 the light wavelength — or 0.02 micron (20 millionths of a millimeter) — is realized.

This measurement technology formed the backbone indispensable to the subsequent development of various aspherical lens-processing technologies.

Photo-8 Precision Aspherical Lenses

Figure-13 Canon's Polar Coordinate Conversion Measurement System

② Establishment of aspherical lens processing system incorporating special grinding and uniform polishing techniques

For precision processing of aspherical lenses, Canon established a special aspherical lens processing system which grinds the lens with high precision to an aspherical shape and then polishes the lens to attain a uniform surface without losing the aspherical shape.

Initially, the aspherical surface processing and ultra-precision shape measurement steps had to be repeated over and over so that each lens was in effect made by hand. Then, in 1974, Canon developed a special machine which had the capability of producing more than 1,000 aspherical lenses per month, thus paving the way for mass production. However, there were limits on the mass production of ground-glass

Photo-9 Spherical Lens Example

Photo-10 Aspherical Lens Example

Figure-14 EF85mm f/1.2L II USM Optical System - Ray Tracing Diagram

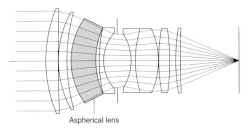

Aspherical lens

Figure-15 EF14mm f/2.8L II USM Optical System - Ray Tracing Diagram

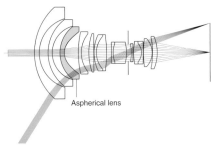

Aspherical lens

Figure-16 EF/FD Zoom Lens: Size Comparison

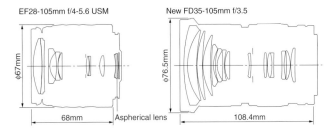

EF28-105mm f/4-5.6 USM   New FD35-105mm f/3.5

φ67mm   φ76.5mm

68mm   Aspherical lens   108.4mm

Figure-17 Principle of Aspherical Lens Effect

Spherical aberration of spherical lens

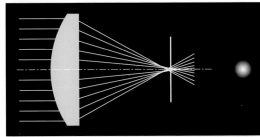

Focal point alignment with aspherical lens

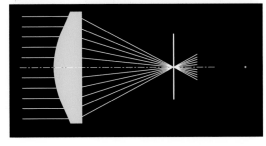

aspherical lenses, so around 1978, Canon succeeded in applying this aspherical processing technology to a die molding process and developed a practical, high-precision plastic molding system for producing small-aperture aspherical lenses in mass quantity and at low cost. Lenses manufactured with this system were employed in compact cameras in the AF rangefinding system and in some shooting lenses (Snappy/AF35MII). In the early 1980s, Canon continued its research and development efforts in the area of large-aperture glass-molded aspherical lenses, and succeeded in developing a practical production system in 1985.

These glass-molded aspherical lenses are manufactured by directly molding glass material in a molding machine incorporating an ultra-high-precision aspherical metal die. This enables high precision sufficient to satisfy the performance requirements of SLR interchangeable lenses as well as mass production at relatively low cost. In 1990, Canon added a fourth aspherical lens production technology to its arsenal by developing technology for producing replica aspherical lenses by using ultraviolet-light-hardening resin to form an aspherical surface layer on a spherical glass lens. In the development of EF lenses, these four aspherical lens types give Canon lens designers great flexibility in being able to choose the best type of lens for each application. Aspherical lenses are particularly useful for

● compensating spherical aberrations in large-aperture lenses,
● compensating distortion in wide-angle lenses, and
● enabling production of compact, high-quality zoom lenses.

Actual examples of such applications are shown in Figure-14 to Figure-16.

Figure-18 Aspherical Surface Shape Precision Measurement Results

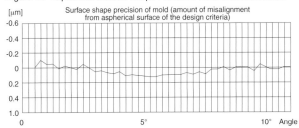

Photo-11 Ultra-High-Precision Glass Molded Aspherical Lens Die

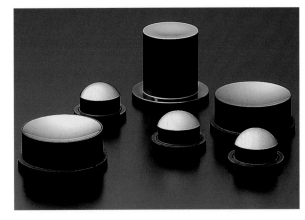

The EF85mm f/1.2L II USM in Figure-14 is designed with aspherical lens elements which cause all light rays passing through the lens to converge at a single point. The image formed by light rays entering the lens along a cross section perpendicular to the paper surface will flare at the maximum aperture. The aspherical lens elements act to both eliminate this flare and compensate the comatic flare component. This lens utilizes two aspherical elements to achieve good compensation over the whole image area from the center to the edges.

The ultra wide-angle lens in Figure-15 incorporates an aspherical lens element designed with a freecurved surface and light ray transmission angle which optimizes the lens' image formation characteristics at every point in the image area. Use of this aspherical lens greatly compensates for the distortion and peripheral image smearing previously unavoidable in ultra wide-angle lenses.

Figure-16 shows a comparison between a previous FD zoom lens constructed only of spherical lens elements and a new EF zoom lens of the same class incorporating an aspherical lens element. Use of the aspherical lens element realizes a shorter overall lens length and significantly reduced curvature of field and distortion.

2 Fluorite and UD Lenses — Sharp Enough to Capture Even the Air

Canon's white-barreled super-telephoto L lens series are continuously extolled by professional photographers throughout the world as being super-high-performance lenses with unrivaled sharpness. The key to this performance is the complete elimination of the secondary spectrum through liberal use of fluorite and UD glass lenses.

Fluorite

● With super-telephoto lenses, there is a limit to the degree of performance improvement possible using optical glass lens elements.

The level of residual chromatic aberration has a significant effect on the degree of image sharpness that can be obtained with telephoto and super-telephoto lenses. As shown in the color-canceling prism example in Figure-19, chromatic aberrations are corrected by utilizing the different dispersion characteristics of different types of optical glass to align the propagation directions of light rays with different wavelengths in the same direction.

In photographic lenses, as well, it is possible bring two wavelengths (such as red and blue) together at the same focal point by combining a

Figure-19 Chromatic Aberration Correction Using Prisms

Figure-20 EF300mm f/2.8L USM Optical System

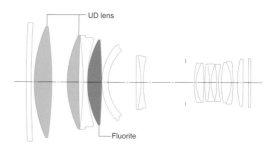

small-dispersion convex lens with a large-dispersion concave lens. A lens in which two colors (wavelengths) are so corrected is called an achromatic lens, or simply an achromat. However, although two colors meet at the same focal point, the intermediate color (green) still converges at a different focal point. This chromatic aberration, which remains even after chromatic aberration correction design measures are carried out, is called secondary chromatic aberration, or secondary spectrum. When using only optical glass lens elements, this secondary spectrum cannot be reduced to less than "focal length x 2/1000 mm" due to theoretical limitations. This is due to the fact that even with different types of optical glass having different rates of dispersion, the proportional amount of dispersion for each wavelength tends to remain fixed.

● Use of fluorite to produce ultra-high-performance lenses
Fluorite is a material that makes it possible to remove the theoretical limit imposed by optical glass and realize virtually ideal correction of chromatic aberrations.

Optical glass is a material produced from silica as the main material together with additives such as barium oxide and lanthanum. During manufacture, these substances are combined in a furnace, melted together at a high temperature of 1,300° to 1,400°C, and then slowly cooled.

Fluorite, on the other hand, has a crystalline structure and is equipped with extraordinary characteristics unobtainable with optical glass-a low index of refraction and low dispersion (Figure-23). Moreover, the dispersion characteristics of fluorite are nearly identical with optical glass for wavelengths in the range from red to green, but differ greatly for wavelengths in the range from green to blue (a characteristic called extraordinary partial dispersion). Use of these special properties makes it possible to significantly improve the imaging performance of super-telephoto lenses, as described below.

① Thorough elimination of the secondary spectrum
When a convex fluorite lens is combined with a large-dispersion optical glass concave lens according to design rules for correcting red and blue wavelengths, the extraordinary partial dispersion characteristics of the fluorite work to effectively compensate for the green wavelength as well, reducing the secondary spectrum to an extremely low level and bringing all three wavelengths-red, green and blue-together at the same focal point, realizing virtually ideal

Figure-21 Secondary Spectrum

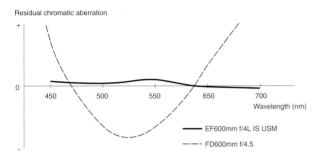

Residual chromatic aberration

—— EF600mm f/4L IS USM

—-—- FD600mm f/4.5

Photo-12 Artificial Fluorite Crystals and Fluorite Lenses

chromatic aberration compensation (apochromatic performance), as shown in Figure-21.

② Image quality improvement over total image area

With telephoto type lenses using a front-convex/rear-concave power distribution design, the overall physical length can be less than the focal length. To achieve a high level of sharpness all the way from the center of the image to the edges with this type of lens, it is desirable for the index of refraction of the front convex lens group to be as small as possible. Accordingly, use of fluorite with its low index of refraction is effective in improving image quality over the total image area.

③ Overall lens length reduction

To reduce the overall length of a telephoto lens, it is desirable to make the mutual power of the convex-concave construction as strong as possible.

With ordinary optical glass, however, increasing the mutual power makes it difficult to correct curvature of field and degrades image quality. With fluorite, on the other hand, the material's low index of refraction is beneficial for the conditions set forth by Petzval's sum, making it possible to achieve significant reductions in lens length while maintaining high image quality.

Although fluorite's extraordinary optical characteristics have been known since the 1800's, natural fluorite only occurs in nature in small sizes usable only for the object lenses in microscopes. Although lens designers long wanted to use fluorite in photographic lenses, it was generally extremely difficult or impossible to obtain naturally formed pieces large enough for lens use. To solve this problem, Canon worked hard at developing synthetic fluorite crystal formation technology and finally succeeded in establishing practical fluorite production technology (calcium fluoride $<CaF_2>$ synthetic crystal formation technology) near the end of the 1960's. This is one example of Canon's undying spirit and efforts to make use of our own abilities to create whatever is necessary to approach the realization of the ideal. The first use of artificially crystallized fluorite in photographic lenses was for the FL-F300mm f/5.6 in 1969, and it has since been incorporated in the FD, New FD, EF, and many other Canon lenses. Today, the only SLR interchangeable lenses incorporating fluorite are the EF lenses.

Figure-22 Comparison of Color Aberration Correction

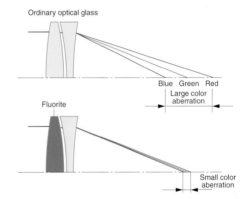

Ordinary optical glass

Blue Green Red
Large color aberration

Fluorite

Small color aberration

Figure-23 Optical Characteristics of Optical Glass and Fluorite

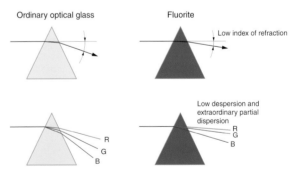

Ordinary optical glass　　　　Fluorite

Low index of refraction

Low despersion and extraordinary partial dispersion

Photo-13 Optimally Coated EF Lenses

UD lenses

The use of fluorite to improve the performance of super-telephoto lenses is well established, but there remains a problem with using fluorite in other types of lenses. That problem is fluorite's extremely high cost arising from the synthetic crystal production process. Because of this, lens designers long desired a special optical glass which could provide characteristics similar to fluorite but at lower cost.

This desire was finally satisfied in the latter half of the 1970's with the development of UD (ultra-low dispersion) glass. The index of refraction and dispersion of UD glass, while not as low as fluorite, are both significantly lower than other types of optical glass. Moreover, UD glass exhibits extraordinary partial dispersion characteristics. Accordingly, use of UD glass can provide nearly the same effect as fluorite (two UD lens elements are equivalent to one fluorite element) by selecting the proper lens combination in consideration of various factors such as focal length.

Fluorite and/or UD glass lens elements are employed in various EF lenses including the EF135mm f/2L USM and EF800mm f/5.6L IS USM telephoto/super telephoto lens group and the EF28-300mm f/3.5-5.6L IS USM, EF70-200mm f/2.8L IS USM, EF70-200mm f/2.8L USM, EF70-200mm f/4L IS USM, EF70-200mm f/4L USM and EF100-400mm f/4.5-5.6L IS USM telephoto zoom lenses. UD lenses are also incorporated into the wide angle EF24mm f/1.4L II USM, EF16-35mm f/2.8L II USM, EF17-40mm f/4L USM and EF24-70mm f/2.8L USM lenses in order to correct chromatic aberration. In 1993, after dramatically improving the performance of conventional UD lenses, a super UD lens was successfully developed reproducing almost the same characteristics as fluorite, and used in the EF400mm f/5.6L USM.

The rapidly expanding field of digital photography has also seen increased emphasis placed on correcting chromatic aberration in photographic lenses. To meet this challenge, fluorite, UD, and super UD lenses will start being used in even more EF lenses in the future, from wide angle to super telephoto.

3 New Possibilities in Optical Systems: The DO Lens (Multi-Layered Diffractive Optical Element)

Diffractive optical elements are, as the name states, optical elements applied to the phenomenon of diffraction. They attracted much attention for their ability to adjust for chromatic aberration, better than UD or fluorite lenses despite being asymmetrical in form. Incorporation of such elements into photographic lenses was nevertheless difficult, mainly due to problems of diffraction flare. Canon solved this problem by developing its uniquely structured "DO lens" and by becoming the first lens manufacturer in the world to incorporate this lens in a photographic lens. The first model to employ this lens — the EF400mm f/4 DO IS USM — is a super telephoto lens achieving both compact and lightweight specifications, and outstanding image quality.

■ Diffraction

This is a phenomenon in which light waves pass around the edges of an object and enter the shadowed area of that object. Diffraction flare is a common diffraction phenomenon seen in photographic lenses when the aperture diameter is small. This phenomenon is caused by the wavelike nature of light. While diffraction flare is actually harmful light rays that adversely affect picture quality by passing around the back of the diaphragm, the same principle can be used to control the direction of the light.

For example, when light enters two slits which are very close together, the same type of flare is produced as when using a small aperture. In this case, as shown in the figure below, a certain direction emerges, along which it is easier for the light waves to propagate. Here, the direction in which the wave movement becomes more intense is the direction in which the phases of the light waves spreading out from the two slits line up. For this reason, the light waves propagate, causing each other to become more intense in several directions, one direction in which the wavelengths shift one cycle and overlap, one direction in which they shift two cycles and overlap, and so on. The direction in which the wavelengths shift one cycle (one wavelength) and overlap is called the primary diffraction, and this slit construction is called a diffraction lattice. The features of the diffraction lattice include:

① Changing the spacing between the slits (the lattice period) changes the direction of diffraction.

② The larger the diffraction cycle, the larger the amount of diffraction (the "diffraction angle").

③ Light with longer wavelengths has a large diffraction angle.

■ Single-Layer Diffractive Optical Elements

Since diffraction lattices utilizing a slit construction (amplitude-type diffraction lattices) generate diffracted light by blocking light, they cannot be employed in optical systems. A phase-type diffraction lattice was suggested, in which the lattice would be in the shape of an axe-blade, and thus not block any light. A phase-

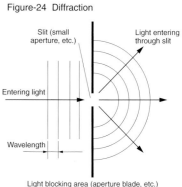

Figure-24 Diffraction

Slit (small aperture, etc.)

Light entering through slit

Entering light

Wavelength

Light blocking area (aperture blade, etc.)

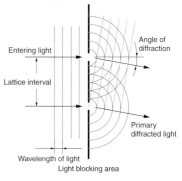

Figure-25 Principle of diffracted light generation

Entering light

Angle of diffraction

Lattice interval

Wavelength of light

Light blocking area

Primary diffracted light

type diffraction lattice would generate diffracted light by forming the diffraction lattice in a concentric circle, like a Fresnel lens. By partially changing the period of the lattice (the spacing of the lattice), an effect identical to that of an aspherical lens could be achieved, making it possible to compensate for a variety of issues, including spherical aberration.

As mentioned above, the light exiting the diffraction lattice has a larger diffraction angle at longer wavelengths. In other words, light with a longer wavelength forms an image closer to the diffraction lattice, while light with a shorter wavelength forms an image farther away. In contrast, for light entering a refraction lens (convex lens) with a positive power, light with a shorter wavelength forms an image closer to the diffraction lattice, while light with a longer wavelength forms an image farther away. This means that the order of the chromatic aberration is reversed with a refractive lens and a diffractive optical element. If they are combined, they cancel out one another's chromatic aberration, making possible an effective chromatic aberration correction. Unlike the previous chromatic aberration compensation technique, which combined convex and concave lenses, the new one is achieved using only convex lenses, making it possible to weaken the power of each element group in the lens, thereby permitting effective correction of other aberrations besides color.

Photo-14 DO lens

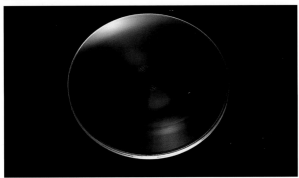

■ Development of the DO Lens

Single-layer diffractive optical elements, while used in the optical readers for CD and DVD players, which use lasers, could not be used in the field of photographic lenses. This is because, unlike laser light, the light used by photographic lenses (the region of visible light) is made up of a number of different wavelengths. To use diffractive optical elements in a photographic lens, all the light entering the lens must be 100% diffracted. The DO lens, with its multi-layered diffractive structure, was developed as a method for transforming all regions of visible light into photographic light. The DO lens in the case of the EF400mm f/4 DO IS USM incorporates two single-layer diffractive optical elements with concentric circle diffraction lattices, which are arranged so that they face one another (Figure-28). Because the light that enters the lens does not generate needless diffracted light, the DO lens succeeds in using almost all of this light as

Figure-26 Construction of DO lens (illustration)

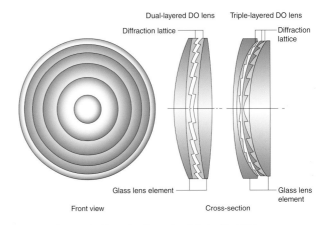

Figure-27 Chromatic Aberration Correction Principal by DO lens

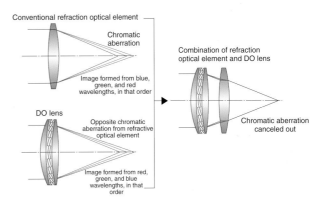

Figure-28 Difference in Diffracted Light between Single-Layered Diffractive Optical Element and DO lens

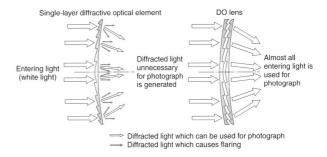

photographic light, making application to photographic lenses possible. The actual DO lens is made up of a spherical glass lens and a diffraction lattice formed in a mold using a special plastic on the surface. The thickness of the diffraction lattice is only a few micrometers, and the lattice period gradually changes from a few millimeters to a few dozen micrometers. In order to form this diffraction lattice, the precision of the diffraction lattice period, height, and positioning has to be controlled to units smaller than a micrometer. Many technologies were used to achieve this level of precision,

Photo-15 With DO lens installed

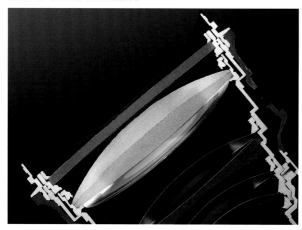

including a 3D ultrahigh-precision micro-fabrication technology developed specifically for this purpose, as well as the replica aspherical lens manufacturing technology gained with the EF lenses, high-precision positioning technology, and much more.

■ Making Smaller Lenses

Using the EF400mm f/4 DO IS USM as an example, let us take a look at the process of how telephoto lenses are made more compact by applying a DO lens.

With diffractive optical elements, the locations where the image is formed along the optical axis for wavelengths of 400nm, 500nm, and 600nm will line up at equal intervals. However, since optical glass has non-linear dispersion characteristics, the locations of image formation for each wavelength will be unequally spaced for refractive optical elements. Accordingly, the following methods were used to maximize the effectiveness of the chromatic aberration compensation of the DO lens.

Figure-29-① shows a 400mm f/4 lens designed using only conventional refractive optical elements. If, as shown in Figure-29-②, the refractive power of each lens element is raised, and the lens elements are placed closer together in order to make the whole lens more compact, the chromatic aberration—particularly for blue—degenerates to a remarkable degree. This means that inclusion of a diffractive optical element will be insufficient to compensate for the chromatic aberration. So, as shown in Figure-29-③, the dispersion of each lens element was optimized to make the chromatic aberration line up in order by wavelength. Lastly, as shown in Figure-29-④, by placing a DO lens with the appropriate refractive power in front of the front lens element, chromatic aberration compensation is complete. Thus, compared with optical systems designed only with conventional refractive optical elements, the EF400mm f/4 DO IS USM achieves a 27% reduction in length (317mm → 232.7mm) and a 31% reduction in weight (3000g → 2080g), making it indeed a compact, lightweight lens (Figure-30).

Figure-29 Principle behind Smaller Optics Thanks to DO lens

① 400mm f/4 lens designed using conventional methods

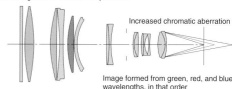

② Lenses arranged closer together for a more compact size

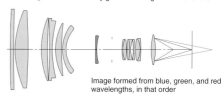

③ Fluorite and UD lens elements replaced with ordinary glass to arrange the order of the chromatic aberration.

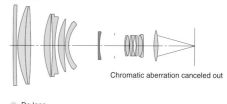

④ Replace front element with DO lens

Figure-30 Compact Single-Focal Length Lens Thanks to DO Lens

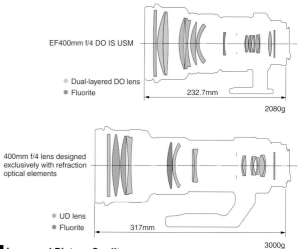

■ Improved Picture Quality

Since the DO lens placed in the front group almost completely cancels out the chromatic aberration generated in the refractive lens group, residual chromatic aberration is suppressed to extremely low levels. And since diffractive optical elements are also characterized by aspherical behavior, spherical aberration is also efficiently corrected, achieving exceptional image quality with high resolution and contrast.

DO Lens will be included in many EF lenses in the future as innovative optical elements which outperform fluorite, UD, and aspherical lenses.

■ Triple-Layered DO Lens

In principle, the DO lens carries the potential to contribute to more compact zoom lenses, as well. However, it would be difficult to employ the dual-layered DO lens used in the EF400mm f/4 DO IS USM in zoom lenses for the following reasons.

In single focal-length lenses such as the EF400mm f/4 DO IS USM, the angle of light entering the lens (incidence angle) is fixed for the most part. In zoom lenses, however, because the angle of view changes in accordance with the focal length, the incidence angle also undergoes significant change. With the conventional DO lens, changes in the incidence angle would cause the generation of diffracted light that is not needed for photography, which would become flares and greatly reduce imaging performance. To resolve this problem, Canon developed a triple-layered DO lens, a new type of DO lens with three diffractive lattices arranged on the optical axis, which can compensate for changes in focal length.

By using three layers of diffractive lattices, even if the angle of light entering the DO lens changes, no unnecessary diffracted light is generated, and almost all of the incident light can be used as photographic light (Figure-32).

The triple-layered DO lens was first applied in the EF70-300mm f/4.5-5.6 DO IS USM lens. Below is an explanation of the processes by which this lens was made compact.

① The refractivity of each lens element in the base lens system (EF75-300mm f/4-5.6 IS USM) was raised, and the space between individual lenses was narrowed.

② Chromatic and spherical aberration, which were worsened

Figure-31   Compact Zoom Lens Thanks to DO Lens

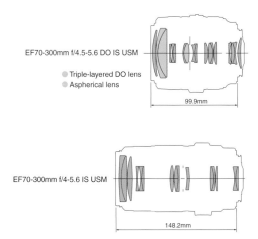

by making the lens more compact, were simultaneously compensated for by the triple-layered DO lens placed in front of the forward lens.

As a result, the EF70-300mm f/4.5-5.6 DO IS USM is 30% shorter (142.8mm→99.9mm) than the conventional EF75-300mm f/4-5.6 IS USM (Figure-31), which has only a refractive optical elements, and it compensates for any remaining chromatic and spherical aberration while achieving high image quality comparable to that of L lenses.

Figure-32   Differences in Diffraction between Dual-Layered and Triple-Layered DO Lenses

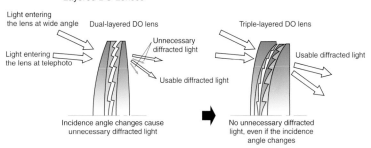

4 Unrivaled Clarity, Ideal Color Reproduction Super Spectra Coating

Lens coating is a technology which uses a vacuum deposition process to form an extremely thin transparent film on the surface of a lens. Reasons for coating a lens include

① improving transmittance and minimizing flare and ghosting,

② achieving optimum color balance, and

③ oxidizing ('burning') the lens surface, and thus is effective for changing or improving the properties of the lens and providing lens surface protection.

When light enters a lens, approximately 4-10% of the light is reflected back at each lens surface (glass-air boundary), resulting in significant light loss in photographic lenses constructed of several elements or more. Also, repeated reflections between the lens surfaces that reach the focal plane may cause flare or ghosting in the image. These harmful reflections can be largely eliminated for a wide range of wavelengths by coating each lens surface with a multi-layer coating consisting of several thin film layers having different indexes of refraction. At Canon, we use several types of multi-layer coatings which are optimized according to the index of refraction of the lens element to be coated.

Also, some types of glass — especially those having high indexes of refraction — tend to absorb blue light due to the components combined to produce the glass, resulting in an overall yellow color. If this yellowish glass were simply coated with a multi-layer coating like other lenses, light passing through the lens would have a slightly yellowish cast, producing a tinge of yellow in the white areas of pictures

Figure-33 Surface Reflections with Non-Coated Glass

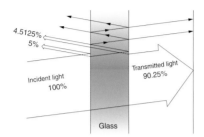

Figure-34 Lens Light Absorption and Surface Reflection

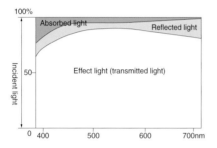

Figure-35 Super Spectra Coating Characteristics (Reflectivity)

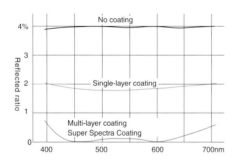

taken on color film. To counteract this, surfaces which have little effect on flare and ghosting are coated with single-layer coatings of appropriate colors such as amber, magenta, purple and blue to ensure identical color balance among all EF interchangeable lenses.

All EF lenses are coated to original standards which are even stricter than the CCI (Color Contribution Index) tolerance range set by the ISO (International Organization for Standardization). This coating process is called Super Spectra Coating within Canon, and offers features such as high transmittance, ultraviolet ray filtering, highly durable surface hardness and stable characteristics.

Through these exacting coating procedures, EF lenses feature superior imaging characteristics such as
① sharp, high-contrast, vivid images
② uniform color balance among all EF lens
③ true color reproduction which does not change over time.

5 Reducing Flare and Ghosting to the Minimum – SWC New Anti-reflection Coating.

SWC (Subwavelength Structure Coating) is an all-new type of anti-reflection coating recently developed by Canon. Reflections that occur on the surface of a lens are the main cause of flare and ghosting. Generally, to prevent such reflections, conventional coatings of vapor-deposition film have been applied to lenses. However, a common problem of this process is that the effectiveness of anti-reflection coating diminishes as the angle of incidence increases. Consequently, a lens with a small curvature radius has a large light incidence, making it difficult to obtain sufficient anti-reflection effectiveness with conventional vacuum vapor deposition coating. For such lenses in particular, SWC is an extremely effective anti-reflection measure because a large angle of incidence is not problematic. Consequently, SWC enables a dramatic reduction in flare and ghosting. (Figure-36)

Figure-36 Anti-reflection effectiveness and increased angle of incidence

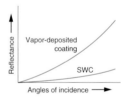

■ Theory and Structure of SWC

The refractive index of air is approximately 1 while that of optical glass ranges from approximately 1.4 to 1.9. Reflections of light occur at the boundary of two media with different refraction indices. Theoretically speaking, by gradually modifying the refractive index difference between two media, it is possible to prevent reflections on lens surfaces — thus creating ideal paths of light through air and optical glass with the desired angle of incidence. (Figure-37)

Based on this theory, Canon developed SWC technology. Though SWC appears to be a thin film, it is actually constructed of nanometer-scale, pyramidal structures as shown in Figure-38, ranging in size from 200-400nm.

The illustration of the lens surface shows this construction in detail. At Level A, most of the space is occupied by air. The

Figure-37 Anti-reflection theory of SWC

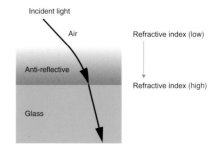

Figure-38 Structure of SWC

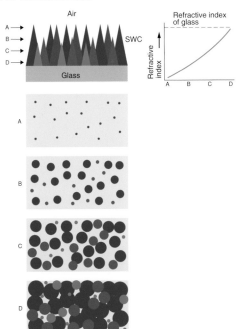

mass of structures occupying the lens surface increases from Levels B to C to D respectively. This gradually modifies the refractive index vertically. Gradual change of the refractive index enables light to enter the lens and pass through the other side of the lens as absorbed by the base of the structures. This is how SWC theory works in practice.

■ Key Technology in Expanding the Freedom of Optical Product Design

As lens manufacturers have pursued ever-higher performance and quality, the relationship between the angle of incidence/emergence and the anti-reflection effectiveness of vacuum vapor deposition coating has long been an issue. For example, even if a lens with a large curvature was essential for improved image quality, developers could not use this lens design due to insufficient anti-reflection effectiveness and limited capabilities of vacuum vapor deposition coating. However, the introduction of SWC will definitely expand the freedom of optical product design. This is demonstrated by the EF24mm f/1.4L II USM, which employs SWC technology for the first time*.

* Among photographic lenses

Figure-39 Optical construction of EF24mm f/1.4L II USM

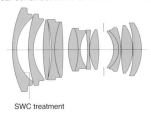

SWC treatment

Photo-16 SWC

6 Born From Innovation: Multi-Group Zoom Lenses

A zoom lens allows the focal length to be continuously varied over a certain range and can maintain focus during zooming (Zoom lenses in which the focus changes with the focal length are known as "vari-focal lenses.") In a zoom lens, part of the lens system is moved along the optical axis to change the focal length, and another part is moved at the same time to compensate for the resulting shift in focus.

Thus, a zoom lens must have at least two lens groups which can be moved along the optical axis. Figure-40 shows the lens construction of EF28-80mm f/3.5-5.6 V USM, a typical two-movable-group short zoom lens (a zoom lens with a length of 40mm or less at the shortest focal length position).

The 2nd group is called a "variator," meaning a group which is moved to change the focal length. The 1st group at the end of the lens moves simultaneously with the 2nd group to compensate focus shift, and is thus called a "compensator." The 2nd group also fulfills the role of focusing by adjusting the focal point.

In a short zoom, the 1st group has negative refraction (divergence), the 2nd group has positive refraction (convergence), and the lens is designed with a retro-focus type construction. This type of design is especially well suited for wide-angle zooms due to the following features:

① The front lens element is given a small diameter, making it easy to achieve a design which is compact and low cost.
② There is little barrel distortion at the short focal length position.
③ The 1st-group-focusing lens design allows focusing down to close distances.

Photo-17
High-Precision Zoom Cam Ring
(EF100-400mm f/4.5-5.6L IS USM)

Figure-40 Short Zoom Lens Construction (EF28-80mm f/3.5-5.6 Ⅴ USM)

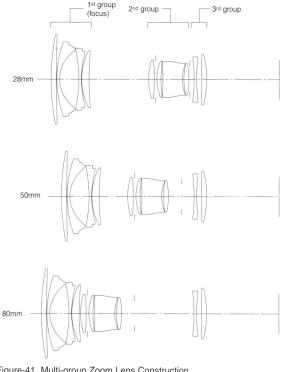

28mm

50mm

80mm

Figure-41 Multi-group Zoom Lens Construction
(EF100-400mm f/4.5-5.6L IS USM)

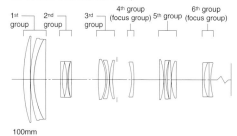

100mm

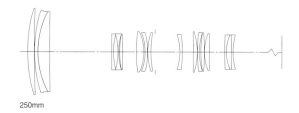

250mm

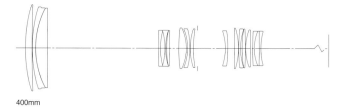

400mm

This type of design, however, presents a problem in that, if the zoom ratio in a short zoom lens is made too large, the movement amount of the 2nd group increases, thus increasing both the length of the lens and the maximum aperture variation amount. A large zoom ratio would also require an increase in the refractive power of the 2nd group, thus necessitating a greater number of lens elements to compensate for aberrations and increasing the overall size of the lens, which would make it very difficult to achieve a large ratio and a compact size. The solution to this problem is the multi-group zoom lens design, a technology developed to break through the limitations of small zoom lenses and achieve both a large ratio and a compact size.

In a short zoom lens, focal length variation (zooming) is carried out by the 2nd group alone; in a multi-group zoom, this task is allotted to several lens groups. Thus, a multi-group zoom is a zoom lens which has three or more movable lens groups.

Advantages of the multi-group zoom design are as follows:

① Since several lens groups are moved to vary the focal length, the movement amount of each lens group can be made small, allowing a compact lens design. Moreover, the change in apertures can be set as desired without requiring a complex diaphragm mechanism.

② Since zooming is distributed among several lens groups, each group can be designed with relatively weak refraction, making it possible to compensate aberrations with relatively few lens elements.

③ Since several lens groups are used, optical design freedom is increased and more options are available for compensating aberrations, such as designing lens groups to mutually cancel out their respective aberrations (cross compensation).

Multi-group zoom technology is high-level optical technology which can meet a wide range of lens design requirements, but it is only made possible with the support of advanced lens barrel design, processing and production technologies that make multiple group movements possible. Currently, the EF16-35mm f/2.8L II USM, EF24-105mm f/4L IS USM, EF100-400mm f/4.5-5.6L IS USM, and all the other EF zoom lenses are designed using multi-group zoom technology, achieving large ratio, compact size, and outstanding picture quality, all at the same time.

7 Quick and Smooth Focusing: Rear and Inner Focusing Systems

General photographic lenses carry out focusing using either the all-group focusing method, in which all lens groups are moved together along the optical axis, or the front-group focusing method, in which only the front lens group is moved. The all-group focusing method has the advantage of introducing relatively little change in aberration with respect to change in shooting distance, and is therefore the most commonly used focusing method in single focal length lenses.

Figure-42 Rear and Inner Focusing Systems

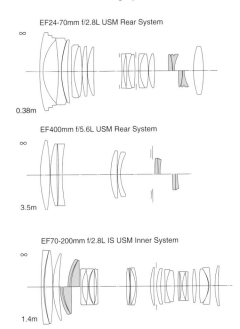

EF24-70mm f/2.8L USM Rear System

∞

0.38m

EF400mm f/5.6L USM Rear System

∞

3.5m

EF70-200mm f/2.8L IS USM Inner System

∞

1.4m

With telephoto and super-telephoto lenses, however, this method becomes less beneficial in terms of operability because of the increased size and weight of the lens system.

Front-group focusing, on the other hand, is primarily used in zoom lenses and has the advantage of affording a comparatively simple lens construction. However, this method has disadvantages because it places restrictions on zoom magnification and size reductions. To overcome the weak points of these two methods, Canon developed an ideal focusing method called rear focusing (or inner focusing) for use in telephoto and super-telephoto lenses. This method divides the lens system into several parts and moves the rear or middle lens group to perform focusing.

Besides the EF telephoto and super-telephoto lenses, rear focusing is currently employed in the EF16-35mm f/2.8L II USM and other zoom lenses. A rear focusing method employing a floating effect was also developed for use in wide-angle lenses such as the EF14mm f/2.8L II USM, EF20mm f/2.8 USM and EF24mm f/2.8.

Canon has also succeeded in employing rear focusing in zoom lenses.

These rear focusing/inner focusing designs have the following features:

① Since a lightweight lens group is moved during focusing, manual focusing operation has an extremely light feel. Moreover, quick-response autofocusing is possible.

② The lens length does not change during focusing. Also, the lens can be designed with a one-piece construction, resulting in improved rigidity.

③ Since the focusing ring can be placed in the optimum

position for focusing, and since the ring does not move back and forth during focusing, superior balance can be achieved.

④ The lens system can be made with a more compact design.

⑤ The minimum focusing distance can be made shorter than with conventional focusing methods.

⑥ Since the filter attachment ring does not rotate during focusing, superior operability is achieved with polarizing filters.

⑦ Since the front frame does not move during focusing, not only can petal hoods with good hooding effect be used, but accessories such as gelatin filter holders can also be used with the autofocus.

At Canon, lenses in which element groups behind the aperture position (towards the film surface) move are called rear focusing, while lenses in which element groups between the aperture and the front element move are called inner focusing.

8 Remarkably Improved Close-Distance Image Quality: Floating System

Conventional lenses are designed to achieve an optimum balance of aberration compensation at only one or possibly two shooting distance points throughout the focus range considered most common for that lens. Thus, although aberrations are well-compensated at the ideal shooting distance(s), aberrations increase and cause image degradation at other shooting distances. The degree to which this image degradation occurs differs according to the lens type and aperture size, with image degradation relatively small in symmetrical lenses but relatively large in asymmetrical lenses such as retro-focus type lenses. With retro-focus type lenses, in particular, aberration fluctuation increases as the focal length decreases or the aperture size increases. With wide-angle interchangeable lenses for SLR cameras — most of which necessarily employ retro-focus designs due to the need for back-focus — aberrations are small when focusing far distances, but curvature of field becomes significantly pronounced at close focusing distances, causing the peripheral image to go out of focus, or causing the central image to go out of focus if the focus is adjusted for the periphery.

To ensure ideal aberration correction throughout the range of focusing distances, Canon developed the floating system, in which the part of the lens system used for correcting aberration moves, or "floats," when adjusting the focus. This system is employed in the EF24mm f/1.4L II USM and other large aperture wide-angle lenses as well as the EF180mm f/3.5L Macro USM to improve close-distance performance.

Canon also developed a method for adding a floating effect to rear-focusing lenses. In the EF14mm f/2.8L II USM, for example, the lens system is divided into front and rear groups and only the rear group is used for focusing. Looking at the lens system as a whole, this rear-group focusing movement changes the distance between lens elements according to the shooting distance and thus provides a floating effect. Since the lens optics were designed from the start with this floating effect in mind, close-distance aberrations are corrected to a high degree.

Another application of the floating effect is to prevent spherical aberration, which tends to become significantly large at close focusing distances with large aperture lenses. This is the main reason why a floating system is employed in lenses such as the EF50mm f/1.2L USM, EF85mm f/1.2L II USM, and EF-S60mm f/2.8 Macro USM. The floating system in these lenses differs from that of wide-angle lenses in that it leaves the rear lens group fixed and extends the remainder of the lens system during focusing. This design achieves almost completely flare-free, high-quality imaging performance at all shooting distances.

Figure-43　EF24mm f/1.4L II USM Floating System　　Figure-44　Floating Effect (at 0.25m)

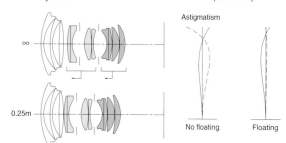

Figure-45　EF85mm f/1.2L II USM Floating System　　Figure-46　Floating Effect (at 0.95m)

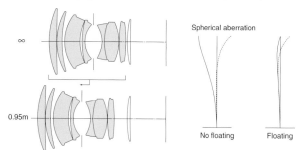

9 Extracting the Utmost in Lens Performance: Elimination of Internal Reflections

Flare and ghosting are caused by harmful light reflections within the lens, adversely affecting picture quality. EF lenses are therefore designed to eliminate reflections both in the lenses and barrel. Each lens element is treated with a special coating to prevent harmful light from occurring by suppressing lens surface reflection. Lens barrel reflection is taken care of

by selecting the best anti-reflection methods for each individual lens from among various techniques listed on the next page.

① Anti-Reflection Coating Techniques

This method employs a special paint on angled surfaces and joining surfaces where the lens elements are held in place by the lens barrel to stop light entering the lens from reflecting from these parts. If a standard coating is used, reflections actually increase due to the large size of the pigment grains and the fact that the coating has a lower index of refraction than the glass. Canon therefore developed several types of special anti-reflection coatings which have a high index of refraction and ultra-fine pigment grains, and can be used according to the location and objective, achieving a superior anti-reflection effect.

② Electrostatic Flocking Techniques

This method is a technique which uses an electrostatic flocking process to directly apply an extremely fine pile to surfaces requiring an anti-reflection finish. Since the pile

Figure-47　EF300mm f/2.8L IS USM Flocked Parts to Eliminate Internal Reflections

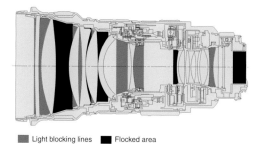

■ Light blocking lines　　■ Flocked area

Figure-48　EF28-135mm f/3.5-5.6 IS USM flare cut moving aperture diaphragm

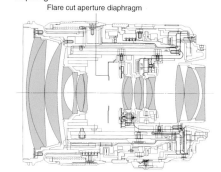

Photo-18　EF300mm f/4L IS USM Flocking Process　　Figure-49　EF24mm f/2.8 Internal Light Blocking Grooves

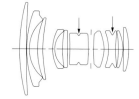

stands perpendicular to the wall surfaces, this technique is extremely effective especially in the long barrel sections of telephoto and super-telephoto single focal length lenses as well as zoom lenses and inside hoods.

③ Anti-Reflection Construction Techniques

In addition to use of special coatings and flocking, prevention of internal reflections is also achieved using various structural techniques such as use of light blocking grooves and knife edges to reduce the reflection surface area (Figure-47 and Figure-48), use of light blocking grooves at the lens' wide edge surface (the groove is filled with anti-reflection coating material and acts as a fixed diaphragm: Figure-49), and fixed and movable diaphragms (in zoom lenses) which double as flare-cutting devices. These measures extend to the blades, as well, with the surface of the aperture blades in the EMD unit (made from plastic and metal) treated with a special anti-reflection coating that also acts as a lubricant, to prevent ghost images from forming in the shape of the maximum apertures.

10 The Key to Quiet, Fast and Smooth Autofocus: Fully Electronic Mount & Lens-incorporated Motor Drive System

The fully electronic mount and lens-incorporated motor drive system is Canon's answer to the problems inherent in body-incorporated drive systems and the key point in the realization of the silent, smooth, fast, high-precision autofocusing the EOS system is known for. This system represents the true realization of Canon's mechatronic camera system design concept, which is "the placement of the optimum actuator close to each corresponding drive unit, and full electronic control of all data transmission and control signals." This extremely streamlined and logical system offers the following advantages over conventional systems.

● Features

① Since each EF lens can be equipped with the optimum actuator matched to its specific AF operation characteristics, strain-free, high-speed lens drive is possible for all lenses ranging from fisheye to super-telephoto. The advantage of this system over body-incorporated drive systems increases as the drive unit becomes farther away from the body in long super-telephoto lenses, enabling Canon to incorporate autofocusing in all of its super-telephoto lenses including the EF800mm f/5.6L IS USM.

② Since the actuator is physically close to the drive unit, drive energy is transmitted efficiently with minimal loss and drive noise.

③ Use of the electronic mount system allows lens designers to select from a wide selection of actuator types.

④ The system allows easy incorporation of new high-performance actuators as they are developed, providing great future development potential.

Canon currently utilizes the following five types of actuators, selecting the best type according to the characteristics of each lens.

● Ring-type USM
● Micro USM
● AFD (Arc-Form Drive: circular deformation brushless motor)
● Coreless DC micro motor
● Cored DC micro motor

Another type of actuator used in EF lenses is the EMD (electromagnetic diaphragm), which integrates an aperture-control deformation stepping motor and a diaphragm blade unit in a single unit. For details, see page 208.

11 Born With The EOS System: Advanced Ultrasonic Motor

The Ultrasonic Motor (USM) is a new type of motor which found its first application as a camera lens motor in Canon EF lenses. The ring USM which made its debut in 1987 in the EF300mm f/2.8L USM amazed the world with its silent, super-fast autofocusing performance. Then, in 1990 Canon established new mass-production technology realizing the development of a ring-type USM for use in popular-class lenses. This was followed by the successful development in 1992 of the Micro USM, a new type of USM enabling the use of automated production techniques, and in 2002 of the ultra-compact Micro USM II, half the length of the Micro USM. With this USM arsenal, the day is very near when Canon will finally realize its dream of employing a USM in every EF lens.

■ Ring-type USM Description

Conventional motors come in many different types and designs, but in principle they all convert electromagnetic force into rotational force. Ultrasonic motors, on the other hand, are based on a completely new principle in which rotational force is generated from ultrasonic vibrational energy. Including USMs still in the research and development phase, three types of USMs-classified by the method used to convert vibrational energy into rotational force-have been announced to date: the standing wave type, the traveling wave type, and the vibrating reed type. According to this classification, all USMs used in Canon lenses are of the traveling wave type. The basic motor construction is very simple, consisting of an elastic stator and a rotating rotor. The stator's bottom section consists of an elastic metal ring with a piezoelectric ceramic element attached, and its top section consists of many uniformly-spaced projections which have trapezoidal cross sections. The stator is made of a special material which has a coefficient of thermal expansion nearly the same as the piezoelectric ceramic element, which minimizes ring distortion due to temperature changes. Because of this, stable operation is guaranteed over a broad temperature range. The rotor is an aluminum ring which has a flange-shaped spring where it contacts the stator, and so is held in contact with the stator under pressure. Since aluminum is a relatively soft material, the location where the rotor contacts the stator is provided with a special abrasion-resistant surface finish.

■ Ring-type USM Features

The basic features of ultrasonic motors are as follows:

① Low-speed, high-torque output characteristics (a USM can generate a larger amount of power at lower speeds than a conventional motor which rotates using electromagnetic force) can be easily realized, enabling direct drive without the need for a speed-reducing gear train.

② Holding torque is large. In other words, when the motor is stopped the lens is automatically held in place by a disc brake effect.

③ Construction is extremely simple.

④ Starting and stopping response and controllability are good. (Quick starting and stopping is possible, and operation can be precisely controlled.)

⑤ Operation is extremely quiet (virtually noiseless).

In addition to the above, Canon's ring USMs also offer the following features:

⑥ High efficiency and low power consumption allow the USM to be powered from the camera's battery.

⑦ The motor's ring shape is the optimum shape for incorporation into a lens barrel.

⑧ Low rotation speed is optimally suited for lens drive purposes.

⑨ Rotation speed can be continuously controlled within a wide range from 0.2 rpm (one rotation every five minutes) to 80 rpm, enabling high-precision, high-speed lens drive control.

⑩ Stable operation is achieved under the harshest of conditions, with a broad range of temperature usability, from −30°C to +60°C.

For any motor, the motor drive control system is an important subsystem necessary for fully extracting the motor's particular characteristics. The same is true for ultrasonic motors. In Canon's USM lenses, functions such as detection of the ultrasonic resonance state with respect to temperature variation, generation of two AC voltages of different phase, starting and stopping control, and electronic manual focus speed adjustment are all controlled by a microcomputer incorporated in the lens.

Photo-19 Ring-type USM

■ Ring-type USM Rotation Principle

The operation principle of a Ring-type USM is as follows: vibrations are applied to the elastic body called the stator, thus generating vibrations in the stator.

Figure-50 Various Lens Actuators

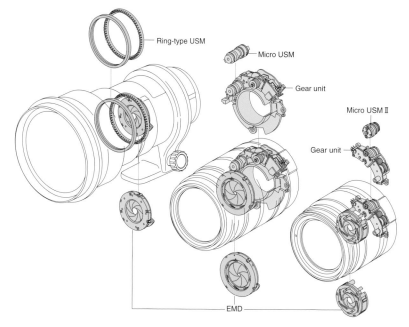

Ring-type USM

Micro USM

Gear unit

Micro USM II

Gear unit

EMD

Figure-51 EF28-135mm f/3.5-5.6 IS USM showing USM

Figure-52 Ring-type USM Construction

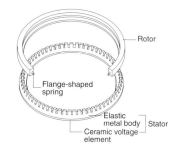

Rotor

Flange-shaped spring

Elastic metal body | Stator
Ceramic voltage element

That vibrational energy is used to continuously rotate the rotor through the pressure contact between the rotor and stator. In more technical terms, the frictional force generated by flexural traveling waves in the stator is the source of rotational motive force. The manner in which the force from the flexural traveling waves generated in the stator is transmitted to the rotor is illustrated in Figure-53. If we watch the movement of the tip of each projection P as the wave advances from left to right, it can be seen that the tip moves in the direction opposite that of the wave. The rotor is driven by the frictional force at each point P, thus completing the operation sequence. As shown in Figure-54 and Figure-55, flexural traveling waves are generated by the piezo-electric ceramic element (an element which expands and contracts when applied with an AC voltage) which is attached to the bottom of the stator and driven by an electronic circuit. This piezoelectric ceramic element is alternately polarized in the direction of its thickness, and is applied with an AC voltage having a frequency near the stator's flexural vibration resonant frequency of approx. 30,000Hz (this frequency is in the ultrasonic range, which is where the USM gets its name). The applied voltage generates vibrations (having an amplitude width of only around 0.001mm) in the stator which are combined with vibrations of a different phase generated by a piezoelectric element attached to the bottom of the stator at a separate location shifted by one-fourth the periodic phase. This combined wave — a flexural traveling wave (7 vibrational waves per cycle) moving along the stator — is the source of the motor's rotational energy.

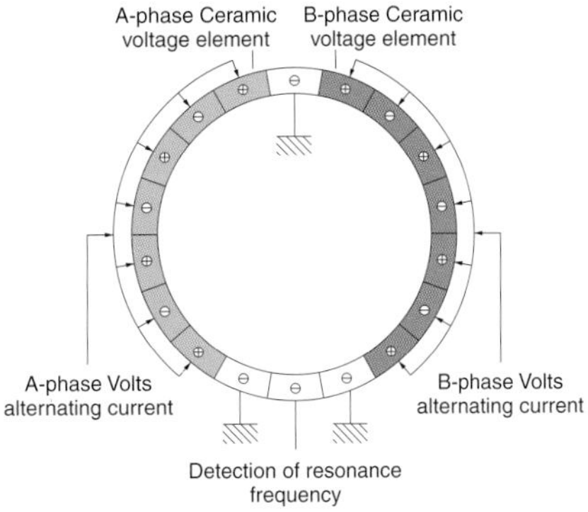

■ Micro USM Description and Features

The Ring-type USM is an ultrasonic motor developed from the

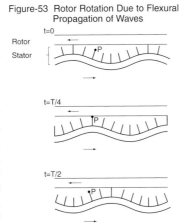

Figure-53 Rotor Rotation Due to Flexural Propagation of Waves

t=0

t=T/4

t=T/2

T: Period of flexural traveling wave

Figure-54 Vibrations Generated by Piezoelectric Ceramic Element

Elastic metal body
Ceramic voltage element
Volts alternating current
⥯ Direction of transformation of voltage elements
⊖ ⊕ Polarity of voltage elements

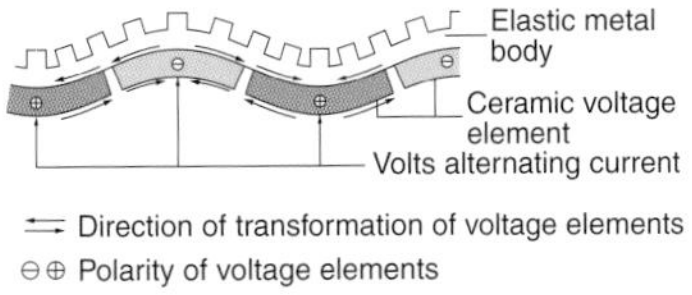

Figure-55 Piezoelectric Ceramic Element Layout (bottom of stator)

A-phase Ceramic voltage element   B-phase Ceramic voltage element

A-phase Volts alternating current   B-phase Volts alternating current

Detection of resonance frequency

beginning for incorporation into round-barreled lenses. In contrast, the Micro USM is a new motor developed as a "multi-purpose miniature ultrasonic motor." Features of the Micro USM are as follows:

● Since there are no lens diameter restrictions, the Micro USM can be incorporated in a wide variety of lenses regardless of optical system construction.

● The stator, rotor and output gear are integrated in a single compact unit approximately half the size and weight of a Ring-type USM.

● Cost is lower than that of the Ring-type USM, enabling use in popularly priced lenses.

■ Micro USM Basic Construction

As shown in Figure-56, the Micro USM has an integrated construction in which the piezoelectric element, stator and rotor are stacked vertically and combined with the output gear in a single compact unit. The stator consists of five piezoelectric element layers, with each layer sandwiched above and below by metal vibrator discs. As a whole, the stator unit functions as an elastic, cylindrical rod.

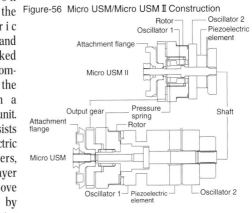

Figure-56 Micro USM/Micro USM II Construction

Rotor
Oscillator 2
Oscillator 1
Piezoelectric element
Attachment flange
Micro USM II
Output gear
Pressure spring
Shaft
Attachment flange
Rotor
Micro USM
Oscillator 1
Piezoelectric element
Oscillator 2

The rotor, which is combined with the spring case, is held in contact with the stator under pressure by the springs built into the inner circumference of the spring case. Rotor rotation is transmitted directly to the output gear in a 1:1 ratio. The various components of the motor – the stator, rotor and output gear – are combined into a single Micro USM unit by a stator shaft which runs through the center of the components and a flange at the top which holds everything together. The motor is incorporated in a lens as shown in Figure-50.

Photo-20 Micro USM (Left) Micro USM II (Right)

■ Micro USM Operation Principle

The ultrasonic vibrations which are the source of rotational energy are generated using an electronic circuit to drive the four layers of piezoelectric elements which have the characteristics shown in Figure-57. Each of the four piezo-electric layers is constructed of two piezoelectric elements divided into two phases — the A phase and the B phase — which are offset from each other positioned by a phase difference of 90°. At the very bottom of the stack is a fifth piezoelectric element layer used for resonant vibration wave detection (Figure-58).

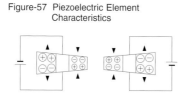

Figure-57 Piezoelectric Element Characteristics

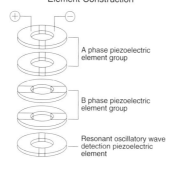

Figure-58 Micro USM Piezoelectric Element Construction

A phase piezoelectric element group

B phase piezoelectric element group

Resonant oscillatory wave detection piezoelectric element

These five layers are incorporated into the base of the stator. If AC voltage is applied only to the A phase of this piezoelectric element group, the expansion and contraction of the piezoelectric elements causes the tip of the stator to vibrate slightly left and right (Figure-59). If AC voltage is applied only to the B phase, the expansion and contraction of the piezoelectric elements cause the tip of the stator to vibrate slightly backward and forward. Finally, if an alternating current which varies by 90° is added to the A phase and the B phase, the vibrations of both phases will combine and generate a small rotational vibration wave (1 vibration wave per cycle, amplitude: 0.002mm) which causes the tip of the stator to swing in a small circular motion as shown in Figure-60. In turn, the rotor which is always in contact with the stator due to the added spring power will also start rotating due to the friction generated by the rotational vibration wave. The rotation of the rotor in turn causes the output gear, to which it is directly connected, to rotate. With a Ring-type USM, the frictional vibration caused by the flexural traveling waves generated in the stator are the operational principle, and where the rotor rotated in the opposite direction of the waves, this basically hold true for the Micro USM.

■ Micro USM II

The Micro USM II is an ultra-compact ultrasonic motor developed to meet the demand for an even smaller space for incorporating the AF drive actuator, due to the increasingly compact size of lens barrels. Its features are as follows.
In conventional Micro USMs, the stator and the rotor are arranged in a row. If the length of the unit were simply shortened without modifying this arrangement, the resonance frequency of the flexural vibration in the stator would become extremely high, preventing achievement of sufficient vibrational amplitude. To overcome this problem, an arrangement which places part of the stator inside the area for the rotor was developed along with a completely new vibrational format for the Micro USM II in order to shorten the length of the unit without raising the resonance frequency. The result is an ultra-compact unit at around half the length and mass of the Micro USM, but with approximately the same performance. The Micro USM II was first included in the EF28-105mm f/4-5.6 USM.

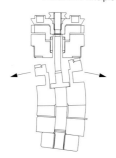

Figure-59 Micro USM Stator Vibration Principle

Figure-60 Micro USM Rotor Rotation Drive Principle

Direction of rotation

Rotor

Stator

Table-2 USM Types and Mounted Lens

Item	Micro USM	Ring-type USM (MI type)		Ring-type USM (LI type)
Integrated lens	EF50mm f/1.4 USM EF70-300mm f/4-5.6 IS USM	EF14mm f/2.8L II USM EF20mm f/2.8 USM EF24mm f/1.4L II USM EF28mm f/1.8 USM EF35mm f/1.4L USM EF50mm f/1.2L USM EF85mm f/1.8 USM EF100mm f/2 USM EF100mm f/2.8L Macro IS USM EF100mm f/2.8 Macro USM EF135mm f/2L USM EF180mm f/3.5L Macro USM EF200mm f/2.8L II USM EF300mm f/4L IS USM EF400mm f/4 DO IS USM EF400mm f/5.6L USM EF-S60mm f/2.8 Macro USM	EF16-35mm f/2.8L II USM EF17-40mm f/4L USM EF24-70mm f/2.8L USM EF24-105mm f/4L IS USM EF28-135mm f/3.5-5.6 IS USM EF28-300mm f/3.5-5.6L IS USM EF70-200mm f/2.8L IS USM EF70-200mm f/2.8L USM EF70-200mm f/4L IS USM EF70-200mm f/4L USM EF70-300mm f/4.5-5.6 DO IS USM EF100-400mm f/4.5-5.6L IS USM EF-S10-22mm f/3.5-4.5 USM EF-S15-85mm f/3.5-5.6 IS USM EF-S17-55mm f/2.8 IS USM EF-S17-85mm f/4-5.6 IS USM	EF85mm f/1.2L II USM EF200mm f/2L IS USM EF300mm f/2.8L IS USM EF400mm f/2.8L IS USM EF500mm f/4L IS USM EF600mm f/4L IS USM EF800mm f/5.6L IS USM
Outer diameter (mm)	φ11	φ62		φ77
Length (mm)	26.7	10		10
Mass (g)	11	26		45

12 Accurate, Unrivaled Digital Electronic Control: EMD

Every EF lens incorporates an EMD (electromagnetic diaphragm) which electronically controls the lens aperture diameter and is designed for use with EOS's fully-electronic data transmission mount system. The EMD is a diaphragm drive control actuator shaped to fit comfortably within the round barrel of a lens, and actually is a component integrating both a deformation stepping motor and a diaphragm blade unit in a single unit. (Photo-21)

Control of the aperture diameter is carried out by an electrical pulse signal which corresponds to a setting value manually selected with the camera's electronic dial or automatically determined by the camera's microcomputer.

Features of the EMD are as follows:

① Since control is carried out electronically, control precision is much higher.

② Since the drive is provided by the stepping motor, superior

Photo-21 EMD Unit

Figure-61 EMD Construction

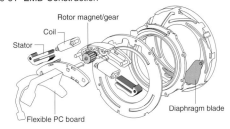

Rotor magnet/gear
Coil
Stator
Flexible PC board
Diaphragm blade

Figure-62 Stepping Motor Construction

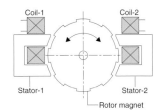

Coil-1
Coil-2
Stator-1
Stator-2
Rotor magnet

start/stop response and controllability are achieved.

③ Since linkage shock inherent in mechanical lever systems is eliminated, operation is extremely quiet.

④ The aperture can be closed down for checking the depth of field with a simple button operation at any time regardless of whether the exposure control mode set on the camera is automatic or manual.

⑤ Superior durability and reliability are realized thanks to less burden during drive.

⑥ By raising the motor drive power, the system can work with large-diameter apertures.

⑦ No need for a mechanical connection to the camera body permits a high degree of freedom in designing the aperture layout.

The actual construction of the EMD (Figure-61) uses a stepping motor and a pinion to control the rotation of a ring engaged with the diaphragm blades. The deformation stepping motor, which acts as the drive source, utilizes the mutual opposing and attracting forces of magnets attached to the stator and rotor arranged as shown in Figure-62 to rotate the rotor one step for every electrical pulse. When an aperture control signal is sent from the camera body to the lens, the lens' built-in microcomputer converts the signal into the corresponding number of pulses and uses digital control to accurately set the diaphragm to the required diameter. In this way, aperture control in EMD-equipped EF lenses is carried out completely within the lens itself once the electrical control signal is received from the camera body. The advantages of this system allow for extensive future development, and have already made it possible for Canon to develop the first tilt-shift lenses (TS-E lenses) in the world equipped with an automatic diaphragm, as well as enabling use of EF lenses on other equipment such as Canon's XL2 interchangeable lens video camera. The newest models of EMD employ a barrel aperture in which the blade shape is optimized for best blur effect.

13 The Fusion of AF and Manual Full-Time Manual Focus

The EOS system was built to deliver completely automated photography, but at the same time has been designed to leave final control over the elements that define the photographer's envisioned image in his or her hands, based on the fundamental concept of delivering automation which conforms to the will of the photographer. This concept can be seen at work in EF lenses, too, in the full time manual focus that allows final focus adjustment after autofocus.

● Full-time mechanical manual focusing

This function allows the photographer to manually focus the lens as soon as one-shot AF control is completed without switching the focus mode switch to manual focus. Full-time manual focusing originally employed an electronic focusing method for the EF85mm f/1.2L USM and other early EF lenses, but today uses a mechanical system in almost all USM lenses equipped with a manual focusing ring and a distance scale, such as the EF16-35mm f/2.8L II USM, and the EF300mm f/2.8L IS USM.

This full-time mechanical manual focus mechanism is a type of differential mechanism comprising three rings and a roller built into one of the rings. A description of the construction follows.

Ring 1 is rotated around the optical axis by the USM, ring 2 rotates around the optical axis when manually turned. The roller is located between the rings 1 and 2, and its rotational axis is connected to the output ring.

Rotating ring 1 or 2 when in autofocus or manual focus causes the roller to move around the optical axis, pushed by the rotation of either of the rings. Since the roller's rotational axis is fixed to the output ring, the movement of the roller in turn rotates the output ring, making the output ring rotate around the optical axis. The focus group is moved by transmitting the rotation of the output ring to a helicoid or cam.

Full-time manual focus is also achieved in the EF50mm f/1.4 USM, which is equipped with a Micro USM, thanks to a differential mechanism built into the gear unit.

Photo-22 Focus Unit Integrated Full-time Mechanical Manual Focus Mechanism

14 Microcomputer-Controlled Electronic Focus Preset

Focus preset is a function currently provided on 6 telephoto lenses (EF200mm f/2L IS USM, EF300mm f/2.8L IS USM, EF400mm f/2.8L IS USM, EF500mm f/4L IS USM, EF600mm f/4L IS USM and EF800mm f/5.6L IS USM) which electronically memorizes a freely selected focus position to allow the photographer to instantly preset the lens to that focus position whenever desired. By pressing the preset switch on the switch panel, the position of the focus lens at that moment is memorized by the microcomputer inside the lens. In this state, normal autofocusing can still be carried out as usual. Then, whenever necessary, turning the playback ring sets the lens to the memorized focus position within 0.5 seconds. This function can be used effectively in situations such as the following:

① Frequently taking pictures at a certain fixed distance

Focus preset is useful in situations such as sports events where most pictures are taken at a certain distance and normal AF operation is used occasionally, or the reverse, where normal AF operation is used most of the time but pictures at a certain fixed distance are sometimes required. Once the focus position is preset, there is no need to refocus the lens to that position for every shot. Moreover, since the focus position is memorized by the lens's microcomputer, focusing to the preset position is possible even if the subject is not covered by the viewfinder's AF frame.

② Memorizing "infinity"

When frequently taking pictures at a shooting distance of "infinity," operability can be significantly improved by using the focus preset function rather than using manual focusing or autofocusing to focus the lens for every shot. (Due to the effect of temperature fluctuations, the infinity position of super-telephoto lenses is provided with a certain amount of play, or "leeway." Because of this, the focus position set when the manual focusing ring is turned all the way in the

Figure-63 Output Power Transmission Mechanism

Figure-64 Manual Focus Mechanism

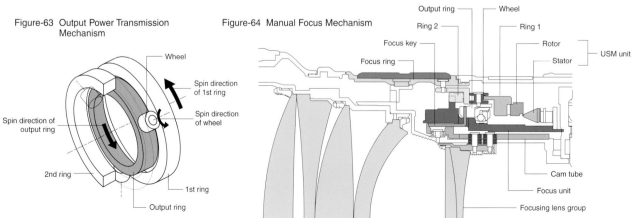

Figure-65 Focus Preset Photography

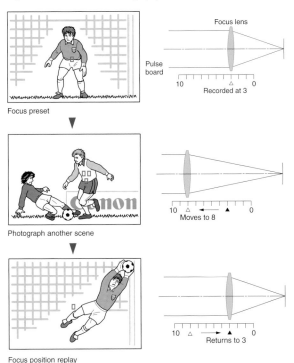

Focus preset

Photograph another scene

Focus position replay

Photo-23 EF300mm f/2.8L IS USM Focus Preset Operation Unit

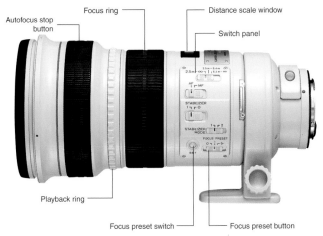

direction of infinity is not actually infinity.)

③ Minimizing time loss caused by AF misfocusing

During AI Servo autofocusing, the lens may shift considerably out of focus if an obstruction should enter the path between the lens and subject. By presetting the focus position to a distance frequently occupied by the main subject, you can use the playback ring whenever this occurs to quickly reset the lens focus to the general subject distance, minimizing the time lost in refocusing.

15 AF Stop Function: Temporarily Turns Off Autofocus

The AF Stop function is available on the EF300mm f/2.8L IS USM and other large aperture super telephoto L type IS series lenses.

It allows the photographer to temporarily turn off autofocus when an obstruction passes between the camera and the subject during AI Servo autofocusing, so the object being focused on will not switch from the subject to the obstruction. AF Stop buttons are at four locations around the grip used for handheld photography at the front of the lens. Pressing an AF Stop button temporarily stops autofocus and releasing the button restarts autofocus.

16 Superior Dust-proof and Drip-proof Construction to withstand even the most Rugged Shooting Conditions

The EF300mm f/2.8L IS USM super telephoto lens, the EF24-70mm f/2.8L USM, and other L-series zoom lenses are designed so they can be used under harsh professional photography conditions by providing dust-proof and drip-proof joints on their external parts.

① A rubber ring on the mount connection blocks the gap between the lens and the camera.

② The moving parts of the manual focus, zoom, and playback rings are shaped to be dust-proof and drip-proof. A dust-proof and drip-proof construction has also been employed on the zooming extension for the EF24-70mm f/2.8L USM.

③ AF Stop and Focus Preset buttons feature dust-proof and drip-proof construction.

④ Dust-proof and drip-proof rubber material is installed on the connections of the switch panel and other external parts.

⑤ Rubber is installed at the opening where the rear drop-in filter holder is inserted, blocking the gap between the lens body and the drop-in filter holder to keep out water droplets and dust particles.

The EOS-1Ds Mark Ⅲ, EOS-1Ds Mark Ⅱ, EOS-1Ds, EOS-1D Mark Ⅳ, EOS-1D Mark Ⅲ, EOS-1D Mark Ⅱ N, EOS-1D Mark Ⅱ, EOS-1D and EOS-1V/HS have dust-proof and drip-proof bodies

17 Breakthrough in Lens Technology: Image Stabilizer

Camera shake is a major cause of blurred images especially when shooting with long focal length lenses. Normally, a shutter speed at least as fast as the reciprocal of the lens focal length (Ex.: 1/300 sec. for 300mm) can prevent a blurred image due to camera shake. However, under low-light conditions or with slow film, a slower shutter speed will be required, resulting in image blur for handheld shots. Canon has developed the Image Stabilizer (IS) to help resolve this problem.

■ How the Image Stabilizer Works

The Image Stabilizer (IS) shifts a lens group in parallel to the focal plane.

When the lens jerks due to camera shake, the light rays from the subject are bent relative to the optical axis, resulting in a blurred image. When the lens is decentered, the light rays are deflected. By shifting the IS lens group on a plane perpendicular to the optical axis to suit the degree of image shake, the light rays reaching the focal plane can be steadied. Figure-66 shows what happens when the lens is jerked downward. The center of the image moves downward on the focal plane. When the IS lens group shifts on the vertical plane, the light rays are refracted so that the image center returns to the center of the focal plane. Since image shake occurs in both the horizontal and vertical directions, the IS lens group can shift vertically and horizontally on a plane perpendicular to the optical axis to counteract the image shake.

Camera shake is detected by two gyro sensors (one each for the yaw and pitch). Shown in Photo-24, the gyro sensors detect the angle and speed of the camera shake caused by handheld shooting.

The IS lens group is driven by an actuator consisting of a pair of fixed magnets and coils. This device is small, light, and highly responsive with excellent control. It can handle a wide frequency range (approx. 0.5 Hz to 20 Hz). (Figure-67)

In the IS unit for the EF-S15-85mm f/3.5-5.6 IS USM, EF-S18-55mm f/3.5-5.6 IS, EF-S18-135mm f/3.5-5.6 IS, EF-S18-200mm f/3.5-5.6 IS and EF-S55-250mm f/4-5.6 IS, the barrel containing the IS lens group is suspended by springs and supported by dampers. This simple structure keeps the unit compact and light. (Figure-68)

Photo-24 Shake-detecting gyro sensor

Figure-66 Image Stabilizer Parallel Movement Principle

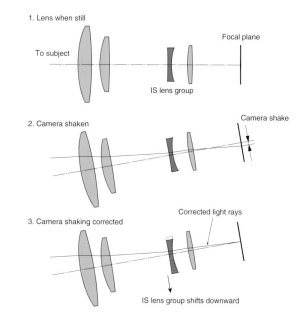

■ Image Stabilizer system

The Image Stabilizer operates as follows.

① When the camera's shutter button is pushed down half way, the vibration gyro starts up.

② The vibration gyro detects the angular velocity component of the lens vibration caused by hand-shake, and transmits a detection signal to the microcomputer.

③ The detection signal is converted to a stabilizer optical system drive signal by the microcomputer, which then transmits this signal to the stabilizer optical system drive circuit.

④ The actuator moves the stabilizer optical system in parallel in response to the drive signal. A fast 16-bit microcomputer is employed to simultaneously control image stabilization, USM, and EMD.

Photo-25 Image Stabilizer Unit

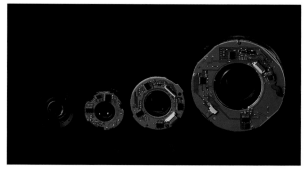

■ Image Stabilizer Mode 2

The stabilization characteristics of the normal Image Stabilizer are set so that it is most effective when photographing stationary subjects, but when panning of a moving subject is attempted, shake-return may affect the finder image, interfering with framing. This occurs because camera movement such as panning is judged to be shaking, activating the image stabilizer.

To resolve this problem, Canon developed Image Stabilizer Mode 2. In this mode, if large movement such as panning continues for a preset time, image stabilization in the direction of the motion is shut off. As this stabilizes the finder image during movement, accurate framing is possible. In Image Stabilizer Mode 2, if you are panning, image stabilization continues vertically relative to the movement of the camera, making it possible to control vertical shaking during panning. (Figure-69)

Image Stabilizer Mode 2 is found in a wide range of lenses, including the EF300mm f/4L IS USM. The EF-S15-85mm f/3.5-5.6 IS USM, EF-S18-55mm f/3.5-5.6 IS, EF-S18-135mm f/3.5-5.6 IS, EF-S18-200mm f/3.5-5.6 IS and EF-S55-250mm f/4-5.6 IS, can distinguish between normal shooting and panning, automatically switching between the two IS modes as needed.

Figure-67 EF70-200mm f/2.8L IS USM Image Stabilizer System

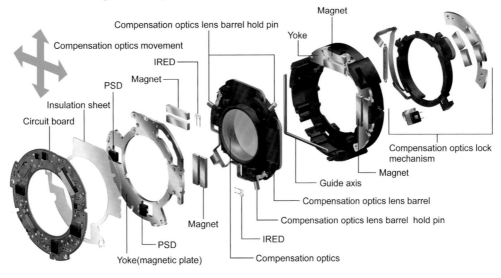

Figure-68 EF-S18-55mm f/3.5-5.6 IS Image Stabilizer System

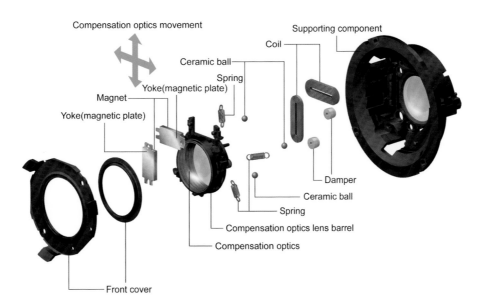

Figure-69 Image Stabilizer Mode 2 stabilization control

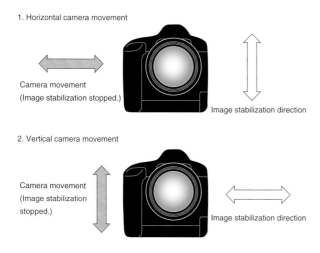

Figure-70 EF70-200mm f/4L IS USM Image Stabilizer Effect Graph

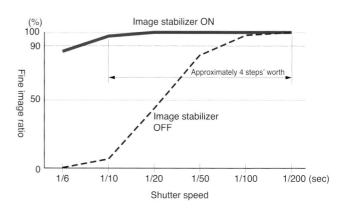

Tripod- and monopod-compatible Image Stabilizer

The EF300mm f/2.8L IS USM and other IS lenses automatically prevent accidental activation of image stabilization when used with a tripod. This eliminates the need for having to manually turn the Image Stabilizer off. With the EF200mm f/2L IS USM and EF800mm f/5.6L IS USM, image stabilization reduces minor blurring caused by camera shake and other factors when shooting with a tripod. And when a monopod is used with any lens in the IS series, image stabilization is identical to that achieved during hand-held photography.

Effect of Image Stabilization

The image stabilization function for EF lenses was first used on the EF75-300mm f/4-5.6 IS USM in 1995. Converted into shutter speed, the effect of image stabilization equalled about two steps. With a 300mm telephoto lens, it permitted hand-held photography at 1/60 second. Later, through improvements to the design of the image stabilizer unit and the algorithm used, the performance of the effect was raised even further, to three steps, with the EF70-200mm f/2.8L IS USM which went on sale in 2001, to four steps with the EF70-200mm f/4L IS USM which went on sale in 2006, and to five steps with the EF200mm f/2L IS USM which went on sale in 2008. The lower limit on hand-held photography at slow shutter speeds was thus reduced significantly.

When the Image Stabilizer Mode 2 is on and an extender is installed, it provides equivalent image stabilization effects. The image stabilizer function is also effective during close-up photography and photography in unstable places.

Hybrid IS

Existing IS technology is highly effective in normal shooting situations, but its benefits are not fully evident when it comes to macro photography. This is because the camera shake that occurs during macro photography, shift camera shake, is different than the shake that occurs in non-macro situations (referred to as angle camera shake). (Figure-71) Canon's proprietary Hybrid IS is the world's first* optical camera shake compensation technology that can detect and compensate for both angle and shift camera shake (Figure-72) simultaneously. Its effectiveness is clearly evident on the EF100mm f/2.8L Macro IS USM.

* For interchangeable SLR camera lenses.

● Angle camera shake and shift camera shake
Conventional IS systems for SLR cameras compensate only for angle camera shake, which is caused by the camera being tilted during exposure. Because the angle of the optical axis changes relative to the camera, the amount of angle camera shake increases as focal length increases, making shooting with telephoto lenses more prone to camera shake than with wide-angle lenses. Conversely, shift camera shake occurs when the camera and the optical axis shift parallel to the image during exposure. Since the effects of shift camera shake decrease as the focus distance increases, they become negligible in non-macro shooting situations. But as the focusing distance decreases and magnification increases into the macro range, the effects of shift camera shake become noticeably larger. When shooting macro photos, both angle and shift camera shake can occur, but conventional IS technologies have been unable to detect and compensate for the latter. Because of this, macro lenses equipped with conventional IS systems cannot solve the problem of camera shake that occurs in macro photography.

Figure-71 The relation between magnification and the amount of camera shake

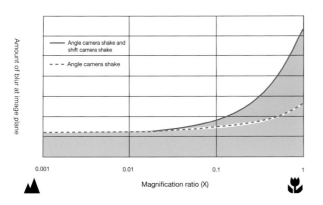

Note: The amount of blur from angle camera shake and shift camera shake varies depending on shooting conditions.

Figure-72 Angle camera shake and shift camera shake

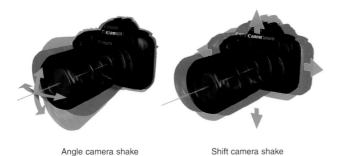

Angle camera shake   Shift camera shake

Photo-26 IS Unit of EF100mm f/2.8L Macro IS USM

Figure-73 Hybrid IS

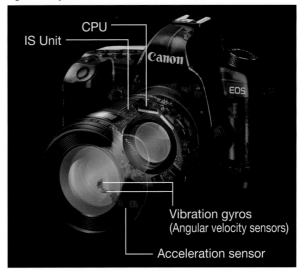

■ Hybrid IS system

Conventional IS systems and Hybrid IS share the same basic principle — each shift IS elements in the lens to counter shifts in the optical axis and thus compensate for camera shake. But the Hybrid IS system is remarkable in that it detects and corrects the effects of both angle camera shake and shift camera shake when shooting in the macro realm.

There are two major elements that make Hybrid IS different than conventional IS:

① Two sensors for two types of camera shake

The Hybrid IS system employs two sensors: one for detecting angle camera shake and the other for shift camera shake. The effectiveness of vibration gyros (angular velocity sensors) in detecting angle camera shake has been amply demonstrated in conventional IS systems. In the Hybrid IS system, however, an acceleration sensor has been added to detect camera shake that occurs parallel to the image plane (referred to as shift camera shake). By monitoring information transmitted by the two sensors, Hybrid IS can detect camera movement in three-dimensional space.

② Dedicated algorithm

There are limits to distinguishing between the two types of camera shake, hence a sensor may be influenced by camera shake it was not intended to detect. For example, the signal output of the angular velocity sensor may be influenced by shift camera shake while the output from the acceleration sensor may be influenced by angle camera shake. To overcome this problem, Canon developed a new algorithm that serves as the nerve center of Hybrid IS. This algorithm calculates the influence of the two types of shake on each sensor by analyzing the correlation between camera shake frequency and output signals from the sensors. This makes it possible for Hybrid IS to simultaneously compensate for the effects of the two types of camera shake at the image plane.

Figure-74 Basic concept of Hybrid IS

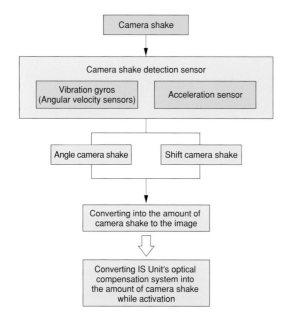

■ Effects of IS in macro photography

A general rule of thumb for reducing the effects of camera shake is to use a shutter speed that is as fast or faster than the reciprocal of lens focal length. For macro photography, however, the slowest shutter speed should be one or two steps faster. The Hybrid IS in the EF100mm f/2.8L Macro IS USM allows handheld shooting at shutter speeds approximately four steps slower than without IS. For macro photography, this translates into usable shutter speeds of approximately three steps slower at 0.5x magnification and about two steps slower at 1x*, thus providing the ability to shoot handheld at 1x magnification.

* Effects of IS may vary depending on shooting conditions. IS allows shooting normal photos using shutter speeds approximately 4 steps slower than with non-IS lenses.

Optical Terminology

What is light to photography?

What is 'light'?

Light is a physical phenomenon which involves creating vision by stimulating the optic nerves, and can be broadly defined as a type of electromagnetic wave.

Types of electromagnetic radiation vary according to wavelength. Starting from the shortest wavelengths, electromagnetic radiation can be classified into gamma rays, X rays, ultraviolet light rays, visible light rays, infrared light rays, far-infrared light rays, microwave radiation, ultra short wave radiation (VHF), short wave radiation, medium wave radiation (MF) and long wave radiation. In photography, the most utilized wavelengths are in the visible light region (400nm~700nm). Since light is a type of electromagnetic radiation, light can be thought of as a type of wave in the category of "light waves." A light wave can be regarded as

Figure-1 Approaching the human eye

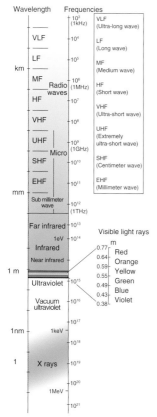

Figure-2 Approaching the human eye

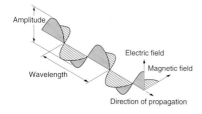

an electromagnetic wave in which an electric field and magnetic field vibrate at right angles to each other in a plane perpendicular to the direction of propagation. The two elements of a light wave which can actually be detected by the human eye are the wavelength and amplitude. Differences in wavelength are sensed as differences in color (within the visible light range) and differences in amplitude are sensed as differences in brightness (light intensity). The third element which cannot be detected by the human eye is the direction of vibration within the plane perpendicular to the light wave's direction of propagation (polarized light).

Basic light-related phenomena

Refraction

A phenomenon whereby the propagation direction of a ray of light changes when the light passes from one medium such as a vacuum or air into a different medium such as glass or water, or vice versa.

Figure-3 Light Refraction

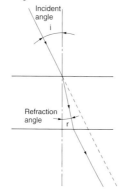

Index of refraction

A numerical value indicating the degree of refraction of a medium, expressed by the formula $n = \sin i / \sin r$. "n" is a constant which is unrelated to the light ray's angle of incidence and indicates the refractive index of the refracting medium with respect to the medium from which the light impinges.

For general optical glass, "n" usually indicates the index of refraction of the glass with respect to air.

Dispersion

A phenomenon whereby the optical properties of a medium vary according to the wavelength of light passing through the medium. When light enters a lens or prism, the dispersion

characteristics of the lens or prism cause the index of refraction to vary depending on the wavelength, thus dispersing the light. This is also sometimes referred to as color dispersion.

Extraordinary partial dispersion

The human eye can sense monochromatic light wavelengths within the range of 400nm (purple) to 700nm (red). Within this range, the difference in index of refraction between two different wavelengths is called partial dispersion. Most ordinary optical materials have similar partial dispersion characteristics. However, partial dispersion characteristics differ for some glass materials, such as glass, which has larger partial dispersion at short wavelengths, FK glass which features a small index of refraction and low dispersion characteristics, fluorite, and glass which has larger partial dispersion at long wavelengths. These types of glass are classified as having extraordinary partial dispersion characteristics. Glass with this property is used in apochromatic lenses to compensate chromatic aberration.

Figure-4 Light Dispersion by A Prism

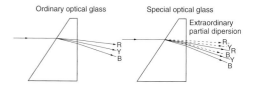

Reflection

Reflection differs from refraction in that it is a phenomenon which causes a portion of the light striking the surface of glass or other medium to break off and propagate in an entirely new direction. The direction of propagation is the same regardless of wavelength. When light enters and leaves a lens which does not have an anti-reflection coating, approximately 5% of the light is reflected at the glass-air boundary. The amount of light reflected depends on the glass material's index of refraction.→Coating (P.209)

Figure-5 Light Reflection

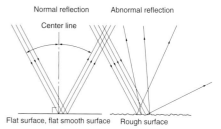

Diffraction

A phenomenon in which light waves pass around the edges of an object and enter the shadowed area of that object, caused because of the wavelike nature of light. Diffraction in a photographic lens is known for causing flare (diffraction flare) which occurs when light rays bend around the edges of the diaphragm. Although diffraction flare tends to appear when the diaphragm diameter is smaller than a certain size, it actually depends not only on the diameter of the diaphragm but also on various factors such as the wavelength of the light, the lens's focal length and the aperture ratio. Diffraction flare causes reductions in image contrast and resolution, resulting in a soft image. The laminated diffraction optical elements developed by Canon control the direction of the light by intentionally creating diffraction.

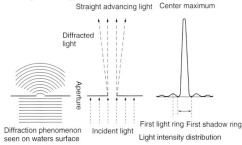

Figure-6 Light Diffraction

Optical terminology related to light passing through a lens

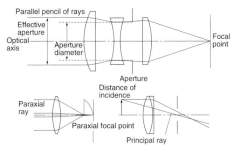

Figure-7 Optical Terminology Related To Light Passing Through A Lens

Optical axis

A straight line connecting the center points of the spherical surfaces on each side of a lens. In other words, the optical axis is a hypothetical center line connecting the center of curvature of each lens surface. In photographic lenses comprised of several lens elements, it is of utmost importance for the optical axis of each lens element to be perfectly aligned with the optical axes of all other lens elements. Particularly in zoom lenses, which are constructed of several lens groups that move in a complex manner, extremely precise lens barrel construction is necessary to maintain proper optical axis alignment.

Paraxial ray

A light ray which passes close to the optical axis and is inclined at a very small angle with respect to the optical axis. The point at which paraxial rays converge is called the paraxial focal point. Since the image formed by a monochromatic paraxial ray is in principle free of aberrations, the paraxial ray is an important factor in understanding the basic operation of lens systems.

Principal ray

A light ray which enters the lens at an angle at a point other than the optical axis point and passes through the center of the diaphragm opening. Principal light rays are the fundamental light rays used for image exposure at all diaphragm openings from maximum aperture to minimum aperture.

Parallel pencil of rays

A group of light rays traveling parallel to the optical axis from an infinitely far point. When these rays pass through a lens, they converge in the shape of a cone to form a point image within the focal plane.

Ray tracing

Use of geometrical optics to calculate the condition of various light rays passing through a lens. Calculations are performed using powerful computers.

Aperture/effective aperture

The aperture of a lens is related to the diameter of the group of light rays passing through the lens and determines the brightness of the subject image formed on the focal plane. The optical aperture (also called the effective aperture) differs from the real aperture of the lens in that it depends on the diameter of the group of light rays passing through the lens rather than the actual lens diameter. When a parallel pencil of rays enters a lens and a group of these rays passes through the diaphragm opening, the diameter of this group of light rays when it enters the front lens surface is the effective aperture of the lens.

Stop/diaphragm/aperture

The opening which adjusts the diameter of the group of light rays passing through the lens. In interchangeable lenses used with single lens reflex cameras, this mechanism is usually constructed as an iris diaphragm consisting of several blades which can be moved to continuously vary the opening diameter. With conventional SLR camera lenses, the aperture is adjusted by turning an aperture ring on the lens barrel. With modern camera lenses, however, aperture adjustment is commonly controlled by operating an electronic dial on the camera body.

Circular aperture diaphragm

With normal aperture diaphragms, closing the aperture causes its shape to become polygonal. A circular aperture diaphragm, on the other hand, optimizes the shape of the blades to achieve a nearly perfect circle even when considerably stopped down from the maximum aperture. Photography with a lens that is equipped with a circular aperture diaphragm achieves a beautiful blur effect for the background, because the point source is circular.

Automatic diaphragm

The general diaphragm operation system used in SLR cameras, referring to a type of diaphragm mechanism which remains fully open during focusing and composition to provide a bright viewfinder image, but automatically closes down to the aperture setting necessary for correct exposure when the shutter button is pressed and automatically opens up again when the exposure is completed. Although conventional lenses use mechanical linkages for controlling this automatic diaphragm operation, EF lenses use electronic signals for more precise control. You can observe this instantaneous aperture stop-down operation by looking into the front of the lens when the shutter is released.

Distance of incidence

Distance from the optical axis of a parallel ray entering a lens.

Entrance pupil/exit pupil

The lens image on the object side of the diaphragm, i.e. the apparent aperture seen when looking from the front of the lens, is called the entrance pupil and is equivalent in meaning to the lens' effective aperture. The apparent aperture seen when looking

Figure-8 Pupils and Angular Aperture

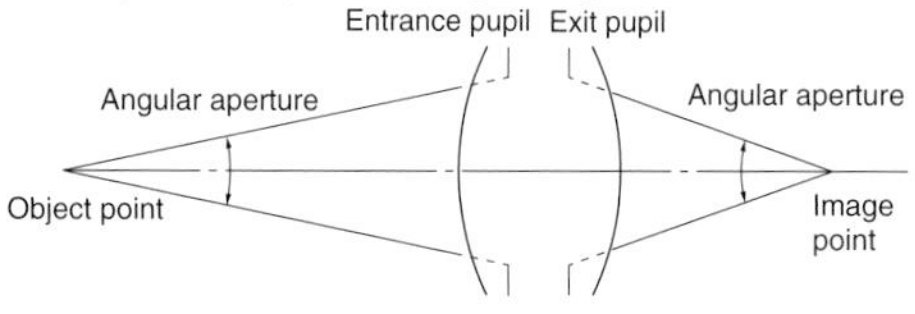

Entrance pupil Exit pupil

Angular aperture ... Angular aperture

Object point ... Image point

from the rear of the lens (the lens image on the image side of the diaphragm), is called the exit pupil. Of the light rays from a certain subject point, the effective light rays which actually form the image create a cone of light rays with the subject point being the point of the cone and the entrance pupil being the base of the cone. At the other end of the lens, the light rays emerge in a cone shape with the exit pupil forming the base of the cone and the point of the cone falling within the image plane. The entrance and exit pupils have the same shape as the actual diaphragm and their size is directly proportional to that of the diaphragm, so even if the construction of the lens system is not known, it is possible to graphically illustrate the effective light rays which actually form the image as long as the positions and sizes of the entrance and exit pupils are known. Thus, knowledge of the entrance and exit pupils is indispensable when considering performance factors such as the total amount of light entering the lens, the manner in which the image blurs and aberrations.

Angular aperture

The angle between the subject point on the optical axis and the diameter of the entrance pupil, or the angle between the image point on the optical axis and the diameter of the exit pupil.

Flange back and back focus

Flange back

Distance from the camera's lens mount reference surface to the focal plane (film

Figure-9 Flange Back and Back Focus

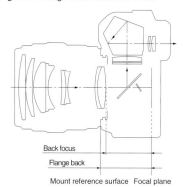

Back focus

Flange back

Mount reference surface Focal plane

plane). In the EOS system, flange back is set at 44.00 mm on all cameras. Flange back is also referred to as flange-focal distance.

Back focus

With a lens focused to infinity, the distance along the optical axis from the apex of the rearmost glass surface to the focal plane is called back focus. Wide-angle lenses with a short back focus cannot be used on SLR cameras that use a mirror that swings up before exposure because the lens will obstruct the mirror movement. Wide-angle lenses for SLR cameras generally employ a retrofocus design which allows a long back focus. The compact size of the quick-return mirror on the EF-S lens compatible digital SLR cameras makes it possible to design lenses like the dedicated EF-S lenses series with a shorter back focus than in other EF lenses.

Focal point and focal length

Focal point, focus

When light rays enter a convex lens parallel to the optical axis, an ideal lens will converge all the light rays to a single point from which the rays again fan out in a cone shape. This point at which all rays converge is called the focal point. A familiar example of this is when a magnifying glass is used to focus the rays of the sun to a small circle on a piece of paper or other surface; the point at which the circle is smallest is the focal point. In optical terminology, a focal point is further classified as being the rear or image-side focal point if it is the point at which light rays from the subject converge on the film plane side of the lens. It is the front or object-side focal point if it is the point at which light rays entering the lens

Figure-10 Focal Point (single lens element)

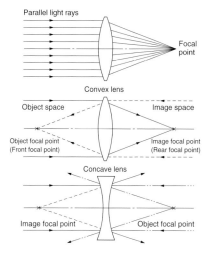

Parallel light rays

Focal point

Convex lens

Object space Image space

Object focal point (Front focal point) Image focal point (Rear focal point)

Concave lens

Image focal point Object focal point

parallel to the optical axis from the focal plane side converge on the object side of the lens.

Focal length

When parallel light rays enter the lens parallel to the optical axis, the distance along the optical axis from the lens' second principal point (rear nodal point) to the focal point is called the focal length. In simpler terms, the focal length of a lens is the distance along the optical axis from the lens' second principal point to the focal plane when the lens is focused at infinity.

Figure-11 Focal Length of Actual Photographic Lens

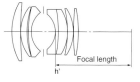

Focal length

h'

Principal point

The focal length of a thin, double-convex, single-element lens is the distance along the optical axis from the center of the lens to its focal point. This center point of the lens is called the principal point. However, since actual photographic lenses consist of combinations of several convex and concave lens elements, it is not visually apparent where the center of the lens might be.

The principal point of a multi-element lens is therefore defined as the point on the optical axis at a distance equal to the focal length measured back toward the lens from the focal point. The principal point measured from the front focal point is called the front principal point, and the principal point measured from the rear focal point is called the rear principal point. The distance between these two

Figure-12 Principal point

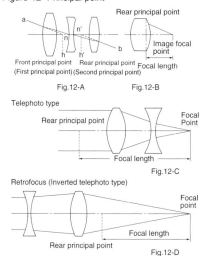

Rear principal point

Image focal point

Front principal point Rear principal point Focal length
(First principal point) (Second principal point)

Fig.12-A   Fig.12-B

Telephoto type

Rear principal point

Focal Point

Focal length

Fig.12-C

Retrofocus (Inverted telephoto type)

Focal point

Focal length

Rear principal point

Fig.12-D

principal points is called the principal point interval.

Front principal point/rear principal point

Light entering a lens from point a in Figure-12-A refracts, passes through n and n' and arrives at b. When this occurs, similar angles are generated between a-n and n'-b with respect to the optical axis, and points h and h' can be defined as where these angles intersect the optical axis. These points, h and h', are principal points indicating the lens reference positions with respect to the subject and image. h is called the front principal point (or first principal point) and h' is called the rear principal point (or second principal point). In general photographic lenses, the distance from h' to the focal point (focal plane) is the focal length. Depending on the lens type, the front-rear relationship of the principal points may be reversed, or h' may fall outside of the lens assembly altogether, but in any case the distance from the rear principal point h' to the focal point is equal to the focal length.

*With telephoto type lenses, the rear principal point h' is actually positioned in front of the frontmost lens element, and with retrofocus type lenses h' is positioned to the rear of the rearmost lens element.

Image circle

The portion of the circular image formed by a lens that is sharp. Interchangeable lenses for 35mm format cameras must have an image circle at least as large as the diagonal of the 24 x 36mm image area. EF lenses therefore generally have an image circle of about 43.2mm diameter. TS-E lenses, however, are designed with larger image circles to cover tilt and shift movements: 67.2mm for the TS-E17mm f/4L and TS-E24mm f/3.5L II; 58.6mm for the TS-E45mm f/2.8 and TS-E90mm f/2.8. EF-S lenses feature a smaller

image circle than other EF lenses, to match the diagonal of the APS-C sized image sensor of EF-S compatible digital SLR cameras.

Angle of view

The area of a scene, expressed as an angle, which can be reproduced by the lens as a sharp image. The nominal diagonal angle of view is defined as the angle formed by imaginary lines connecting the lens' second principal point with both ends of the image diagonal (43.2mm). Lens data for EF lenses generally includes the horizontal (36mm) angle of view and vertical (24mm) angle of view in addition to the diagonal angle of view.

Terms related to lens brightness

Aperture ratio

A value used to express image brightness, calculated by dividing the lens' effective aperture (D) by its focal length (f). Since the value calculated from D/f is almost always a small decimal value less than I and therefore difficult to use practically, it is common to express the aperture ratio on the lens barrel as the ratio of the effective aperture to the focal length, with the effective aperture set equal to 1. (For example, the EF85mm f/1.2L II USM lens barrel is imprinted with 1 : 1.2, indicating that the focal length is 1.2 times the effective aperture when the effective aperture is equal to 1.) The brightness of an image produced by a lens is proportional to the square of the aperture ratio. In general, lens brightness is expressed as an F number, which is the inverse of the aperture ratio (f/D). F number

Figure-14 Lens Brightness

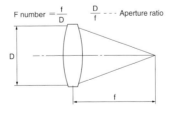

$$F \text{ number} = \frac{f}{D} \quad \frac{D}{f} \text{ --- Aperture ratio}$$

F number

Since the aperture ratio (D/f) is almost always a small decimal value less than one and therefore difficult to use practically, lens brightness is often expressed for convenience' sake as the inverse of the aperture ratio (f/D), which is called the F number. Accordingly, image

brightness is inversely proportional to the square of the F number, meaning that the image becomes darker as the F number increases. F number values are expressed as a geometrical series starting at 1 with a common ratio of √2, as follows: 1.0, 1.4, 2, 2.8, 4, 5.6, 8, 16, 22, 32, etc. (However, there are many cases where only the maximum aperture value deviates from this series.) The numbers in this series, which may at first seem difficult to become familiar with, merely indicate values which are close to the actual FD values based on the diameter (D) of each successive diaphragm setting which decreases the amount of light passing through the lens by half. Thus, changing the F number from 1.4 to 2 halves the image brightness, while going the other direction from 2 to 1.4 doubles the image brightness. (A change of this magnitude is generally referred to as "1 stop".) With recent cameras employing electronic displays, smaller divisions of 1/2 stop or even 1/3 stop are used.

Numerical aperture (NA)

A value used to express the brightness or resolution of a lens' optical system. The numerical aperture, usually indicated as NA, is a numerical value calculated from the formula $n\sin\theta$, where 2θ is the angle (angular aperture) at which an object point on the optical axis enters the entrance pupil and n is the index of refraction of the medium in which the object exists. Although not often used with photographic lenses, the NA value is commonly imprinted on the objective lenses of microscopes, where it is used more as an indication of resolution than of brightness. A useful relationship to know is that the NA value is equal to half the inverse of the F number. For example, F 1.0 = NA 0.5, F 1.4 = NA 0.357, F2 = NA 0.25, and so on.

Focus and depth of field

Focus, focal point

The focal point is the point where parallel light rays from an infinitely far subject converge after passing through a lens. The plane perpendicular to the optical axis which contains this point is called the focal plane. In this plane, which is where the film or the image sensor is positioned in a camera, the subject is sharp and said to be "in focus." With general photographic lenses consisting of several lens elements, the focus can be adjusted so that light rays

Figure-13 Angle of view and image circle

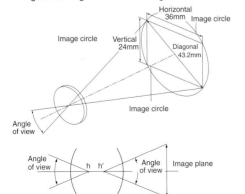

from subjects closer than "infinity" converge at a point in the focal plane.

Figure-15 Relationship Between the Ideal Focal Point and the Permissible Circle of Confusion and Depth of Field

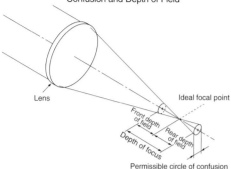

Circle of confusion

Since all lenses contain a certain amount of spherical aberration and astigmatism, they cannot perfectly converge rays from a subject point to form a true image point (i.e., an infinitely small dot with zero area). In other words, images are formed from a composite of dots (not points) having a certain area, or size. Since the image becomes less sharp as the size of these dots increases, the dots are called "circles of confusion." Thus, one way of indicating the quality of a lens is by the smallest dot it can form, or its "minimum circle of confusion." The maximum allowable dot size in an image is called the "permissible circle of confusion."

Permissible circle of confusion

The largest circle of confusion which still appears as a "point" in the image. Image sharpness as sensed by the human eye is closely related to the sharpness of the actual image and the "resolution" of human eyesight. In photography, image sharpness is also dependent on the degree of image enlargement or projection distance and the distance from which the image is viewed. In other words, in practical work it is possible to determine certain "allowances" for producing images which, although actually blurred to a certain degree, still appear sharp to the observer. For 35mm single lens reflex cameras, the permissible circle of confusion is about 1/1000~1/1500 the length of the film diagonal, assuming the image is enlarged to a 5"×7" (12 cm × 16.5 cm) print and viewed from a distance of 25~30 cm/0.8~1 ft. EF lenses are designed to produce a minimum circle of confusion of 0.035 mm, a value on which calculations for items such as depth of field are based.

Depth of field

The area in front of and behind a focused subject in which the photographed image appears sharp. In other words, the depth of sharpness to the front and rear of the subject where image blur in the focal plane falls within the limits of the permissible circle of confusion. Depth of field varies according to the lens' focal length, aperture value and shooting distance, so if these values are known, a rough estimate of the depth of field can be calculated using the following formulas:

Front depth of field $= d \cdot F \cdot a^2/(f^2 + d \cdot F \cdot a)$
Rear depth of field $= d \cdot F \cdot a^2/(f^2 - d \cdot F \cdot a)$
f: focal length F: F number d: minimum circle of confusion diameter
a: subject distance (distance from the first principal point to subject)

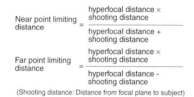

$$\text{Near point limiting distance} = \frac{\text{hyperfocal distance} \times \text{shooting distance}}{\text{hyperfocal distance} + \text{shooting distance}}$$

$$\text{Far point limiting distance} = \frac{\text{hyperfocal distance} \times \text{shooting distance}}{\text{hyperfocal distance} - \text{shooting distance}}$$

(Shooting distance: Distance from focal plane to subject)

If the hyperfocal distance is known, the following formulas can also be used:
In general photography, depth of field is characterized by the following attributes:
① Depth of field is deep at short focal lengths, shallow at long focal lengths.
② Depth of field is deep at small apertures, shallow at large apertures.
③ Depth of field is deep at far shooting distances, shallow at close shooting distances.
④ Front depth of field is shallower than rear depth of field.

Figure-16 Depth of Field and Depth of Focus

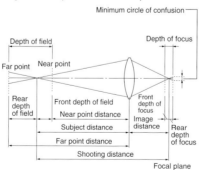

Depth of focus

The area in front of and behind the focal plane in which the image can be photographed as a sharp image. Depth of focus is the same on both sides of the image plane (focal plane) and can be determined by multiplying the minimum

circle of confusion by the F number, regardless of the lens focal length. With modern autofocus SLR cameras, focusing is performed by detecting the state of focus in the image plane (focal plane) using a sensor which is both optically equivalent (1:1 magnification) and positioned out of the focal plane, and automatically controlling the lens to bring the subject image within the depth of focus area.

Figure-17 Relationship Between Depth of Focus and Aperture

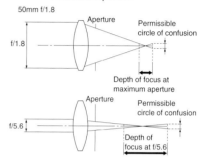

Hyperfocal distance

Using the depth of field principle, as a lens is gradually focused to farther subject distances, a point will eventually be reached where the far limit of the rear depth of field will be equivalent to "infinity." The shooting distance at this point, i,e., the closest shooting distance at which "infinity" falls within the depth of field, is called the hyperfocal distance. The hyperfocal distance can be determined as follows:

$$\text{Hyperfocal distance} = \frac{f^2}{d \cdot F \text{ number}}$$

f: focal length F: F number d: minimum circle of confusion diameter

Thus, by presetting the lens to the hyperfocal distance, the depth of field will extend from a distance equal to half the hyperfocal distance to infinity. This method is useful for presetting a large depth of field and taking snapshots without having to worry about adjusting the lens focus, especially when using a wide-angle lens. (For example, when the EF20mm f/2.8 USM is set to f/16 and the shooting distance is set

Photo-1 Hyperfocal Length Set Condtion

to the hyperfocal distance of approximately 0.7m/2.3ft, all subjects within a range of approximately 0.4m/1.3ft from the camera to infinity will be in focus.)

Lens aberration

Aberration

The image formed by an ideal photographic lens would have the following characteristics:

① A point would be formed as a point.

② A plane (such as a wall) perpendicular to the optical axis would be formed as a plane.

③ The image formed by the lens would have the same shape as the subject.

Also, from the standpoint of image expression, a lens should exhibit true color reproduction. If only light rays entering the lens close to the optical axis are used and the light is monochromatic (one specific wavelength), it is possible to realize virtually ideal lens performance. With real photographic lenses, however, where a large aperture is used to obtain sufficient brightness and the lens must converge light not only from near the optical axis but from all areas of the image, it is extremely difficult to satisfy the above-mentioned ideal conditions due to the existence of the following obstructive factors:

● Since most lenses are constructed solely of lens elements with spherical surfaces, light rays from a single subject point are not formed in the image as a perfect point. (A problem unavoidable with spherical surfaces.)

● The focal point position differs for different types (i.e., different wavelengths) of light.

● There are many requirements related to changes in angle of view (especially with wide-angle, zoom and telephoto lenses).

The general term used to describe the difference between an ideal image and the actual image affected by the above factors is "aberration." Thus, to design a high-performance lens, aberration must be extremely small, with the ultimate objective being to obtain an image as close as possible to the ideal image. Aberration can be broadly divided into chromatic aberrations, and monochromatic aberrations → Chromatic

aberration → Five aberrations of Seidel

Chromatic aberration

When white light (light containing many colors uniformly mixed so that the eye does not sense any particular color and thus perceives the light as white) such as sunlight is passed through a prism, a rainbow spectrum can be observed. This phenomenon occurs because the prism's index of refraction (and rate of dispersion) varies depending on the wavelength (short wavelengths are more strongly refracted than long wavelengths). While most visible in a prism, this phenomenon also occurs in photographic lenses, and since it occurs at different wavelengths is called chromatic aberration. There are two types of chromatic aberration: "axial chromatic aberration," where the focal point position on the optical axis varies according to the wavelength, and "chromatic difference of magnification," where the image magnification in peripheral areas varies according to the wavelength. In actual photographs, axial chromatic aberration appears as color blur or flare, and chromatic difference of magnification appears as color fringing (where edges show color along their borders). Chromatic aberration in a photographic lens is corrected by combining different types of optical glass having different refraction and dispersion characteristics. Since the effect of chromatic aberration increases at longer focal lengths, precise chromatic aberration correction is particularly important in super-telephoto lenses for good image sharpness. Although there is a limit to the degree of correction possible with optical glass, significant performance improvements can be achieved using man-made crystal such as fluorite or UD glass. Axial chromatic aberration is also sometimes referred to as "longitudinal chromatic aberration" (since it occurs longitudinally with respect to the optical axis), and chromatic difference of

Figure-18 Chromatic Aberration

●This phenomenon occurs because the prism's index of refraction varies depending on the wavelength (color).

Transverse chromatic aberration
(lateral chromatic aberration)

Parallel light rays

Optical axis

Off-axis object point

Axial chromatic aberration
(longitudinal chromatic aberration)

magnification can be referred to as "lateral chromatic aberration" (since it occurs laterally with respect to the optical axis).

Note: While chromatic aberration is most noticeable when using color film, it affects black-and-white images as well, appearing as a reduction in sharpness.

Achromat

A lens which corrects chromatic aberration for two wavelengths of light. When referring to a photographic lens, the two corrected wavelengths are in the blue-violet range and yellow range.

Apochromat

A lens which corrects chromatic aberration for three wavelengths of light, with aberration reduced to a large degree particularly in the secondary spectrum. EF super-telephoto lenses are examples of apochromatic lenses.

Five aberrations of Seidel

In 1856, a German named Seidel determined through analysis the existence of five lens aberrations which occur with monochromatic (single wavelength) light. These aberrations, described below, are called the five aberrations of Seidel.

① Spherical aberration

This aberration exists to some degree in all lenses constructed entirely of spherical elements. Spherical aberration causes parallel light rays passing through the edge of a lens to converge at a focal point closer to the lens than light rays passing through the center of the lens. (The amount of focal point shift along the optical axis is called longitudinal spherical aberration.) The degree of spherical aberration tends to be larger in large-aperture lenses. A point image affected by spherical aberration is sharply formed by light rays near the optical axis but is affected by flare from the peripheral light rays (this flare is also called halo, and its radius is called lateral spherical aberration). As a result, spherical

Figure-19 Spherical Aberration

●This is the phenomenon where the focus is not concentrated on one point on the light ray but rather is offset to the front or back.
Occurrence of a halo——The image becomes flare.

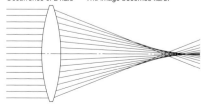

Table-1 Lens Aberrations

Aberrations seen in the continuous spectrum
■ Chromatic aberrations
 ● Axial chromatic aberration (longitudinal chromatic aberration)
 ● Transverse chromatic aberration (lateral chromatic aberration)

Aberrations seen at specific wavelengths
■ Five aberrations of Seidel
 ① Spherical aberration
 ② Chromatic aberration
 ③ Astigmatism
 ④ Curvature of field
 ⑤ Distortion

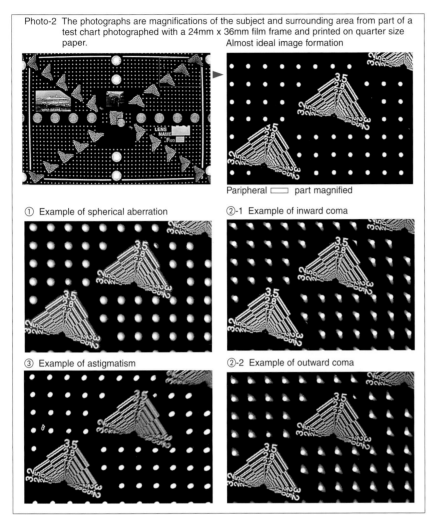

Photo-2 The photographs are magnifications of the subject and surrounding area from part of a test chart photographed with a 24mm x 36mm film frame and printed on quarter size paper.

Almost ideal image formation

Paripheral ☐ part magnified

① Example of spherical aberration

②-1 Example of inward coma

③ Example of astigmatism

②-2 Example of outward coma

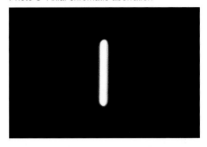

Photo-3 Axial chromatic aberration

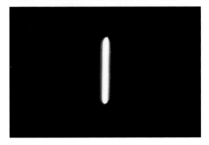

Photo-4 Transverse chromatic aberration

aberration affects the entire image area from the center to the edges, and produces a soft, low-contrast image which looks as if covered with a thin veil. Correction of spherical aberration in spherical lenses is very difficult. Although commonly carried out by combining two lenses — one convex and one concave — based on light rays with a certain height of incidence (distance from the optical axis), there is a limit to the degree of correction possible using spherical lenses, so some aberration always remains. This remaining aberration can be largely eliminated by stopping down the diaphragm to cut the amount of peripheral light. With large aperture lenses at full aperture, the only effective way to thoroughly compensate spherical aberration is to use an aspherical lens element. → Aspherical lens

② Coma, comatic aberration
Coma, or comatic aberration, is a phenomenon visible in the periphery of an image produced by a lens which has been corrected for spherical aberration, and

causes light rays entering the edge of the lens at an angle to converge in the form of a comet instead of the desired point, hence the name. The comet shape is oriented radially with the tail pointing either toward or away from the center of the image. The resulting blur near the edges of the image is called comatic flare. Coma, which can occur even in lenses which correctly reproduce a point as a point on the optical axis, is caused by a difference in refraction between light rays from an off-axis point passing through the edge of the lens and the principal light ray from

Figure-20 Comatic Aberration

● This is the phenomenon where the diagonal light rays do not focus on one point on the image surface.

This is the phenomenon where there is a tail like that of a comet.
— Inward coma
— Outward coma

Off-axis parallel pencil of rays

Optical axis

the same point passing through the lens center. Coma increases as the angle of the principal ray increases, and causes a decrease in contrast near the edges of the image. A certain degree of improvement is possible by stopping down the lens. Coma can also cause blurred areas of an image to flare, resulting in an unpleasing effect. The elimination of both spherical aberration and coma for a subject at a certain shooting distance is called aplanatism, and a lens corrected as such is called an aplanat.

③ Astigmatism
With a lens corrected for spherical and comatic aberration, a subject point on the optical axis will be correctly reproduced as a point in the image, but an off-axis subject point will not appear as a point in the image, but rather as an ellipse or line. This type of aberration is called astigmatism, It is possible to observe this phenomenon near the edges of the image by slightly shifting the lens focus to a position

Figure-21 Astigmatism

● This is the phenomenon where there is no point image

P2

Principle ray

P1

Lens

Optical axis

Sagittal image

Po

Meridional image

P

where the subject point is sharply imaged as a line oriented in a direction radiating from the image center, and again to another position.

④ Curvature of Field

This is the phenomenon where, when focusing on a flat surface, the image does not become flat, but where the image is formed in a bowed shape to the inside of the bowl. Therefore, when focusing on the center of the frame, the circumference is blurred, and conversely, when focusing on the circumference, the center is blurred. This image bending is mainly changed using the astigmatism correction method, which creates an image between a sagittal image and a meridional image, so the more the astigmatism is corrected, the smaller the image becomes. Because there is almost no corrective effect from stopping down the lens, various efforts are made during designing, such as changing the shape of the single lenses of the lens configuration and selecting the aperture position, but one of the requirements for

Figure-22 Curvature of field

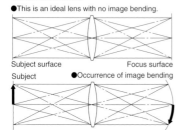

This is the phenomenon where a good image focus surface is bent.

● This is an ideal lens with no image bending.

Subject surface | Focus surface

Subject | ● Occurrence of image bending

Photo-5 Example of curvature of field

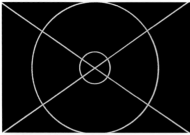

Focusing on center of screen causes corners to go out of focus.

Photo-6 Example of curvature of field

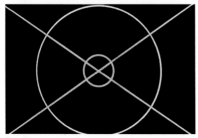

Focusing on corners of screen causes center to go out of focus.

correcting astigmatism and image bending at the same time is Petzval's condition (1843). This condition is that the inverse of the product of the index of refraction for each of the single lenses of the lens configuration and the focal distance added with the number of single lenses used in the lens configuration must produce a sum of 0. This sum is called Petzval's sum.

⑤ Distortion

One of the conditions for an ideal lens is that "the image of the subject and the image formed by the lens are similar," and the deviation from this ideal where the straight lines are bent is called distortion. The extended shape in the diagonal view angle direction (+) is called pincushion distortion, and, conversely, the contracted shape (–) is called barrel distortion. With an ultra wide-angle lens, rarely do both of these distortions exist together. Although this seldom occurs in lenses where the lens combination configuration is at the aperture boundary, it occurs easily in configuration lens. Typical zoom lenses

Figure-23 Distortion

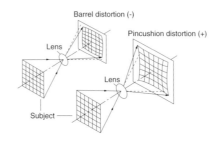

Barrel distortion (-)

Pincushion distortion (+)

Lens

Lens

Subject

Photo-7 Example of distortion

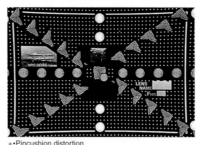

+·Pincushion distortion

Photo-8 Example of distortion

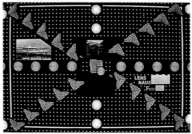

-·Barrel distortion

tend to exhibit barrel distortion at the shortest focal lengths and pincushion distortion at the longest focal lengths (the distortion characteristics change slightly during zooming), but in zoom lenses that use an aspherical lens, the aspherical lens is effective at removing distortion, so the correction is good. This difference is caused by the difference in refraction of the principal rays passing through the center of the lens, so it cannot be improved no matter how much the aperture is stopped down.

Meridional

A plane that includes a principal ray that tries to capture a point outside the optical axis and the optical axis is called a meridional plane. The position linked to the focal point by the light ray entering through a lens of this shape is called the meridional image plane. This is the image plane where the image of concentric circles in the frame are at the best. If the spherical surface of the lens is compared to a portion of the earth's curvature and if the optical axis is compared to the earth's axis, the meridional plane would be where the earth's meridian is, which is why this name is used. The curve that expresses the characteristics of this image plane using a MTF characteristics graph, etc., is often abbreviated as "M."

Sagittal

The plane that is perpendicular to the meridional plane is called the sagittal plane, and this is the image plane where the radial image is at its best. The word comes from the Greek word for arrow. The name comes from the shape of the focal point, which spreads radially. The position linked to the focal point of a light ray that passes through a sagittal plane shape and into a lens is called the sagittal image plane, and when the characteristics of this image plane are expressed using a MTF characteristics graph, etc., it is often abbreviated using the initial "S."

How to Read Distortion Graphs

A simple way of reading the aberration graphs that accompany test report articles in camera magazines.

● **Spherical Distortion Characteristics Graph (Graph1)**

The vertical axis of the graph shows the height of entry above the axis entering the lens system (distance above the diagonal from the center of the frame), and the horizontal axis shows the image point offset captured by the film surface shape. The unit is mm. The horizontal axis symbols are "–" (minus), which shows the subject's side direction, and "+" (plus), which shows the film's side direction. The ideal lens characteristic is for the horizontal axis zero point to form a straight line with the entry height. The difference between this ideal and the actual lens is shown as a curve. Spherical distortion correction is generally said to be good if there is a core in the image and the focal point moves little when the lens is stopped down, in other words, there is slightly insufficient correction in the middle area while at the maximum entry height there is perfect correction where it returns nearly to zero.

Figure-24 Spherical Distortion
Characteristics Graph (Graph 1)

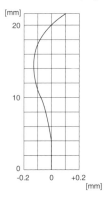

● Astigmatism curve (Graph 2)

The graph's vertical axis is the axial height of incidence (distance from the image center) of the ray entering the lens system, and the horizontal axis is the amount of shift of the image point formed in the focal plane. Units and signs are the same as in the spherical aberration curve. The curve for an ideal lens would be a straight line at the horizontal axis' zero point with respect to the height of incidence. The difference between the ideal lens and actual lens is indicated by two curved lines in the S direction (sagittal/radial direction) and M direction (meridional/concentric circle direction). If the difference between S and M (astigmatic difference) is large, a point will not be formed as a point and the image will smear. Moreover, the blur image in front of and behind the image formation plane will be unnatural.

● Distortion curve (Graph 3)

The graph's vertical axis is the axial height of incidence (distance from the image center; unit: mm) of the ray entering the

lens system, and the horizontal axis is percent (%) distortion. The curve indicates the difference between the ideal image and the actual image formed at the focal plane. A minus sign indicates negative, or barrel, distortion where the length of the diagonal of the actual image is shorter than the diagonal of the ideal image. A plus sign indicates positive, or pincushion, distortion. An ideal lens would exhibit ±0% distortion at any image height. Distortion curves for zoom lenses generally show barrel distortion at wide-angle positions and pincushion distortion at telephoto positions.

Figure-25 Astigmatism   Distortion Curve
Curve (Graph2)   (Graph3)

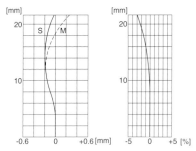

How to minimize the effects of aberrations

Modern lenses are designed using large-scale computers to perform mind-boggling calculations and high-level simulations to minimize all types of aberration and achieve superior image formation performance. Even with this technology, however, it is impossible to completely remove all aberrations, meaning that all lenses on the market still have at least a small amount of aberration remaining. This aberration is called residual aberration. The type of residual aberration in a lens generally determines the lens' imaging characteristics such as its sharpness and blur effect. Because of this,

modern lenses are often designed with consideration given to achieving a pleasing blur effect (image characteristics outside the image formation plane) by using computer simulation techniques to analyze lens performance at the design stage. As mentioned in the various aberration descriptions, the effects of some aberrations can be minimized by stopping down the lens, while others cannot. The relationships between aperture and aberrations are shown in Table 2.

Lens performance evaluation

Resolving power/resolution

The resolution of a lens indicates the capacity of reproduction of a subject point of the lens. The resolution of the final photograph depends on three factors: the resolution of the lens, the resolution of the film or image sensor, and the resolution of the printer or printing paper. Resolution is evaluated by photographing, at a specified

Figure-26 Resolution Measurement Charts

Resolution chart (koana)

Resolution chart (JIS)

Siemens star

Projection-use resolution chart   Howllet chart

Table-2 Relationship between aperture and aberration

Cause of drop in image quality	Areas affected on the screen	Improvement by smaller aperture
Axial color aberration	Center and edges	Slight effect
Magnification color aberration	Edges	No effect
Spherical aberration	Center and edges	Effect present
Comatic aberration	Edges	Effect present
Astigmatism	Edges	Slight effect
Curvature of field	Edges	Slight effect
Distortion	Edges	No effect
Ghosting/flaring	Center and edges	No effect
Drop in peripheral illumination	Edges	Effect present

magnification, a chart containing groups of black and white stripes that gradually decrease in narrowness, then using a microscope to observe the negative image at a magnification of 50x.

It is common to hear resolution expressed as a numerical value such as 50 lines or 100 lines. This value indicates the number of lines per millimeter of the smallest black and white line pattern which can be clearly recorded on the film. To test the resolution of a lens alone, a method is used in which a fine resolution chart is positioned in the location corresponding to the focal plane and projected through the test lens onto a screen. The numerical value used for expressing resolving power is only an indication of the degree of resolution possible, and does not indicate resolution clarity or contrast.

Contrast

The degree of distinction between areas of different brightness levels in a photograph, i.e., the difference in brightness between light and dark areas. For example, when the reproduction ratio between white and black is clear, contrast is said to be high,

Figure-27 Contrast Concept Diagram

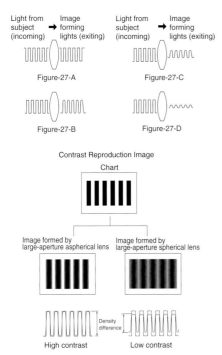

Figure-27-E MTF Measurement-Use Slit Chart

and when unclear, contrast is said to be low. In general, lenses producing high quality images have both high resolution and high contrast.

MTF (modulation transfer function)

Modulation transfer function is a lens performance evaluation method used to determine the contrast reproduction ratio, or sharpness, of a lens. When evaluating the electrical characteristics of audio equipment, one important measure of performance is frequency response. In this case, where the source sound is recorded through a microphone and then played back through speakers, frequency response indicates the fidelity of the reproduced sound with respect to the source sound. If the reproduced sound is very close to the source sound, the equipment is classified as "hi-fi," or "high fidelity." By thinking of the optical system of a lens as a "system for transmitting optical signals" in the same way as an audio system transmits electrical signals, it is possible to find out how accurately optical signals are transmitted as long as the frequency response of the optical system can be measured. In an optical system, the equivalent of frequency is "spatial frequency," which indicates how many patterns, or cycles, of a certain sine density are present in a 1 mm width. Accordingly, the unit of spatial frequency is lines per mm. Figure-27-A shows the MTF characteristics of an ideal "hi-fi" lens for a certain spatial frequency, with the output equal to the input. A lens of this type is said to provide a contrast of 1:1. However, since actual lenses contain residual aberration, actual contrast ratios are always less than 1:1. As the spatial frequency increases (i.e., as the black-and-white sine wave pattern becomes finer, or more dense), the contrast decreases as shown in Figure-27-D until finally becoming gray with no distinction between black and white (no contrast, 1:0) at the spatial frequency limit. Illustrating this phenomenon in graph form with spatial frequency as the horizontal axis and contrast as the vertical axis results in the curve shown in Graph-4. In other words, the graph makes it possible to check resolution and contrast repro-ducibility (i.e., the degree of modulation) in a continuous manner. However, since it only shows the characteristics for one point in the image area, it is necessary to use data for several points in order to

determine the MTF characteristics of the overall image. Because of this, for the EF lens MTF characteristics presented in this book, two typical spatial frequencies (10 lines/mm and 30 lines/mm) are selected and sophisticated computer simulation techniques are used to determine the MTF characteristics of the entire image area, graphed with the horizontal axis corresponding to the distance from the center of the image along the diagonal line, and the vertical axis corresponding to contrast.

How to read the MTF graphs

The MTF graphs shown for the lenses in this book place image height (with the image center having an image height of 0) on the horizontal axis and contrast on the vertical axis. MTF characteristics are provided for spatial frequencies of 10 lines/mm and 30 lines/mm. The test chart's spatial frequency, lens aperture value and direction in the image area are as shown in the following table.

Basic information on the performance of a lens can be extracted from the MTF chart as follows: The closer the 10-line/mm curve is to 1, the better the contrast and separation ability of the lens, and the closer the 30-line/mm curve is to 1, the better the resolving power and sharpness of the lens. Additionally, the closer the characteristics of M and S are, the more natural the background blur becomes. Although a good balance between these characteristics is important, it can generally be assumed that a lens will provide excellent image quality if the 10-line/mm curve is greater than 0.8, and that satisfactory image quality can be obtained if the l0-line/mm curve is greater than 0.6. Looking at the MTF characteristics of EF super-telephoto L-series lenses with this frame of reference, it is obvious from just the data that these lenses possess extremely high-performance imaging characteristics.

Graph-4 MTF Characteristics for A Single Image Point

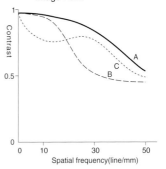

A: Resolving power and contrast are both good

B: Contrast is good and resolving power is bad

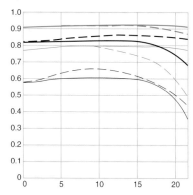
C: Resolving power is good and contrast is bad

Table-3

Spatial frequency	Maximum aperture		F 8	
	S	M	S	M
10 lines/mm	▬▬▬	▬ ▬ ▬	▬▬▬	▬ ▬ ▬
30 lines/mm	───	─ ─ ─	───	─ ─ ─

Graph-5 MTF Characteristics

Color balance

The color reproduction fidelity of a photo taken through a lens compared to the original subject. Color balance in all EF lenses is based on ISO recommended reference values and maintained within a strict tolerance range narrower than ISO's CCI allowable value range.→ CCI

CCI (color contribution index)

Color reproduction in a color photograph depends on three factors: the color characteristics of the film or digital imaging system, the color temperature of the light source illuminating the subject, and the light transmission characteristics of the lens. The color contribution index, or CCI, is an index indicating "the amount of color variation caused by filtering effect differences between lenses" when using a standard film and light source, and is expressed by three numbers in the form 0/5/4. These three numbers are relative values expressed as logarithms of lens transmittance at the blue-violet/green/red wavelengths corresponding to the three light sensitive emulsion layers of color film, with larger numbers representing higher transmittance. However, since photographic lenses absorb most ultraviolet wavelengths, the blue-violet transmittance value is usually zero, so color balance is judged by comparing the green and red values to ISO-specified reference lens values. The ISO reference lens light transmission characteristics were set according to a method proposed by Japan which involved taking the average transmittance values of 57 standard lenses

Graph-6 ISO Tolerance Range Graphed on CCI Coordinates

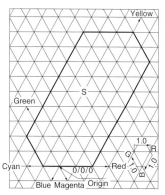

comprising five models from representative lens manufacturers including Canon. The resulting recommended reference value of 0/5/4 is used by film manufacturers as a reference when designing the color production characteristics of color films. In other words, if the light transmission characteristics of a lens do not match the ISO reference values, the color reproduction characteristics of a color film cannot be obtained as intended by the manufacturer.

Peripheral illumination

The brightness of a lens is determined by the F number, but this value only indicates the brightness at the optical axis position, i.e., at the center of the image. The brightness (image surface illuminance) at the edge of the image is called peripheral illumination and is expressed as a percent (%) of the amount of illumination at the image center. Peripheral illumination is affected by lens vignetting and the cos4 (cosine 4) law and is inevitably lower than the center of the image.→ Vignetting, Cos4 law

Graph-7 Image Plane Illuminance Ratio Showing the Peripheral Illumination Characteristics

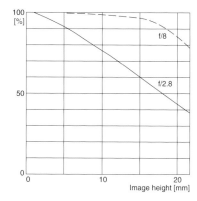

Optical vignetting

Light rays entering the lens from the edges of the picture area are partially blocked by the lens frames in front of and behind the diaphragm, preventing all the rays from passing through the effective aperture (diaphragm diameter) and causing light fall-off in the peripheral areas of the image. This type of vignetting can be eliminated by stopping down the lens.

Figure-28 Vignetting

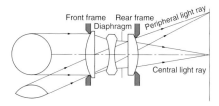

Cosine law

The cosine law, also called the cosine law, states that light fall-off in peripheral areas of the image increases as the angle of view increases, even if the lens is completely free of vignetting. The peripheral image is formed by groups of light rays entering the lens at a certain angle with respect to the optical axis, and the amount of light fall-off is proportional to the cosine of that angle raised to the

Graph-8 Peripheral Light Reduction According to
Cosine Law

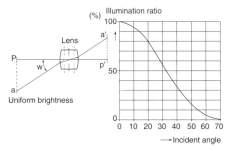

fourth power. As this is a law of physics, it cannot be avoided. However, with wide-angle lenses having a large angle of view, decreases in peripheral illumination can be prevented by increasing the lens' aperture efficiency (ratio of the area of the on-axis entrance pupil to the area of the off-axis entrance pupil).

Hard vignetting

A phenomenon where light entering the lens is partially blocked by an obstruction such as the end of a lens hood or the frame of a filter, causing the corners of the image to darken or the overall image to lighten. Shading is the general term used for the case where the image is degraded by some type of obstacle that blocks light rays which should actually reach the image.

Flare

Light reflected from lens surfaces, the inside of the lens barrel and the inner walls of the camera's mirror box can reach the film or image sensor and fog part or all of the image area, degrading image sharpness. These harmful reflections are called flare. Although flare can be reduced to a large extent by coating the lens surfaces and using anti-reflection measures in the lens barrel and camera, flare cannot be completely eliminated for all subject conditions. It is therefore

Figure-29 Flare and Ghosting

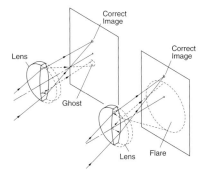

desirable to use an appropriate lens hood whenever possible. The term "flare" is also used when referring to the effects of blurring and halo caused by spherical and comatic aberration.

Ghost image

A type of flare occurring when the sun or other strong light source is included in the scene and a complex series of reflections among the lens surfaces causes a clearly defined reflection to appear in the image in a position symmetrically opposite the light source. This phenomenon is differentiated from flare by the term "ghost" due to its ghost-like appearance. Ghost images caused by surface reflections in front of the aperture have the same shape as the aperture, while a ghost image caused by reflections behind the aperture appears as an out-of-focus area of light fogging. Since ghost images can also be caused by strong light sources outside the picture area, use of a hood or other shading device is recommended for blocking undesired light. Whether or not ghosting will actually occur when the picture is taken can be verified beforehand by looking through the viewfinder and using the camera's depth-of-field check function to close down the lens to the actual aperture to be used during exposure.

Coating

When light enters and exits an uncoated lens, approximately 5% of the light is reflected back at each lens-air boundary due to the difference in index of refraction. This not only reduces the amount of light passing through the lens but can also lead to repeating reflections which can cause unwanted flare or ghost images. To prevent such reflections, lenses are processed with a special coating. Generally, this is carried out using vacuum vapor deposition to coat the lens with a thin film having a thickness 1/4 the wavelength of the light to be affected, with the film made of a substance (such as magnesium fluoride) which has an index of refraction of $\sqrt{n}$, where n is the index of refraction of the lens glass. Instead of a single coating affecting only a single wavelength, however, EF lenses feature a superior multi-layer coating (multiple layers of vapor deposited film reducing the reflection rate to 0.2-0.3%), which effectively prevents reflections of all wavelengths in the visible light range. Moreover, Canon has introduced SWC

(Subwavelength Structure Coating), which effectively prevents reflection by a method different from the vapor-deposited film process. Lens coating not only prevents reflections but also plays an important role in providing the overall lens system with optimum color balance characteristics.

Optical Glass

Optical Glass

Optical glass is specially made for use in precision optical products such as photographic lenses, video lenses, telescopes and microscopes. In contrast to general-purpose glass, optical glass is provided with fixed, precise refraction and dispersion characteristics (precision to six decimal points) and subjected to strict requirements regarding transparency and lack of defects such as striae, warps and bubbles. Types of optical glass are classified according to their composition and optical constant (Abbe number), and more than 250 types are in existence today. For high-performance lenses, different types of optical glass are optimally combined. Glass with an Abbe number of 50 or less is called flint glass (F), and glass with an Abbe number of 55 or more is called crown glass (K). Each type of glass is further classified in other ways such as specific gravity, and a corresponding serial name is assigned to each type.

Abbe number

A numerical value indicating the dispersion of optical glass, using the Greek symbol ν. Also called the optical constant. The Abbe number is determined by the following formula using the index of refraction for three Fraunhofer's lines: F (blue), d (yellow) and c (red).

Abbe number = $\nu d = nd - 1/nF - nc$

Fraunhofer's lines

Absorption lines discovered in 1814 by a German physicist named Fraunhofer (1787~1826), comprising the absorption spectrum present in the continuous spectrum of light emitted from the sun created by the effect of gases in the sun's and earth's atmospheres. Since each line is located at a fixed wavelength, the lines are used for reference in regard to the color (wavelength) characteristics of optical glass. The index of refraction of optical glass is measured based on nine wavelengths selected from among Fraunhofer's lines (see Table 4). In lens design, calculations for correcting chromatic aberrations are also based on these wavelengths.

Table-4 Light Wavelengths and Spectrum Lines

Spectrum line code	i	h	g	F
Wavelength (mm)	365.0	404.7	435.8	486.1
Color	Ultra-violet	Violet	Blue-violet	Blue

Spectrum line code	e	d	c	r	t
Wavelength (mm)	546.1	587.6	656.3	706.5	1014
Color	Green	Yellow	Red	Red	Infrared

Note: 1 nm = 10⁻⁶mm

Fluorite

Fluorite has extremely low indexes of refraction and dispersion compared to optical glass and features special partial dispersion characteristics (extraordinary partial dispersion), enabling virtually ideal correction of chromatic aberrations when combined with optical glass. This fact has long been known, and in 1880 natural fluorite was already in practical use in the apochromatic objective lenses of microscopes. However, since natural fluorite exists only in small pieces, it cannot be used practically in photographic lenses. In answer to this problem, Canon in 1968 succeeded in establishing production technology for manufacturing large artificial crystals, thus opening the door for fluorite use in photographic lenses.

UD lens

A lens made of special optical glass possessing optical characteristics similar to fluorite. UD lens elements are especially effective in correcting chromatic aberrations in super-telephoto lenses. Two UD lens elements are characteristically equivalent to one fluorite element. "UD" stands for "ultra-low dispersion."

Lead-Free Glass

This is a type of optical glass which contains no lead, to relieve the burden on the environment. Lead is used in many types of optical glass because it raises the refractive power of glass. While the lead cannot leak out of the glass it is contained in, it does nevertheless pose a threat to the environment when it escapes in the form of waste produced when grinding and polishing the glass. With the goal of eliminating lead from the manufacturing process, Canon worked with a glass manufacturer to develop lead free glass, and is in the process of phasing out glass which contains lead from its lens lineup. Lead free glass uses titanium, which, unlike lead, poses no problems for the environment or humans, but still delivers optical characteristics equal to conventional leaded glass.

Lens shapes and lens construction fundamentals

Lens shapes

Figure-30 Lens Shapes

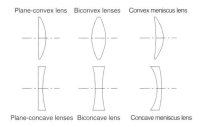

Fresnel lens

A type of converging lens, formed by finely dividing the convex surface of a flat convex lens into many concentric circle-shaped ring lenses and combining them to extremely reduce the thickness of the lens while retaining its function as convex lens. In an SLR, to efficiently direct peripheral diffused light to the eyepiece, the side opposite the matte surface of the focusing screen is formed as a fresnel lens with a 0.05 mm pitch Fresnel lenses are also commonly used in flash units, indicated by the concentric circular lines visible on the white diffusion screen covering the flash tube. The projection lens used to project light from a lighthouse is an example of a giant fresnel lens.

Figure-31 Fresnel Lens

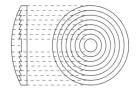

Aspherical lens

Photographic lenses are generally constructed of several single lens elements, all of which, unless otherwise specified, have spherical surfaces. Because all surfaces are spherical, it becomes especially difficult to correct spherical aberration in large-aperture lenses and distortion in super-wide-angle lenses. A special lens element with a surface curved with the ideal shape to correct these aberrations, i.e., a lens having a free-curved surface which is not spherical, is called an aspherical lens. The theory and usefulness of aspherical lenses. have been known since the early days of lens making, but due to the extreme difficulty of actually processing and accurately measuring aspherical surfaces, practical aspherical lens manufacturing methods were not realized until fairly recently. The first SLR photographic lens to incorporate a large diameter aspherical lens was Canon's FD 55mm f/1.2AL released in March 1971. Due to revolutionary advances in production technology since that time, Canon's current EF lens group makes abundant use of various aspherical lens types such as ground and polished glass aspherical lens elements, ultra-precision glass molded (GMo) aspherical lens elements, composite aspherical lens elements and replica aspherical lens elements.

Air lens

The air spaces between the glass lens elements making up a photographic lens can be thought of as lenses made of glass having the same index of refraction as air (1.0). An air space designed from the beginning with this concept in mind is called an air lens. Since the refraction of an air lens is opposite that of a glass lens, a convex shape acts as a concave lens and a concave shape acts as a convex lens. This principle was first propounded in 1898 by a man named Emil von Hoegh working for the German company Goerz.

Figure-32 Air Lens Concept Diagram

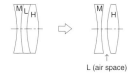

L (air space)

Actual photographic lenses

When looking at the enlarged image of an object through a magnifying glass, it is common for the edges of the image to be distorted or discolored even if the center is clear. As this indicates, a single-element lens suffers from many types of aberrations and cannot reproduce an image which is clearly defined from corner to corner. Because of this, photographic lenses are constructed of several lens elements having different shapes and characteristics in order to obtain a sharp image over the entire picture area. The basic construction of a lens is listed in the specifications section of brochures and instruction manual in terms of elements and groups. Figure 33 shows an example of the EF85mm f/1.2L II USM, constructed of 8 elements in 7 groups.

Figure-33 EF85mm f/1.2L II USM Lens Construction

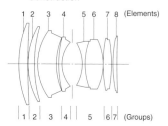

Fundamentals of lens construction

There are five basic constructions used for general-purpose single focal length lenses. ① The single type is the simplest — comprised of a single element or a doublet made of two conjoined elements. ② and ③ are of the double type, comprised of two independent elements. ④ is a triplet type, comprised of three independent lens elements in a convex-concave-convex sequence. ⑤ is a symmetrical type, consisting of two groups of one or more lenses of the same shape and configuration symmetrically oriented around the diaphragm.

Figure-34 Fundamental Lens Groupings

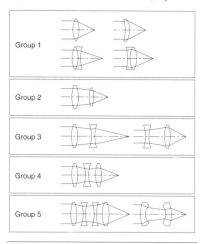

Typical photographic lens types

● Single focal length lenses
① Symmetrical type

In this type of lens, the lens group behind the diaphragm has nearly the same configuration and shape as the lens group in front of the diaphragm. Symmetrical lenses are further classified into various types such as the Gauss type, triplet type, Tessar type, Topcon type and orthometer type. Of these, the Gauss type and its derivations is the most typical configuration used today because its symmetrical design allows well balanced correction of all type of aberrations, and a comparatively long back focus can be achieved. The Canon 50mm f/1.8 released back in 1951 succeeded in eliminating the comatic aberration which was the sole weak point of Gauss type lenses of that day, and thus became famous as a historical landmark lens due to the remarkable improvement in performance it afforded. Canon still uses a Gauss type construction in current lenses such as the EF50mm f/1.4 USM, EF50mm f/1.8 II and EF85mm f/1.2L II USM. The Tessar and triplet type symmetrical configurations are commonly used today in compact cameras equipped with single focal length lenses.

Figure-35 Typical Photographic Lens Types

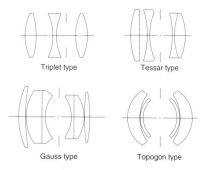

Triplet type   Tessar type

Gauss type   Topogon type

② Telephoto type (teletype)

With general photographic lenses, the overall length of a lens (the distance from the apex of the frontmost lens element to the focal plane) is longer than its focal length. This is not usually the case with lenses of particularly long focal length, however, since using a normal lens construction would result in a very large, unwieldy lens. To keep the size of such a lens manageable while still providing a long focal length, a concave (negative) lens assembly is placed behind the main convex (positive) lens assembly, resulting in a lens which is shorter than its focal length. Lenses of this type are called telephoto lenses. In a telephoto lens, the second principal point is located in front of the frontmost lens element.

● Telephoto ratio

The ratio between the overall length of a telephoto lens and its focal length is called the telephoto ratio. Put another way, it is the value of the distance from the apex of the frontmost lens element to the focal plane divided by the focal length. For telephoto lenses, this value is less than one. For reference, the telephoto ratio of the EF300mm f/2.8L IS USM is 0.94, and that of the EF600mm f/4L IS USM is 0.81.

Figure-36 Telephoto Type

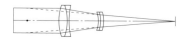

③ Retrofocus type

Conventionally designed wide-angle lenses have such a short back focus that they cannot be used in SLR cameras because they would obstruct the up/down swinging movement of the main mirror. Because of this, wide-angle lenses for SLRs have a construction opposite that of telephoto lenses, with a negative lens assembly placed in front of the main lens assembly. This moves the second principal point behind the lens (between the rearmost lens element and the film plane) and creates a lens having a back focus which is longer than the focal length. This type of lens is generally called a retrofocus lens from the name of a product marketed by Angenieux Co. of France. In optical terms, this type of lens is classified as an inverted telephoto type lens.

Figure-37 Inverted Telephoto Types (Retrofocus)

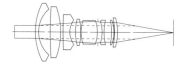

Zoom lenses

④ 4-group zoom type

An orthodox zoom lens configuration which clearly divides the functions of the lens into four groups (focusing group, magnification variation group, correction group and image formation group). Two groups — the magnification variation group and correction group — move during zooming. Since a high-magnification zoom ratio can be easily obtained with this type of construction, it is commonly used for movie camera lenses and SLR telephoto zoom lenses. However, due to problems incurred when designing compact zoom lenses, its use is becoming less common in modern non-telephoto zoom lenses.

⑤ Short zoom type

Explanation → P.212

⑥ Multi-group zoom type
Explanation → P.212

Focusing and lens movement

Focusing and lens movement techniques
Methods of lens movement for focusing can be broadly classified into the five types described below.

① Overall linear extension
The entire lens optical system moves straight backward and forward when focusing is carried out. This is the simplest type of focusing used in mainly in wide-angle through standard single focal length lenses, Such as the EF15mm f/2.8 Fisheye, lense, the EF50mm f/1.4 USM, the TS-E 90mm f/2.8, and other EF lenses.

② Front group linear extension
The rear group remains fixed and only the front group moves straight backward and forward during focusing. Examples of front group linear extension lenses are the EF50mm f/2.5 Compact Macro, MP-E 65mm f/2.8 Macro Photo and EF85mm f/1.2L II USM.

③ Front group rotational extension
The lens barrel section holding the front lens group rotates to move the front group backward and forward during focusing. This type of focusing is used only in zoom lenses and is not found in single focal length lenses. Representative examples of lenses using this method are the EF-S18-55mm f/3.5-5.6 IS, EF70-300mm f/4-5.6 IS USM and other EF lenses.

④ Inner focusing
Focusing is performed by moving one or more lens groups positioned between the front lens group and the diaphragm.
→ P.212

⑤ Rear focusing
Focusing is performed by moving one or more lens groups positioned behind the diaphragm. → P.212

Floating system
This system varies the interval between certain lens elements in accordance with the extension amount in order to compensate for aberration fluctuation caused by camera distance. This method is also referred to as a close-distance aberration compensation mechanism. → P.213

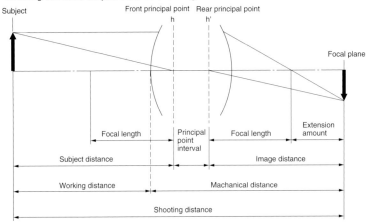

Figure-38 Shooting Distance, Subject Distance and Image Distance

Shooting distance/subject distance/image distance

Camera distance
The distance from the focal plane to the subject. The position of the focal plane is indicated on the top of most cameras by a "⊖" symbol.

Subject distance
The distance from the lens' front principal point to the subject.

Image distance
The distance from the lens' rear principal point to the focal plane when the lens is focused on a subject at a certain distance.

Extension amount
With a lens which moves the entire optical system backward and forward during focusing, the amount of lens movement necessary to focus a subject at a limited distance from the infinity focus position.

Mechanical distance
The distance from the front edge of the lens barrel to the focal plane.

Working distance
The distance from the front edge of the lens barrel to the subject. An important factor especially when shooting close-ups and enlargements.

Image magnification
The ratio (length ratio) between the actual subject size and the size of the image reproduced on film. A macro lens with a magnification indication of 1:1 can reproduce an image on film the same size as the original subject (actual size). Magnification is generally expressed as a proportional value indicating the size of the image compared to the actual subject. (For example, a magnification of 1:4 is expressed as 0.25x.)

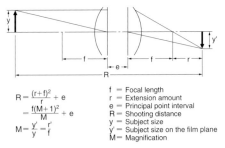

Figure-39 Relationship Between the Focal Length, Extension Amount (Overall Extension) and Magnification

$$R = \frac{(r+f)^2}{r} + e$$
$$= \frac{f(M+1)^2}{M} + e$$
$$M = \frac{y'}{y} = \frac{r'}{f}$$

f = Focal length
r = Extension amount
e = Principal point interval
R = Shooting distance
y = Subject size
y' = Subject size on the film plane
M = Magnification

Polarized light and polarizing filters

Polarized light
Since light is a type of electromagnetic wave, it can be thought of as uniformly vibrating in all directions in a plane perpendicular to the direction of propagation. This type of light is called natural light (or natural polarized light). If the direction of vibration of natural light becomes polarized for some reason, that light is called polarized light. When

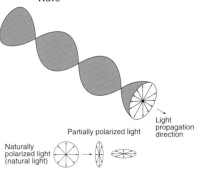

Figure-40 Naturally Polarized Electromagnetic Wave

natural light is reflected from the surface of glass or water, for example, the reflected light vibrates in one direction only and is completely polarized. Also, on a sunny day the light from the area of the sky at a 90° angle from the sun becomes polarized due to the effect of air molecules and particles in the atmosphere. The half-mirrors used in autofocus SLR cameras also cause light polarization.

Linear polarizing filter
A filter which only passes light vibrating in a certain direction. Since the vibrational locus of the light allowed to pass through the filter is linear in nature, the filter is called a linear polarizing filter. This type of filter eliminate reflections from glass and water the same way as a circular polarizing filter, but it cannot be used effectively with most auto exposure and autofous cameras as it will cause exposure errors in AE cameras equipped with TTL metering systems using half-mirrors, and will cause focusing errors in AF cameras incorporating AF range-finding systems using half-mirrors.

Circular polarizing filter
A circular polarizing filter is functionally the same as a linear polarizing filter as it only passes light vibrating in a certain direction. However, the light passing through a circular polarizing filter differs from light passing through a linear polarizing filter in that the vibrational locus rotates in a spiral pattern as it propagates. Thus, the effect of the filter does not interfere with the effect of half-mirrors, allowing normal operation of TTL-AE and AF functions. When using a polarizing filter with an EOS camera, be sure to always use a circular polarizing filter. The effectiveness of a circular polarizing filter in eliminating reflected light is the same as that of a linear polarizing filter.

Digital Terminology

Image sensor
A semiconductor element which converts image data into an electric signal, playing the role of the film in a regular film camera. Also known as an imager. The two most common image elements used in digital cameras are CCD (Charge-Coupled Devices) and CMOS (Complementary Metal-Oxide Semiconductors). Both are area sensors containing a large number of receptors (pixels) on a flat surface which convert variations in light into electric signals. The higher the number of receptors, the more accurate the image reproduction is. Since these receptors are only sensitive to brightness and not color, RGB or CMYG color filters are placed before them in order to capture both brightness and color data at the same time.

Low-pass filter
With general image elements used in digital cameras, RGB or CMYG color information is collected for each receptor arranged on the surface. This means that when light with a high spatial frequency hits a single pixel, false colors, moiré, and other colors which do not exist in the subject appear in the image. In order to reduce the occurrence of these types of false colors, the light must made to enter many different receptors, and in order to do that, the receptors used are low-pass filters. Low-pass filters use liquid crystal and other crystal structures which are characterized by double refraction (a phenomenon where two streams of refracted light are created), placed before the image elements. By double-refracting light with a high spatial frequency using low-pass filters, it becomes possible to receive light using multiple elements.

The human eye and viewfinder diopter

Eyesight, visual acuity
The ability of the eye to distinguish details of an object's shape. Expressed as a numerical value which indicates the inverse of the minimum visual angle at which the eye can clearly distinguish two points or lines, i.e. the resolution of the eye in reference to a resolution of 1'. (Ratio with a resolution of 1' assumed as 1.)

Eye accommodation

Figure-41 Human Eye Construction

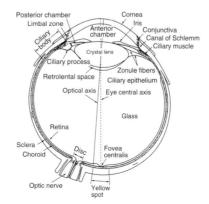

The ability of the eye to vary its refractive power in order to form an image of an object on the retina. The state in which the eye is at its minimum refractive power is called the accommodation rest state.

Normal vision, emmetropia
The eye condition in which the image of an infinitely distant point is formed on the retina when the eye is in the accommodation rest state.

Far-sightedness
The eye condition in which the image of an infinitely distant point is formed to the rear of the retina when the eye is in the accommodation rest state.

Near-sightedness, myopia
The eye condition in which the image of an infinitely distant point is formed in front of the retina when the eye is in the accommodation rest state.

Astigmatism
The eye condition in which astigmatism exists on the eye's visual axis.

Presbyopia
The eye condition in which the ability of the eye to focus decreases as a person becomes older. In camera terms, this is similar to having a fixed focal point with a shallow depth of field.

Least distance of distinct vision
The closest distance at which an eye having normal vision can observe an object without straining. This distance is normally assumed to be 25 cm/0.8 ft.

Diopter
The degree to which the light ray bundles leaving the viewfinder converge or disperse. The standard diopter of all EOS cameras is set at −1 dpt. This setting is designed to allow the finder image to appear to be seen from a distance of 1 m. Thus, if a person cannot see the viewfinder image clearly, the person should attach to the camera's eyepiece a dioptric adjustment lens having a power which, when added to the viewfinder's standard diopter, makes it possible to easily see an object at one meter. The numerical values printed on EOS dioptric adjustment lenses indicate the total diopter obtained when the dioptric adjustment lens is attached to the camera.

MTF Characteristics

How to read the MTF Characteristics

An MTF characteristic of 0.8 or more at 10 lines/mm indicates a superior lens.

An MTF characteristic of 0.6 or more at 10 lines/mm indicates a satisfactory image.

Curve showing contrast at maximum aperture

Curve showing resolution at maximum aperture

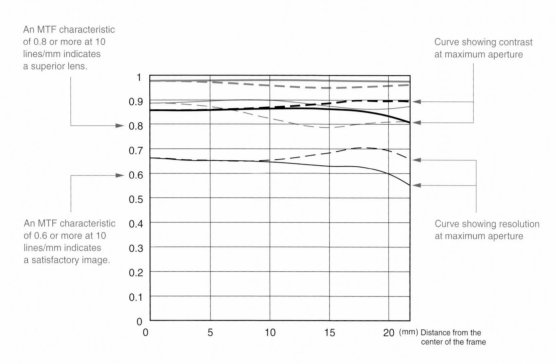

Spatial frequency	Maximum aperture		f/8	
	S	M	S	M
10 lines/mm	▬▬▬	╍╍╍	▬▬▬	╍╍╍
30 lines/mm	────	─────	────	─────

The more the S and M curves are in line, the more natural the blurred image becomes.

Resolving power and contrast are both good

Contrast is good and resolving power is bad

Resolving power is good and contrast is bad

Single Focal Length Lenses

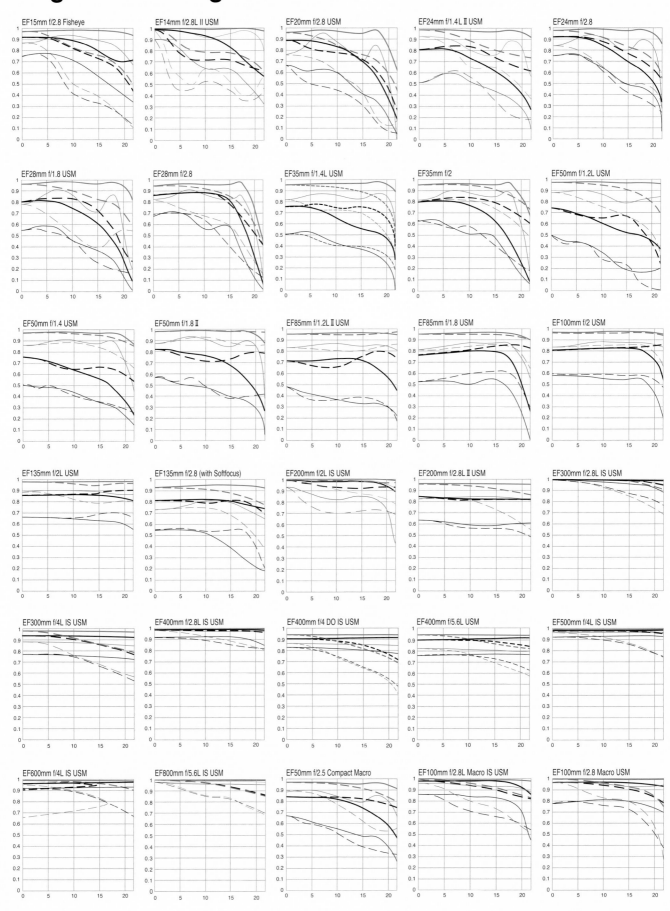

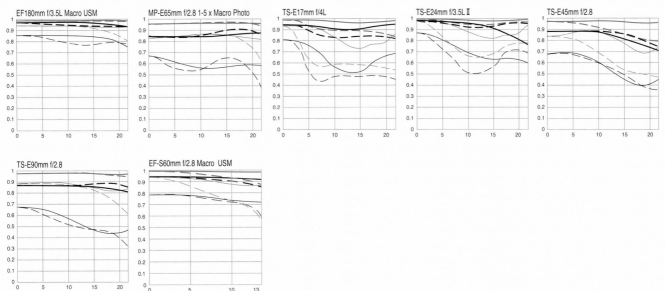

Zoom Lenses

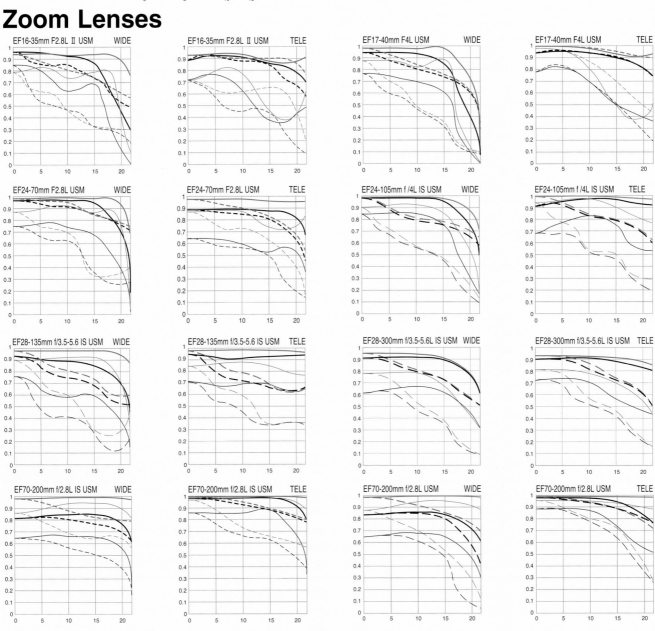

Zoom Lenses

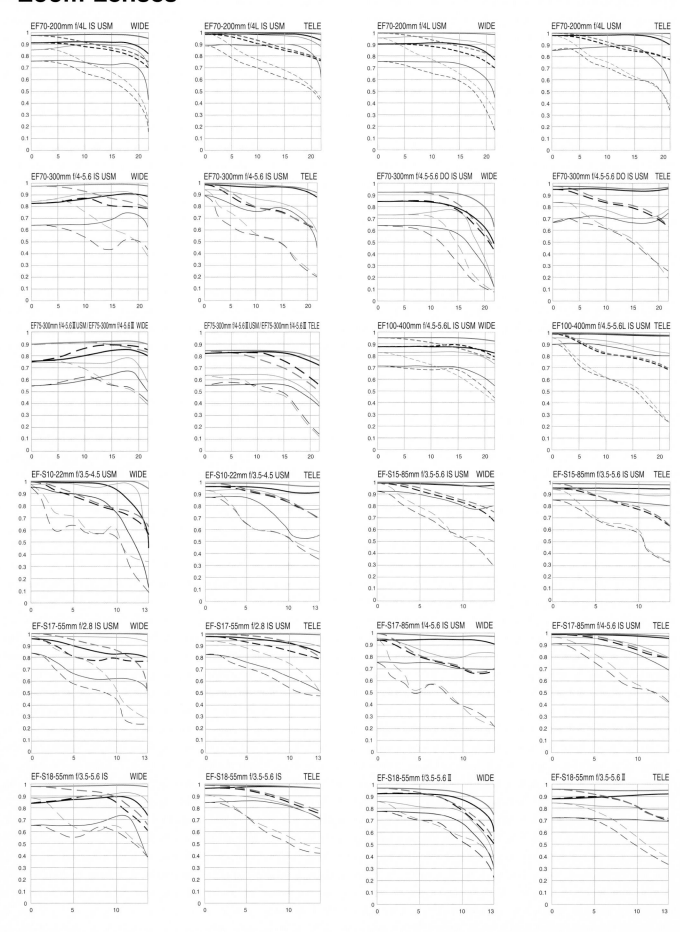

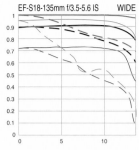

EF-S18-135mm f/3.5-5.6 IS   WIDE

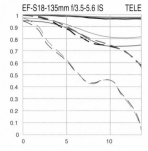

EF-S18-135mm f/3.5-5.6 IS   TELE

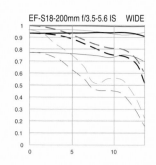

EF-S18-200mm f/3.5-5.6 IS   WIDE

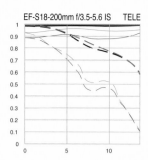

EF-S18-200mm f/3.5-5.6 IS   TELE

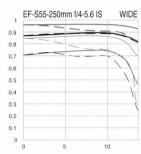

EF-S55-250mm f/4-5.6 IS   WIDE

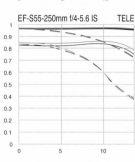

EF-S55-250mm f/4-5.6 IS   TELE

Extenders
EF1.4x Ⅱ

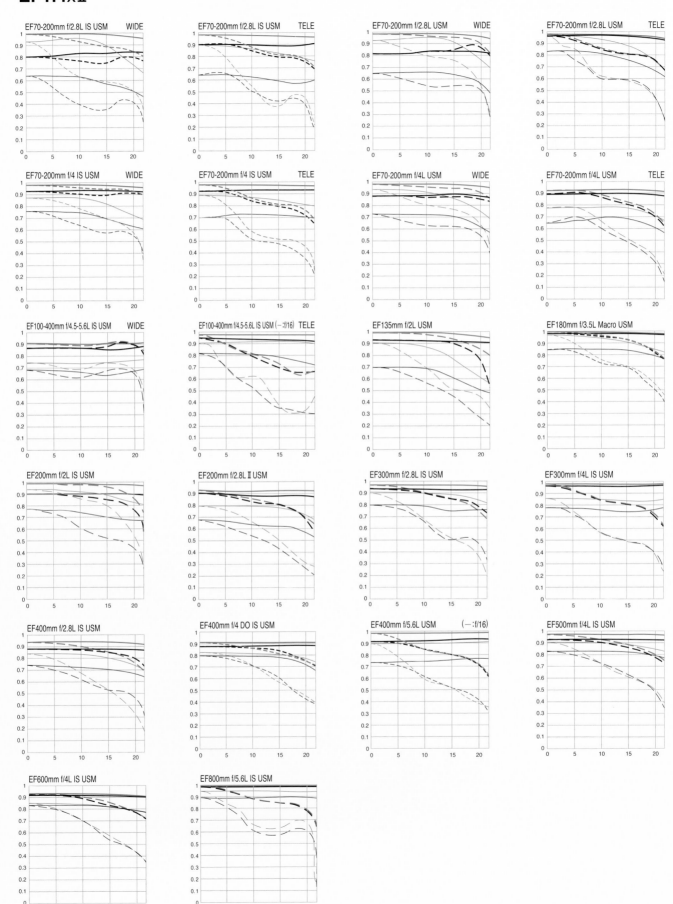

EF2xⅡ

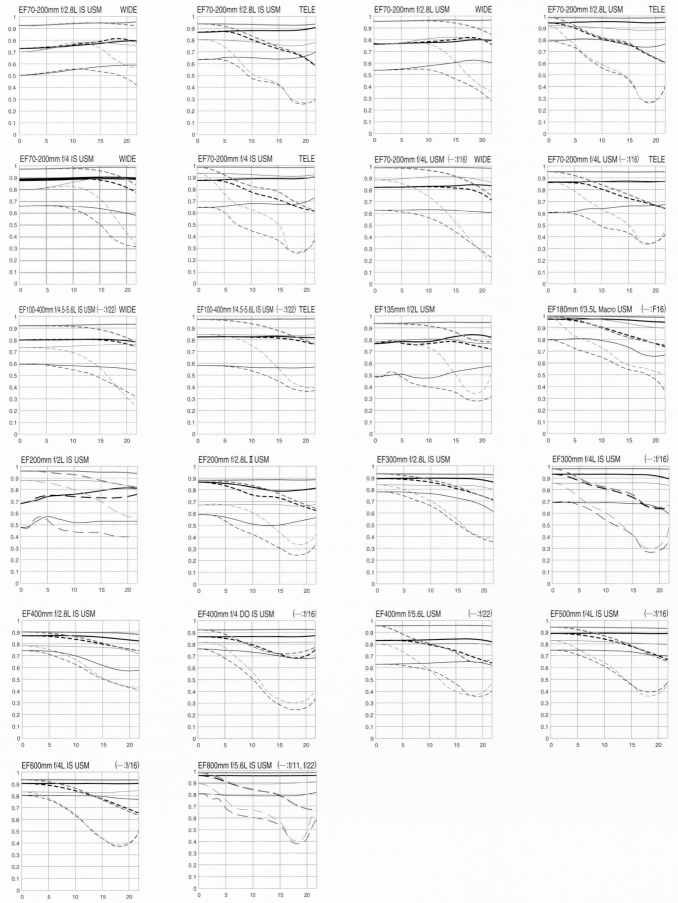

EF Lens Specifications

Lens	Angle of View (horizontal·vertical·diagonal)	Construction (groups-elements)	No. of Diaphragm Blades	Minimum Aperture	Closest Focusing Distance (m/ft)
EF15mm f/2.8 Fisheye	—·—·180°	7-8	5	22	0.2/0.7
EF14mm f/2.8L II USM	104°·81°·114°	11-14	6	22	0.2/0.7
EF20mm f/2.8 USM	84°·62°·94°	9-11	5	22	0.25/0.8
EF24mm f/1.4L II USM	74°·53°·84°	10-13	8	22	0.25/0.8
EF24mm f/2.8	74°·53°·84°	10-10	6	22	0.25/0.8
EF28mm f/1.8 USM	65°·46°·75°	9-10	7	22	0.25/0.8
EF28mm f/2.8	65°·46°·75°	5-5	5	22	0.3/1.0
EF35mm f/1.4L USM	54°·38°·63°	9-11	8	22	0.3/1.0
EF35mm f/2	54°·38°·63°	5-7	5	22	0.25/0.8
EF50mm f/1.2L USM	40°·27°·46°	6-8	8	16	0.45/1.5
EF50mm f/1.4 USM	40°·27°·46°	6-7	8	22	0.45/1.5
EF50mm f/1.8 II	40°·27°·46°	5-6	5	22	0.45/1.5
EF85mm f/1.2L II USM	24°·16°·28°30'	7-8	8	16	0.95/3.1
EF85mm f/1.8 USM	24°·16°·28°30'	7-9	8	22	0.85/2.8
EF100mm f/2 USM	20°·14°·24°	6-8	8	22	0.9/3.0
EF135mm f/2L USM	15°·10°·18°	8-10	8	32	0.9/3.0
EF135mm f/2.8 (with Softfocus)	15°·10°·18°	6-7	6	32	1.3/4.3
EF200mm f/2L IS USM	10°·7°·12°	12-17	8	32	1.9/6.2
EF200mm f/2.8L II USM	10°·7°·12°	7-9	8	32	1.5/4.9
EF300mm f/2.8L IS USM	6°50'·4°35'·8°15'	13-17	8	32	2.5/8.2
EF300mm f/4L IS USM	6°50'·4°35'·8°15'	11-15	8	32	1.5/4.9
EF400mm f/2.8L IS USM	5°10'·3°30'·6°10'	13-17	8	32	3/9.8
EF400mm f/4 DO IS USM	5°10'·3°30'·6°10'	13-17	8	32	3.5/11.5
EF400mm f/5.6L USM	5°10'·3°30'·6°10'	6-7	8	32	3.5/11.5
EF500mm f/4L IS USM	4°·2°45'·5°	13-17	8	32	4.5/14.8
EF600mm f/4L IS USM	3°30'·2°20'·4°10'	13-17	8	32	5.5/18.0
EF800mm f/5.6L IS USM	2°35'·1°40'·3°5'	14-18	8	32	6/19.69
EF50mm f/2.5 Compact Macro	40°·27°·46°	8-9	6	32	0.23/0.8
Life-size Converter EF (exclusive for EF50mm f/2.5 Compact Macro)	—·—·—	3-4	—	—	0.24/0.8
EF100mm f/2.8L Macro IS USM	20°·14°·24°	12-15	9	32	0.3/1.0
EF100mm f/2.8 Macro USM	20°·14°·24°	8-12	8	32	0.31/1.0
EF180mm f/3.5L Macro USM	11°25'·7°40'·13°40'	12-14	8	32	0.48/1.6
MP-E65mm f/2.8 1-5 x Macro Photo	15°40'·10°35'·18°40'	8-10	6	16	0.24/0.8
TS-E17mm f/4L	93°·70°30'·104°	12-18	8	22	0.25/0.8
TS-E24mm f/3.5L II	74°·53°·84°	11-16	8	22	0.21/0.7
TS-E45mm f/2.8	44°·30°·51°(without tilt or shift)*1	9-10	8	22	0.4/1.3
TS-E90mm f/2.8	22°37'·15°11'·27°(without tilt or shift)*1	5-6	8	32	0.5/1.6
Extender EF 1.4 x II	—·—·—	4-5	—	—	—
Extender EF 2 x II	—·—·—	5-7	—	—	—
EF16-35mm f/2.8L II USM	98°~54°·74°10'~38°·108°10'~63°	12-16	7	22	0.28/0.9
EF17-40mm f/4L USM	93°~49°20'·70°30'~34°·104°~57°30'	9-12	7	22	0.28/0.9
EF24-70mm f/2.8L USM	74°~29°·53°~19°30'·84°~34°	13-16	8	22	0.38(Macro)/1.3(Macro)
EF24-105mm f/4L IS USM	74°~19°20'·53°~13°·84°~23°20'	13-18	8	22	0.45(Macro)/1.5(Macro)
EF28-135mm f/3.5-5.6 IS USM	65°~15°·46°~10°·75°~18°	12-16	6	22~36	0.5(Macro)/1.6(Macro)
EF28-300mm f/3.5-5.6L IS USM	65°~6°50'·46°~4°35'·75°~8°15'	16-23	8	22~38(40)*2	0.7/2.3
EF70-200mm f/2.8L IS USM	29°~10°·19°30'~7°·34°~12°	18-23	8	32	1.4/4.6
EF70-200mm f/2.8L USM	29°~10°·19°30'~7°·34°~12°	15-18	8	32	1.5/5.0
EF70-200mm f/4L IS USM	29°~10°·19°30'~7°·34°~12°	15-20	8	32	1.2/3.9
EF70-200mm f/4L USM	29°~10°·19°30'~7°·34°~12°	13-16	8	32	1.2/3.9
EF70-300mm f/4-5.6 IS USM	29°~6°50'·19°30'~4°35'·34°~8°15'	10-15	8	32~45	1.5/4.9
EF70-300mm f/4.5-5.6 DO IS USM	29°~6°50'·19°30'~4°35'·34°~8°15'	12-18	6	32~38(40)*2	1.4/4.9
EF75-300mm f/4-5.6 III USM	27°~6°50'·18°11'~4°35'·32°11'~8°15'	9-13	7	32~45	1.5/4.9
EF75-300mm f/4-5.6 III	27°~6°50'·18°11'~4°35'·32°11'~8°15'	9-13	7	32~45	1.5/4.9
EF100-400mm f/4.5-5.6L IS USM	20°~5°10'·14°~3°30'·24°~6°10'	14-17	8	32~38(40)*2	1.8/5.9
EF-S60mm f/2.8 Macro USM*5	20°40'·14°10'·24°30'	8-12	7	32	0.2/0.7
EF-S10-22mm f/3.5-4.5 USM*5	97°10'~54°30'·74°10'~37°50'·107°30'~63°30'	10-13	6	22-27(29)*2	0.24/0.8
EF-S15-85mm f/3.5-5.6 IS USM*5	74°10'~15°25'·53°30'~10°25'·84°30'~18°25'	12-17	7	22-38(36)*2	0.35/1.2
EF-S17-55mm f/2.8 IS USM*5	68°40'~23°20'·48°~15°40'·78°30'~27°50'	12-19	7	22	0.35/1.2
EF-S17-85mm f/4-5.6 IS USM*5	68°40'~15°25'·48°~10°25'·78°30'~18°25'	12-17	6	22-32	0.35/1.2
EF-S18-55mm f/3.5-5.6 IS*5	64°30'~23°20'·45°30'~15°40'·74°20'~27°50'	9-11	6	22-38(36)*2	0.25/0.8
EF-S18-55mm f/3.5-5.6 II*5	64°30'~23°20'·45°30'~15°40'·74°20'~27°50'	9-11	6	22-38(36)*2	0.28/0.9
EF-S18-135mm f/3.5-5.6 IS*5	64°30'~9°30'·45°30'~6°20'·74°20'~11°30'	12-16	6	22-38(36)*2	0.45(at 135mm)/1.5
EF-S18-200mm f/3.5-5.6 IS*5	64°30'~6°30'·45°30'~4°20'·74°20'~7°50'	12-16	6	22-36(38)*2	0.45/1.5
EF-S55-250mm f/4-5.6 IS*5	23°20'~5°20'·15°40'~3°30'·27°50'~6°15'	10-12	7	22-32	1.1/3.6

*1 Image circle ø58.6mm *2 The aperture is for bodies using 1/2-step displays. In the case of 1/3-step displays, the aperture values of some lenses are shown in parentheses. *3 Equipped with a full-time manual mechanism. *4 Micro motor
*5 Can be used only with EOS digital SLR cameras designed to take EF-S lenses.

Lens	Maximum Magnification (X)	Drive System	Distance Scale	Water/dust-resistance*	Filter Size (mm)	Max. Diameter X Length (mm/in)	Weight(g/oz)
EF15mm f/2.8 Fisheye	0.14	AFD	—	—	Gelatin	73x62.2/2.9"x2.5"	330/11.6
EF14mm f/2.8L II USM	0.15	Ring-type USM*3	O	O	Gelatin	80x94/3.2"x3.7"	645/1.4 lbs.
EF20mm f/2.8 USM	0.14	Ring-type USM*3	O	—	72	77.5x70.6/3.1"x2.8"	405/14.3
EF24mm f/1.4L II USM	0.17	Ring-type USM*3	O	O	77	83.5x86.9/3.3"x3.4"	650/1.4 lbs.
EF24mm f/2.8	0.16	AFD	—	—	58	67.5x48.5/2.7"x1.9"	270/9.5
EF28mm f/1.8 USM	0.18	Ring-type USM*3	O	—	58	73.6x55.6/2.9"x2.2"	310/10.9
EF28mm f/2.8	0.13	AFD	—	—	52	67.4x42.5/2.7"x1.7"	185/6.5
EF35mm f/1.4L USM	0.18	Ring-type USM*3	O	—	72	79x86/3.1"x3.4"	580/1.3 lbs.
EF35mm f/2	0.23	AFD	—	—	52	67.4x42.5/2.7"x1.7"	210/7.4
EF50mm f/1.2L USM	0.15	Ring-type USM*3	O	O	72	85.8x65.5/3.4"x2.6"	590/1.3 lbs.
EF50mm f/1.4 USM	0.15	Micro USM	—	—	58	73.8x50.5/2.9"x2"	290/10.2
EF50mm f/1.8 II	0.15	MM*4	—	—	52	68.2x41/2.7"x1.6"	130/4.6
EF85mm f/1.2L II USM	0.11	Ring-type USM*3	O	—	72	91.5x84/3.6"x3.3"	1,025/2.3 lbs.
EF85mm f/1.8 USM	0.13	Ring-type USM*3	O	—	58	75x71.5/3"x2.8"	425/15
EF100mm f/2 USM	0.14	Ring-type USM*3	O	—	58	75x73.5/3"x2.9"	460/1 lb.
EF135mm f/2L USM	0.19	Ring-type USM*3	O	—	72	82.5x112/3.2"x4.4"	750/1.7 lbs.
EF135mm f/2.8 (with Softfocus)	0.12	AFD	—	—	52	69.2x98.4/2.7"x3.9"	390/13.8
EF200mm f/2L IS USM	0.12	Ring-type USM*3	O	O	52 drop-in	128x208/5"x8.2"	2,520/5.6 lbs.
EF200mm f/2.8L II USM	0.16	Ring-type USM*3	O	—	72	83.2x136.2/3.3"x5.4"	765/1.7 lbs.
EF300mm f/2.8L IS USM	0.13	Ring-type USM*3	O	O	52 drop-in	128x252/5"x9.9"	2,550/5.6 lbs.
EF300mm f/4L IS USM	0.24	Ring-type USM*3	O	—	77	90x221/3.5"x8.7"	1,190/2.6 lbs.
EF400mm f/2.8L IS USM	0.15	Ring-type USM*3	O	O	52 drop-in	163x349/6.4"x13.7"	5,370/11.8 lbs.
EF400mm f/4 DO IS USM	0.12	Ring-type USM*3	O	O	52 drop-in	128x232.7/5"x9.4"	1,940/4.3 lbs.
EF400mm f/5.6L USM	0.12	Ring-type USM*3	O	—	77	90x256.5/3.5"x10.1"	1,250/2.8 lbs.
EF500mm f/4L IS USM	0.12	Ring-type USM*3	O	O	52 drop-in	146x387/5.8"x15.2"	3,870/8.5 lbs.
EF600mm f/4L IS USM	0.12	Ring-type USM*3	O	O	52 drop-in	168x456/6.6"x18"	5,360/11.8 lbs.
EF800mm f/5.6L IS USM	0.14	Ring-type USM*3	O	O	52 drop-in	163x461/6.4"x18.1"	4,500/9.9 lbs.
EF50mm f/2.5 Compact Macro	0.5	AFD	—	—	52	67.6x63/2.7"x2.5"	280/9.9
Life-size Converter EF (exclusive for EF50mm f/2.5 Compact Macro)	1	—	—	—	—	67.6x34.9/2.7"x1.4"	160/5.6
EF100mm f/2.8L Macro IS USM	1	Ring-type USM*3	O	O	67	77.7x123/3.1"x4.8"	625/1.4 lbs.
EF100mm f/2.8 Macro USM	1	Ring-type USM*3	O	—	58	78.6x118.6/3.1"x4.7"	580/1.3 lbs.
EF180mm f/3.5L Macro USM	1	Ring-type USM*3	O	—	72	82.5x186.6/3.3"x7.4"	1,090/2.4 lbs.
MP-E65mm f/2.8 1-5 x Macro Photo	5	—	O	—	58	81x98/3.2"x3.9"	710/1.6 lbs.
TS-E17mm f/4L	0.14	—	O	—	—	88.9x106.7/3.5"x4.2"	820/1.8 lbs.
TS-E24mm f/3.5L II	0.34	—	O	—	82	88.5x106.9/3.5"x4.2"	780/1.7 lbs.
TS-E45mm f/2.8	0.16	—	—	—	72	81x90.1/3.2"x3.5"	645/1.4 lbs.
TS-E90mm f/2.8	0.29	—	—	—	58	73.6x88/2.9"x3.5"	565/1.2 lbs.
Extender EF 1.4 x II	—	—	—	O	—	72.8x27.2/2.9"x1.1"	220/7.8
Extender EF 2 x II	—	—	—	O	—	71.8x57.9/2.8"x2.3"	265/9.3
EF16-35mm f/2.8L II USM	0.22(at 35mm)	Ring-type USM*3	O	O	82	88.5x111.6/3.5"x4.4"	640/1.4 lbs.
EF17-40mm f/4L USM	0.24(at 40mm)	Ring-type USM*3	O	O	77	83.5x96.8/3.3"x3.8"	475/1 lb.
EF24-70mm f/2.8L USM	0.29(at 70mm)	Ring-type USM*3	O	O	77	83.2x123.5/3.3"x4.9"	950/2.1 lbs.
EF24-105mm f/4L IS USM	0.23(at 105mm)	Ring-type USM*3	O	O	77	83.5x107/3.3"x4.2"	670/1.5 lbs.
EF28-135mm f/3.5-5.6 IS USM	0.19(at 135mm)	Ring-type USM*3	Scale	—	72	78.4x96.8/3.1"x3.8"	540/1.2 lbs.
EF28-300mm f/3.5-5.6L IS USM	0.3(at 300mm)	Ring-type USM*3	O	O	77	92x184/3.6"x7.2"	1,670/3.7 lbs.
EF70-200mm f/2.8L IS USM	0.17(at 200mm)	Ring-type USM*3	O	O	77	86.2x197/3.4"x7.8"	1,470/3.2 lbs.
EF70-200mm f/2.8L USM	0.16(at 200mm)	Ring-type USM*3	O	—	77	84.6x193.6/3.3"x7.6"	1,310/2.9 lbs.
EF70-200mm f/4L IS USM	0.21(at 200mm)	Ring-type USM*3	O	O	67	76x172/3"x6.8"	760/1.7 lbs.
EF70-200mm f/4L USM	0.21(at 200mm)	Ring-type USM*3	O	—	67	76x172/3"x6.8"	705/1.6 lbs.
EF70-300mm f/4-5.6 IS USM	0.26(at 300mm)	Micro USM	O	—	58	76.5x142.8/3.0"x5.6"	630/1.4 lbs.
EF70-300mm f/4.5-5.6 DO IS USM	0.19(at 300mm)	Ring-type USM*3	O	—	58	82.4x99.9/3.2"x3.9"	720/1.6 lbs.
EF75-300mm f/4-5.6 III USM	0.25(at 300mm)	Micro USM	—	—	58	71x122/2.8"x4.8"	480/1.1 lbs.
EF75-300mm f/4-5.6 III	0.25(at 300mm)	MM*4	—	—	58	71x122/2.8"x4.8"	480/1.1 lbs.
EF100-400mm f/4.5-5.6L IS USM	0.2(at 400mm)	Ring-type USM*3	O	—	77	92x189/3.6"x7.4"	1,380/3 lbs.
EF-S60mm f/2.8 Macro USM	1	Ring-type USM*3	O	—	52	73x69.8/2.9"x2.8"	335/11.8
EF-S10-22mm f/3.5-4.5 USM	0.17(at 22mm)	Ring-type USM*3	O	—	77	83.5x89.8/3.3"x3.5"	385/13.6
EF-S15-85mm f/3.5-5.6 IS USM	0.21(at 85mm)	Ring-type USM*3	O	—	72	81.6x87.5/3.2"x3.4"	575/1.3 lbs.
EF-S17-55mm f/2.8 IS USM	0.17(at 55mm)	Ring-type USM*3	O	—	77	83.5x110.6/3.3"x4.4"	645/1.41 lbs.
EF-S17-85mm f/4-5.6 IS USM	0.2(at 85mm)	Ring-type USM*3	O	—	67	78.5x92/3.1"x3.6"	475/1 lb.
EF-S18-55mm f/3.5-5.6 IS	0.34(at 55mm)	MM*4	O	—	58	68.5x70/2.7"x2.8"	200/7.1
EF-S18-55mm f/3.5-5.6 II	0.28(at 55mm)	MM*4	O	—	58	68.5x66/2.7"x2.6"	190/6.7
EF-S18-135mm f/3.5-5.6 IS	0.21(at 135mm)	MM*4	O	—	67	75.4x101/3.0"x4.0"	455/1 lb.
EF-S18-200mm f/3.5-5.6 IS	0.24(at 200mm)	MM*4	O	—	72	78.6x102/3.1"x4.0"	595/1.3 lbs.
EF-S55-250mm f/4-5.6 IS	0.31(at 250mm)	MM*4	O	—	58	70x108/2.8"x4.3"	390/15.4

* Water- and dust-resistant lenses have a cam ring which improves dust and drip resistance and which may cause slight scratching around the camera mount, but this in no way affects use of either the camera or the lens.

With Extender EF1.4xII attached

When used with EF Lens	EF135mm f/2L USM	EF180mm f/3.5L Macro USM	EF200mm f/2L IS USM	EF200mm f/2.8L II USM	EF300mm f/2.8L IS USM	EF300mm f/4L IS USM	EF400mm f/2.8L IS USM	EF400mm f/4 DO IS USM	EF400mm f/5.6L USM
Focal length (mm)	189	252	280	280	420	420	560	560	560
Maximum aperture (f/)	2.8~45	4.5~45(5~45)*1	2.8~45	4~45	4~45	5.6~45	4~45	5.6~45	8~45
Maximum magnification (X)	0.27	1.4	0.18	0.22	0.19	0.33	0.22	0.17	0.18
AF	○	○*2	○	○	○	○	○	○	○*3
IS	—	—	○	—	○	○	○	○	—

When used with EF Lens	EF500mm f/4L IS USM	EF600mm f/4L IS USM	EF800mm f/5.6L IS USM	EF70-200mm f/2.8L IS USM	EF70-200mm f/2.8L USM	EF70-200mm f/4L IS USM	EF70-200mm f/4L USM	EF100-400mm f/4.5-5.6L IS USM
Focal length (mm)	700	840	1,120	98~280	98~280	98~280	98~280	140~560
Maximum aperture (f/)	5.6~45	5.6~45	8~45	4~45	4~45	5.6~45	5.6~45	6.7~54 (6.3~57)*1
Maximum magnification (X)	0.17	0.17	0.2	0.24	0.22	0.31	0.31	0.28
AF	○	○	○*3	○	○*4	○	○	○*3
IS	○	○	○	○	—	○	—	○*5

With Extender EF2xII attached

When used with EF Lens	EF135mm f/2L USM	EF180mm f/3.5L Macro USM	EF200mm f/2L IS USM	EF200mm f/2.8L II USM	EF300mm f/2.8L IS USM	EF300mm f/4L IS USM	EF400mm f/2.8L IS USM	EF400mm f/4 DO IS USM	EF400mm f/5.6L USM
Focal length (mm)	270	360	400	400	600	600	800	800	800
Maximum aperture (f/)	4~64	6.7~64(7.1~64)*5	4~64	5.6~64	5.6~64	8~64	5.6~64	8~64	11~64
Maximum magnification (X)	0.38	2.0	0.24	0.32	0.28	0.47	0.31	0.24	0.25
AF	○	X	○	○	○	○*3	○	○*3	X
IS	—	—	○	—	○	○*5	○	○*5	—

When used with EF Lens	EF500mm f/4L IS USM	EF600mm f/4L IS USM	EF800mm f/5.6L IS USM	EF70-200mm f/2.8L IS USM	EF70-200mm f/2.8L USM	EF70-200mm f/4L IS USM	EF70-200mm f/4L USM	EF100-400mm f/4.5-5.6L IS USM
Focal length (mm)	1,000	1,200	1,600	140~400	140~400	140~400	140~400	200~800
Maximum aperture (f/)	8~64	8~64	11~64	5.6~64	5.6~64	8~64	8~64	9.5~76 (9~81)*5
Maximum magnification (X)	0.25	0.24	0.28	0.36	0.33	0.45	0.45	0.41
AF	○*3	○*3	X	○	○*4	○*3	○*3	X
IS	○*5	○*5	○	○	—	○*5	—	○*5

When using the Extender EF1.4xII the autofocus drops in speed by approximately one half, and when using the Extender EF2xII it drops 1/4.

*1 The aperture is for bodies using 1/2-step displays. In the case of 1/3-step displays, the aperture values of some lenses are shown in parentheses.

*2 Autofocus use range is 0.8m to ∞.

*3 AF can be used only with the center measuring point when using the EOS-1Ds Mark III, EOS-1Ds Mark II, EOS-1Ds, EOS-1D Mark IV, EOS-1D Mark III, EOS-1D Mark II N, EOS-1D Mark II, EOS-1D, EOS-1V/HS, EOS-3. With other EOS cameras only manual focus is available.

*4 AF is possible using only the center measuring point when using a multi-point measurement EOS.

*5 Cameras with which the image stabilizing function is available are the EOS-1Ds Mark III, EOS-1Ds Mark II, EOS-1Ds, EOS-1D Mark IV, EOS-1D Mark III, EOS-1D Mark II N, EOS-1D Mark II, EOS-1D, EOS 5D Marh II, EOS 5D, EOS 7D, EOS 50D, EOS 40D, EOS 30D, EOS 20D, EOS 20Da, EOS 10D, EOS D60, EOS D30, EOS Kiss X3/REBEL T1i/500D, EOS Kiss X2/DIGITAL REBEL XSi/450D, EOS Kiss F/DIGITAL REBEL XS/1000D, EOS Kiss Digital X/DIGITAL REBEL XTi/400D DIGITAL, EOS Kiss Digital N/DIGITAL REBEL XT/350D DIGITAL, EOS Kiss Digital/DIGITAL REBEL/300D DIGITAL, EOS D6000, EOS D2000, EOS·DCS 1, EOS·DCS 3, EOS-1V/HS, EOS-1N/DP/HS/RS, EOS 7s/ELAN 7NE/ELAN 7N/30V/33V, EOS 7/ELAN 7E/ELAN 7/33/30, EOS-3, EOS 55/ELAN II E/ELAN II/50E/50, EOS Kiss 7/REBEL T2/300X, EOS Kiss Lite/REBEL K2/3000V, EOS Kiss 5/REBEL Ti/300V, EOS Kiss III L, EOS Kiss III/REBEL 2000/300, New EOS Kiss/REBEL G/500N, EOS REBEL G II, EOS REBEL X, EOS Kiss/REBEL XS/500, EOS 3000N/XSN, EOS 3000/88, EOS 5000/888, EOS IX 50/Lite/7 and EOS IX E/IX.

EF Lens Accessory Chart

Lens	Extension Tube EF12 II	Extension Tube EF25 II	LENS CAP	LENS HOOD	Lens Pouch/Case	Gelatin Filter Holder III (Hood III *1)	Gelatin Filter Holder IV (Hood IV *1)
EF15mm f/2.8 Fisheye	—	—	Exclusive	Built-in	LP814	NC*2	NC*2
EF14mm f/2.8L II USM	—	—	Exclusive	Built-in	LP1016	NC*2	NC*2
EF20mm f/2.8 USM	0.72~0.60X	—	E-72U	EW-75 II	LP1214	NC	0
EF24mm f/1.4L II USM	0.67~0.50X	—	E-77U	EW-83K	LP1319	NC	0
EF24mm f/2.8	0.64~0.50X	1.22~1.11X	E-58	EW-60 II	LP811	0	0
EF28mm f/1.8 USM	0.61~0.43X	1.13~0.96X	E-58U	EW-63 II	LP814	0	0
EF28mm f/2.8	0.56~0.43X	1.09~0.95X	E-52	EW-65 II	LP1011	1	1
EF35mm f/1.4L USM	0.54~0.36X	0.97~0.79X	E-72U	EW-78C	LP1214	NC	0
EF35mm f/2	0.58~0.35X	1.00~0.77X	E-52	EW-65 II	LP1011	2	2
EF50mm f/1.2L USM	0.39~0.24X	0.67~0.53X	E-72U	ES-78	LP1214	0	1
EF50mm f/1.4 USM	0.39~0.24X	0.68~0.53X	E-58U	ES-71 II	LP1014	2*3	2
EF50mm f/1.8 II	0.39~0.24X	0.68~0.53X	E-52	ES-62+ADP	LP1014	2	1
EF85mm f/1.2L II USM	0.25~0.15X	0.42~0.33X	E-72U	ES-79 II	LP1219	4	4
EF85mm f/1.8 USM	0.27~0.15X	0.44~0.32X	E-58U	ET-65 III	LP1014	5	4
EF100mm f/2 USM	0.27~0.13X	0.42~0.28X	E-58U	ET-65 III	LP1014	5	4
EF135mm f/2L USM	0.29~0.09X	0.41~0.20X	E-72U	ET-78 II	LP1219	5	5
EF135mm f/2.8 (with Softfocus)	0.22~0.09X	0.33~0.20X	E-52	ET-65 III	LP1016	5	4
EF200mm f/2L IS USM	0.19~0.06X	0.26~0.14X	E-145B	ET-120B	Lens Case 200	NC*5	NC*5
EF200mm f/2.8L II USM	0.23~0.06X	0.32~0.14X	E-72U	ET-83B II	LP1222	5	5
EF300mm f/2.8L IS USM	0.18~0.04X	0.24~0.09X	E-145	ET-120	Lens Case 300	NC*5	NC*5
EF300mm f/4L IS USM	0.30~0.04X	0.37~0.09X	E-77U	Built-in	LZ1128	5*6	4
EF400mm f/2.8L IS USM	0.19~0.03X	0.23~0.06X	E-180C	ET-155	Lens Case 400	NC*5	NC*5
EF400mm f/4 DO IS USM	0.16~0.03X	0.20~0.07X	E-145	ET-120	Lens Case 400B	NC*5	NC*5
EF400mm f/5.6L USM	0.16~0.03X	0.21~0.07X	E-77U	Built-in	LZ1132	5*6	5
EF500mm f/4L IS USM	0.15~0.03X	0.18~0.05X	E-163	ET-138	Lens Case 500	NC*5	NC*5
EF600mm f/4L IS USM	0.14~0.02X	0.17~0.05X	E-185	ET-160	Lens Case 600	NC*5	NC*5
EF800mm f/5.6L IS USM	0.16~0.02X	0.19~0.04	E-180C	ET-155	Lens Case 800	NC*5	NC*5
EF50mm f/2.5 Compact Macro	0.74~0.24X	1.04~0.54X	E-52	—	LP814	2	2
Life-size Converter EF (exclusive for EF50mm f/2.5 Compact Macro)	—	—	R-F-3	—	LP811	5*4	5*4
EF100mm f/2.8L Macro IS USM	1.17~0.12X	1.37~0.27X	E-67U	ET-73	LP1219	4	4
EF100mm f/2.8 Macro USM	1.19~0.12X	1.39~0.26X	E-58U	ET-67	LP1219	4	4
EF180mm f/3.5L Macro USM	1.09~0.07X	1.21~0.15X	E-72U	ET-78 II	LZ1324	5	5
MP-E65mm f/2.8 1-5 x Macro Photo	—	—	E-58	Exclusive	LP1216	0	0
TS-E17mm f/4L	—	—	Lens Cap 17	—	LP1219	NC	NC
TS-E24mm f/3.5L II	Not recommended	Not recommended	E-82	EW-88B	LP1319	NC	NC
TS-E45mm f/2.8	0.44~0.27X	—	E-72	EW-79B II	LP1216	0	0
TS-E90mm f/2.8	0.43~0.14X	0.60~0.31X	E-58	ES-65 III	LP1016	1	1
Extender EF 1.4 x II	—	—	Extender Cap E II	—	LP811	—	—
Extender EF 2 x II	—	—	Extender Cap E II	—	LP811	—	—
EF16-35mm f/2.8L II USM	0.62~0.36X	1.11~0.80X	E-82U	EW-88	LP1319	NC	0*8
EF17-40mm f/4L USM	0.83~0.32X	1.02~0.70X	E-77U	EW-83E	LP1319	NC	0*8
EF24-70mm f/2.8L USM	0.63~0.18X	0.75~0.40X	E-77U	EW-83F	LP1219	0*8	0*8
EF24-105mm f/4L IS USM	0.60~0.12X	0.61~0.27X	E-77U	EW-83H	LP1219	NC	0
EF28-135mm f/3.5-5.6 IS USM	0.53~0.09X	1.09~0.21X	E-72U	EW-78B II	LP1116	NC	0
EF28-300mm f/3.5-5.6L IS USM	0.50~0.04X	0.50~0.09X	E-77U	EW-83G	LZ1324	NC	6*8
EF70-200mm f/2.8L IS USM	0.24~0.06X	0.41~0.14X	E-77U	ET-86	LZ1324	0	1
EF70-200mm f/2.8L USM	0.22~0.06X	0.41~0.14X	E-77U	ET-83 II	LZ1324	2	2
EF70-200mm f/4L IS USM	0.28~0.06X	0.42~0.14X	E-67U	ET-74	LP1224	2	3
EF70-200mm f/4L USM	0.29~0.06X	0.39~0.13X	E-67U	ET-74	LP1224	2	3
EF70-300mm f/4-5.6 IS USM	0.32~0.04X	0.40~0.09X	E-58U	ET-65B	LP1222	2	3
EF70-300mm f/4.5-5.6 DO IS USM	0.26~0.04X	0.46~0.09X	E-58U	ET-65B	LP1116	4	4
EF75-300mm f/4-5.6 III USM	0.31~0.04X	0.39~0.09X	E-58	ET-60	LP1019	5	4
EF75-300mm f/4-5.6 III	0.31~0.04X	0.39~0.09X	E-58	ET-60	LP1019	5	4
EF100-400mm f/4.5-5.6L IS USM	0.25~0.03X	0.35~0.07X	E-77U	ET-83C	LZ1324	4	5
EF-S60mm f/2.8 Macro USM	1.28~0.20X	1.61~0.44X	E-52U	ET-67B	LP1016	6	6
EF-S10-22mm f/3.5-4.5 USM	0.77~0.58X	Not recommended	E-77U	EW-83E	LP1319	NC	0
EF-S15-85mm f/3.5-5.6 IS USM	0.44~0.15X	—	E-72U	EW-78E	LP1116	NC	0
EF-S17-55mm f/2.8 IS USM	0.45~0.23X	Not recommended	E-77U	EW-83J	LP1219	NC	0
EF-S17-85mm f/4-5.6 IS USM	0.43~0.14X	0.72~0.33X	E-67U	EW-73B	LP1116	NC	0
EF-S18-55mm f/3.5-5.6 IS	0.64~0.23X	1.00~0.51X	E-58	EW-60C	LP814	0	0
EF-S18-55mm f/3.5-5.6 II	0.81~0.23X	0.92~0.51X	E-58	EW-60C	LP814	0	0
EF-S18-135mm f/3.5-5.6 IS	0.38~0.09X	0.59~0.21X	E-67	EW-73B	LP1116	NC	0
EF-S18-200mm f/3.5-5.6 IS	0.39~0.06X	0.56~0.14X	E-72	EW-78D	LP1116	0	0
EF-S55-250mm f/4-5.6 IS	0.6~0.05X	0.48~0.11X	E-58	ET-60	LP1019	5	5

- The Extension Tube EF12 II can be used with all lenses except the EF15mm f/2.8 Fisheye, EF14mm f/2.8L II USM, MP-E65mm f/2.8 1-5x Macro Photo, TS-E17mm f/4L, EF16-35mm f/2.8L II USM at wide angles, EF-S10-22mm f/3.5-4.5 USM at wide angles, EF-S15-85mm f/3.5-5.6 IS USM at wide angles, EFS17-55mm f/2.8 IS USM at wide angles, EF-S17-85mm f/4-5.6 IS USM at wide angles, EF-S18-55mm f/3.5-5.6 IS at wide angles, EF-S18-135mm f/3.5-5.6 IS at wide angles, EF-S18-200mm f/3.5-5.6 IS at wide angles.
- The Extension Tube EF25 II can be used with all lenses except the EF15mm f/2.8 Fisheye, EF14mm f/2.8L II USM, EF20mm f/2.8 USM, EF24mm f/1.4L II USM, MP-E 65mm f/2.8 1-5x Macro Photo, and TS-E17mm f/4L, TS-E 45mm f/2.8, EF16-35mm f/2.8L II USM at wide angles, EF17-40mm f/4L USM at wide angles, EF24-70mm f/2.8L USM at wide angles, EF24-105mm f/4L IS USM at wide angles, EF28-300mm f/3.5-5.6L IS USM at wide angles, EF-S10-22mm f/3.5-4.5 USM at wide angles, EF-S15-85mm f/3.5-5.6 IS USM, EF-S17-85mm f/3.5-5.6 IS USM, EF-S18-55mm f/3.5-5.6 IS at wide angles, EF-S18-135mm f/3.5-5.6 IS at wide angles, EF-S18-200mm f/3.5-5.6 IS at wide angles. (We do not recommend use of the Extension Tube EF25II with TS-E24mm f/3.5L II, EF-S10-22mm f/3.5-4.5 USM at near the tele end EF-S17-55mm f/2.8 IS USM at near the tele end, since it radically reduces working distance.)

*1 Maximum number of gelatin filter holder hood III or IV which can be used. "0" indicates that only the gelatin filter holder can be used. *2 Use a rear drop-in gelatin filter holder. *3 Use the special Gelatin Filter Holder Adapter III when attaching the Gelatin Filter Holder III to the EF50mm f/1.4 USM. *4 Maximum number of gelatin filter holder hood III or IV which can be used with the EF50mm f/2.5 Compact Macro. *5 Use the 52mm Drop-in Gelatin Filter Holder. *6 The securing pin may be slightly difficult to use. *7 Use the 48mm Drop-in Gelatin Filter Holder II *8 Vignetting occurs at wide angles. (We recommend using the built-in rear gelatin filter holder for the EF16-35mm f/2.8L II USM and EF17-40mm f/4L USM.) *9 Vignetting occurs during tilt and shift. NC: Not compatible with gelatin filter holder III or IV.

EF Lens Map

EF15mm f/2.8 Fisheye

EF14mm f/2.8L II USM

EF20mm f/2.8 USM

EF24mm f/1.4L II USM

EF24mm f/2.8

EF28mm f/1.8 USM

EF28mm f/2.8

EF35mm f/1.4L USM

EF35mm f/2

EF50mm f/1.2L USM

EF50mm f/1.4 USM

EF50mm f/1.8 II

EF50mm f/2.5
Compact Macro

Life-Size Converter EF

MP-E65mm f/2.8
1-5 × Macro Photo

EF85mm f/1.2L II USM

EF85mm f/1.8 USM

EF100mm f/2 USM

EF100mm f/2.8L Macro IS USM

EF100mm f/2.8 Macro USM

EF135mm f/2L USM

EF135mm f/2.8 (with Softfocus)

EF180mm f/3.5L Macro USM

EF200mm f/2.8L II USM

EF200mm f/2L IS USM

TS-E17mm f/4L

TS-E24mm f/3.5L II

TS-E45mm f/2.8

TS-E90mm f/2.8

EF300mm f/2.8L IS USM

EF300mm f/4L IS USM

EF400mm f/2.8L IS USM

EF400mm f/4 DO IS USM

EF400mm f/5.6L USM

EF500mm f/4L IS USM

EF600mm f/4L IS USM

Extender EF1.4x II

Extender EF2x II

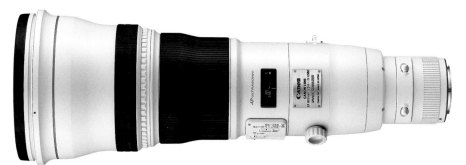

EF800mm f/5.6L IS USM

EF16-35mm f/2.8L II USM

EF17-40mm f/4L USM

EF24-70mm f/2.8L USM

EF24-105mm f/4L IS USM

EF28-135mm f/3.5-5.6 IS USM

EF28-300mm f/3.5-5.6L IS USM

EF70-200mm f/2.8L IS USM

EF70-200mm f/2.8L USM

EF70-200mm f/4L IS USM

EF70-200mm f/4L USM

EF70-300mm f/4-5.6 IS USM

EF70-300mm f/4.5-5.6 DO IS USM

EF75-300mm f/4-5.6 III USM

EF75-300mm f/4-5.6 III

EF100-400mm f/4.5-5.6L IS USM

EF-S lenses Exclusively for EF-S compatible DIGITAL SLR cameras

Compatible EOS SLR cameras: EOS 7D, EOS 50D, EOS 40D, EOS 30D, EOS 20D, EOS 20Da, EOS Kiss X3/REBEL T1i/500D, EOS Kiss X2/DIGITAL REBEL XSi/450D, EOS Kiss F/REBEL XS/1000D, EOS Kiss Digital X/DIGITAL REBEL XTi/DIGITAL 400D, EOS Kiss Digital N/EOS DIGITAL REBEL XT/350D DIGITAL, EOS Kiss Digital/DIGITAL REBEL/300D DIGITAL. (as of October 2009)

EF-S60mm f/2.8 Macro USM

EF-S10-22mm f/3.5-4.5 USM

EF-S15-85mm f/3.5-5.6 IS USM

EF-S17-55mm f/2.8 IS USM

EF-S17-85mm f/4-5.6 IS USM

EF-S18-55mm f/3.5-5.6 IS

EF-S18-55mm f/3.5-5.6 II

EF-S18-135mm f/3.5-5.6 IS

EF-S18-200mm f/3.5-5.6 IS

EF-S55-250mm f/4-5.6 IS

The Professional Eye/Introducing Our Photographers

Adherents of the rockabilly subculture reject the internet and opt for 50s fashions, 50s furniture for their houses, even 50s-style tattoos – in a word, they give over their entire being to living in the 50s. I had always been interested in people who live their lives in an extreme fashion, and these people were no exception. This photograph was taken at the famous Hemsby Rockabilly Festival in England, held twice a year and attended by around 5,000 rockabilly enthusiasts from around the globe. I spent four hectic days in Hemsby taking pictures and doing interviews, and one day when out for a drive along the nearby coast I found a British rockabilly aficionado in his car. He took a drag on his cigarette just as I lifted the camera for the shot. He was probably going for a James Dean look. I've used Canon ever since I became a photographer. The Canon EOS-1N and the EF28mm f/1.8 USM are the mainstays of my equipment. I've also got a backup camera with a 17-35mm. But the EF28mm f/1.8 USM is my favorite. It's very sensitive and produces photographs with excellent sharpness and contrast. I've used Canon equipment under all sorts of conditions, including some pretty rough situations, but I've never been let down by it.

Erik Refner
Born in Copenhagen, 1971. After representing Denmark in the modern pentathlon, did stints as an assistant photographer before working as a photo-journalist for Night & Day, and Berlingske Tidende, a major Danish newspaper (www.berlingske.dk). Has worked at the Jalozai refugee camp in Pakistan, Lourdes, Cambodia, and has covered the Tour de France. Participated in the Swedish Rockabilly Project (of people who live their lives as though it were still 1950). Major awards received include the Visa d'Or Perpignan 2001, the World Press Photo 2002 Award, two awards for people in the news in 2002, photograph publishing report POY, Feature Picture Story NPPA, the Scanpix Prize Best Book Award, and more.

All these photographs are from a real wedding I was hired to photograph. I always try to capture people at their most natural in order to bring out their true selves. By approaching my subjects in a gentle, reassuring manner, they relax and forget that there is a camera pointed at them. For wedding photographs I pay attention to all details, because I have to change my approach for each shot, be it a fashion photograph, a landscape, a portrait, photo journalism, or something more like an advertisement. Each moment is in "real time" during weddings, and there are no second takes. The EOS and EF lenses adapt to each unscripted change in the situation with the sharpness I am looking for. I have used the Digital EOS for two years now, and it is an SLR camera with everything I have every hoped for and expected in the perfect camera. The EF lenses I use now are the EF20mm f/2.8 USM, EF50mm f/1.8 II, EF16-35mm f/2.8L USM, EF28-70mm f/2.8L USM, EF28-135mm f/3.5-5.6 IS USM, EF70-200mm f/2.8L IS USM and EF75-300mm f/4-5.6 IS USM.

Yervant Zanazanian
Armenian photographer born in Ethopia. Studied in Venice and has lived in Australia for over 25 years. Master Photographer 3 Gold Bars. Has received many awards in Australia for portraits and weddings. Has introduced digital imaging and graphic design into the field of professional wedding photography, and is known for his pioneering work in magazine-type wedding albums.

This scene of gnus crossing the river was shot in Masai Mara, Kenya. It was shot with an EOS-1V using an EF500mm f/4L IS USM set at 1/640 sec, f/6.3. I highly evaluate the quality Canon lenses, excellent ergonomically designed body, and the solidness and reliability of the product itself. This is because I often work under very extreme conditions. Because I almost always use the program mode, the accuracy of the automatic exposure is very important to me. In particular, the very high 100% viewfinder coverage and auto focus speed of the EOS-1V are a big plus for a wildlife photographer. In addition, the image stabilizer is a great strength of the Canon lens.
I recently used the EOD-1D and EOS-1Ds digital bodies in Africa for the first time and fell in love with them. Using a digital SLR camera makes the image marking process unbelievably simple. Now I can look at the photos on the day I shot them instead of having to wait two months to see them. Now I can't imagine going out into the field without a digital EOS.

Michel Denis-Huot
Born in 1953. He is one of France's representative animal photographers. He has been interested in wild animals since he was small. In October 1972 he successfully photographed two wild boars fighting, and those photographs would eventually be published repeatedly. Michel, who visited Kenya for the first time in 1973, became enamored with the expansive wild world of East Africa and quit his studies of veterinary medicine to become a wildlife photographer. Since then, he has spent almost all his time in Africa. He has continued photographing mainly in the Masai Mara, Kenya. Together with his wife Christine, he has published many books about African wildlife. He has been the frequent recipient of the World Press Photographer Award for Nature Photography and has been chosen the BG Wildlife Photographer of the Year.

One early morning in Karri Valley in western Australia I came upon a lone fisherman in his fishing boat, lit up by a single sliver of sunlight. Two nearby hills blocked out all other light, creating this unbelievable view. The dark background presented the risk of an extreme overexposure, so I switched my Canon EOS to fine-spot mode and measured just the fisherman. The exposure was perfect. I was using the EF70-200mm f/2.8L IS USM. (Photo on right.) Milford Sound on the west coast of South Island, one of New Zealand's more mountainous areas. Unfortunately when I got there it had rained for a week and all flights in and out were canceled. The weather report predicted even stronger rains for the next few days after that. But the next day I woke up to a clear blue sky with a beautiful dawn breaking over Meter Peak. This amazing mountain soars one mile above the fjord and its shape and the mirror-like water surface created a calming effect. Not expecting the good weather or lighting conditions to continue, I grabbed my EOS-1 and EF20-35mm f/3.5-4.5 USM and got a few angles on film. (Photo on left.) I started using the Canon EOS and the EF lenses not only because they are tough and accurate, but more than anything because the Canon System lets me work quickly and instinctively in even the toughest situations. Exceptional photographs are the product of unusual light and ever-changing conditions. The ergonomically unrivaled EOS operation combines with the high resolution optical system of the EF lenses for an absolutely reliable system that allows me to focus on nothing but my creativity. I will continue pushing the envelope with the EOS – EF combination, confident that I will produce even more wonderful photographs.

R. Ian Lloyd
Born in Canada. After studying photography in the US, moved to Australia. Later, moved to Singapore and started his office in 1983. Has contributed to over 30 magazines related to countries and regions in Asia, including National Geographic, Travel Holiday, Gourmet, Time, and Fortune. Has received many awards and a 20-year retrospective of his work sponsored by the National Geographic Channel has been shown in six cities in Asia. Is currently based in Singapore and Sydney.

Suzuka is the home of the Japanese GP, a favorite with the majority of F1 drivers and photographers alike. Held in autumn with a late start for the European audience it provides soft late afternoon light, and unique angles such as this shot taken from below the level of the car and from a perfect rear angle. The heat haze from the Mercedes 850BHP engine mixes with the colours from the 200,000 capacity crowd lining the circuit. Canon EOS cameras and EF lenses are simply the best "tools" on the market for my sphere of photography. Shooting F1 cars requires equipment to be light, fast, versatile and ergonomic. My Canons provide this and therefore are used as an extension of me. Digital SLR cameras are the future and my EOS-1D is used and feels the same way as my EOS-1V.

Steven Tee
Steven Tee is managing Director of LAT Photographic, a specialist motorsports agency with the worlds largest motorsport archive. Having covered F1 for 15 years he heads up an on track team of 7 photographers covering the Grands Prix for media and commercial clients.

This photograph was taken on a snowy mountain at night using only night-lights. Nothing could be more difficult than photographing a fast-moving subject in the dark, and until now it would have been natural to produce a grainy shot due to the high film sensitivity required or a blurry picture due to the camera shaking at a slow shutter speed. However, with the advent of image stabilizer technology it has been possible to turn such stereotypes on their head. I used a daylight ISO 100 film and a shutter speed of 1/60 with the large-aperture EF300mm f/2.8L with the IS switch on. The result is amazing – no graininess and no out-of-focus blurriness due to the camera shaking. I can get the shots I want, thanks to the EF300mm f/2.8L IS. I believe a 300mm is the standard for sport photography. And since the 300mm is such a great lens, the other large-aperture EF telephoto lenses also have high potential. As a professional photographer, I don't want to compromise in my work. As the large-aperture IS telephoto EF lenses stabilize images (as the name says), they are an essential part of my equipment lineup.

Takahito Mizutani
Born in Tokyo, 1968. Moved to France upon graduation from the Tokyo School of Photography. Worked in Europe focusing on motor sports, winter sports, soccer, rugby, and other sports before returning to Japan. With Japan as a base, continues to cover sporting events in Europe and North America. Published "Never End," a collection of photographs in conjunction with an exhibition of the same name in 2001. Member of AJPS (Association Japonaise de la Presse Sportive) and AIPS (Association Internationale de la Presse Sportive).

The Canon Camera International Service Network

As of October 2009.

Repairs to the Canon product you have purchased can be done by the Canon-authorized repair companies listed here. Products with an international warranty (those marked with the above Canon International Warranty System symbol) will be repaired during the warranty period by the repair companies indicated by the ⊕ mark, even outside the country or region of purchase. When repair is performed during the warranty period, be sure to show the warranty form. If you do not show the warranty, or if the warranty does not bear the name of the seller and date of purchase, a fee will be charged for repair work.

• Depending on the type of repair, there may be cases when a part must be specially ordered and it might take longer than usual for the work to be completed.
• Information subject to change.
• Contact your local repair dealer for service locations not listed here.

(***) - Country & Area Code

JAPAN — http://canon.jp

REGIONAL HEADQUARTERS ⊕ **CANON MARKETING JAPAN INC.** Phone: (81) 03-3455-9353

*For service center location, please contact the phone number above.

ASIA — http://www.canon-asia.com

HONG KONG ⊕ **Canon HongKong Co. Ltd. - Domestic Sales Office** Phone: (852) 3191-2333
11/F Oterprise Square, 26 Nathan Road, Tsim Fax: (852) 2428-3963
Sha Tsui Kowloon, Hong Kong

MALAYSIA ⊕ **Canon Marketing (Malaysia) Sdn. Bhd.** Phone: (60) 03-7845-0055
Block D, Peremba Square, Saujana Resort, Section Fax: (60) 03-7844-6044
U2, 40150 Shah Alam, Selangor Darul Ehsan
Malaysia

PHILIPPINES ⊕ **Canon Marketing (Philippines) Inc.** Phone: (63) 02-812-6047
Marvin Plaza Building, 2153 Don Chino Roces Ave. Fax: (63) 02-812-0067
Makati City, Metro Manila

SINGAPORE ⊕ **Canon Singapore Pte. Ltd.** Phone: (65) 6799-8888
1 HarbourFront Avenue #04-01 Keppel Bay Tower Fax: (65) 6799-8882
Singapore 098632

TAIWAN ⊕ **Rainbow Photo & Image Equipment Co. Ltd.** Phone: (886) 02-2571-1166
No. 20 Chiling Road, Taipei 10424, Taiwan Fax: (886) 02-2537-1169

THAILAND ⊕ **Canon Marketing (Thailand) Co.Ltd** Phone: (66) 02-344-9999
10th Floor, Bangkok City Tower, Fax: (66) 02-344-9910
179/34-45 South Sathorn Road, Bangkok 10120

UNITED STATES OF AMERICA — http://www.usa.canon.com

REGIONAL HEADQUARTERS ⊕ **CANON U.S.A., INC.** Phone: 1-800-OK-CANON
(1-800-652-2666)

*For service center location, please visit our website or contact the phone number above.

CANADA — http://www.canon.ca

REGIONAL HEADQUARTERS ⊕ **CANON CANADA, INC.** Phone: 1-800-OK-CANON
(1-800-652-2666)

*For service center location, please visit our website or contact the phone number above.

CENTRAL & SOUTH AMERICA — http://www.canonlatinamerica.com

REGIONAL HEADQUARTERS (Except Mexico) ⊕ **CANON LATIN AMERICA, INC.** Phone: 1-305-260-7400

*For service center location, please visit our website or contact the phone number above.

MEXICO — http://www.canon.com.mx

REGIONAL HEADQUARTERS ⊕ **CANON MEXICANA, S.DE R.L. DE C.V.** Phone: 01-800-710-7168*
Manuel Avila Camacho No. 138, *Within Mexico only
PB y pisos 15,16 y 17 Col. Lomas de (52) 052-494-905
Chapultepec Delegacion Miguel Hidalgo, Fax: (52) 052-494-944
C.P. 11000 Mexico, D.F.

*For service center location, please contact the phone number above or send an e-mail to: canonmx_soporte@cusa. canon. com

Asia/Oceania

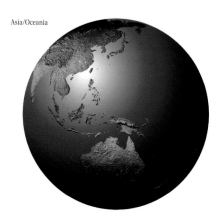

North America/South America

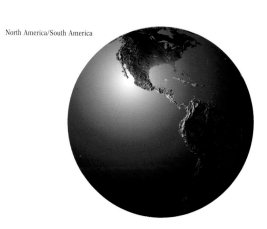

Europe

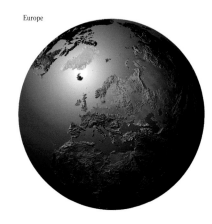

Africa/Middle East

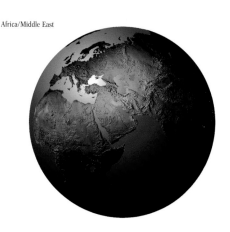

(***) - Country & Area Code

EUROPE/MIDDLE EAST/AFRICA http://www.canon-europa.com

For support please visit: http://www.support.canon-europe.com

REGIONAL HEADQUARTERS	⊕ CANON EUROPA N.V P.O. Box 2262, Bovenkerkerweg 59-61 1180 EG Amstelveen, The Netherlands	Phone: (31) 020-545-8545 Fax: (31) 020-545-8211

*For general Inquiry only. For repair, please contact one of service center listed below.
*Within Local only for non-Country & Area Code No.

AUSTRIA	⊕ Canon Ges.m.b.H http://www.canon.at	Phone: 0810-081009
BELGIUM	⊕ Canon Belgium N.V. / S.A. http://www.canon.be	Phone: 070-300-012
CYPRUS	⊕ TSP PHOTOMARKET LTD http://www.canon-paroutis.com	Phone: (357) 25-568274
CZECH REP.	⊕ Canon CZ s.r.o. http://www.canon.cz	Phone: (420)02-25280-111
	⊕ AWH service http://www.awh.cz	Phone: (420)02-22721-525
DENMARK	⊕ Canon Denmark http://www.canon.dk	Phone: 70-2055-15
FINLAND	⊕ Canon Oy http://www.canon.fi	Phone: 020-366-466
FRANCE	⊕ Canon France Regional Competence Center http://www.canon.fr	Phone: 0825-002-923
GERMANY	⊕ Canon Germany Regional Competence Center http://www.canon.de	Phone: 0180-500-6022
GREECE	⊕ Intersys SA http://www.intersys.gr	Phone: (30) 0210-955-4000
HUNGARY	⊕ Camera Kft http://www.camerakft.hu	Phone: (36) 01-2668085
ICELAND	⊕ Beco ehf http://www.beco.is	Phone: (354) 533-3411
IRAN	⊕ Aphomar Co. Ltd. 10th Floor Sarve Trade Center, Sarve Ave, Saadatabad, P.O.Box 11367-1167 Tehran	Phone: (98) 021-8752442
IRELAND	⊕ Canon Ireland Ltd. http://www.canon.ie	Phone:(353)01890-200-563
ISRAEL	⊕ Karat Israel Ltd. http://www.karat.co.il	Phone: (972) 03-6888525
ITALY	⊕ Canon Italy Regional Competence Center http://www.canon.it	Phone: 848-800-519
LUXEMBOURG	⊕ Canon Luxembourg S.A. http://www.canon.lu	Phone: 27-302-054
THE NETHERLANDS	⊕ Canon Netherland N.V http://www.canon.nl	Phone: 0900-202-2915
NORWAY	⊕ Canon Norge A/S http://www.canon.no	Phone: 235-00143
POLAND	⊕ Canon Polska SP.Z.O.O. http://www.canon.pl	Phone: (48) 022-572-30-00
	⊕ CSI Foto Video http://www.e-csi.pl	Phone: (48) 022-862-41-38
PORTUGAL	⊕ Canon Portugal http://www.canon.pt	Phone: (351) 021-3242830
SAUDI ARABIA	⊕ AlQuraishi Leisure Services http://www.alquraishi.com	Phone: (966) 02-6970779/ 6970652
SLOVAKIA	⊕ Pro Laika http://www.prolaika.sk	Phone: (421) 02-5441-4880
SLOVENIA	⊕ 3A AUDIO VIDEO Servis http://www.3a-servis.si	Phone: (386) 01-5461000
SOUTH AFRICA	⊕ Canon South Africa. http://www.canon-sa.com	Phone: (27) 011-2667162
SPAIN	⊕ Canon España, S.A. http://www.canon.es	Phone: 901900012
SWEDEN	⊕ Canon Nordic Regional Competence Center http://www.canon.se	Phone: 08-51992369
SWITZERLAND	⊕ Canon Schweiz AG http://www.canon.ch	Phone: 0848-833-838
UNITED KINGDOM	⊕ Canon UK Regional Competence Center http://www.canon.co.uk	Phone: 08-705-143723

(***) - Country & Area Code

OCEANIA http://www.canon.com.au

REGIONAL HEADQUARTERS	⊕ CANON AUSTRALIA PTY. LTD.	Phone: 13-13-83 *Within Australia only (61) 02-9805-2555 Fax: (61) 02-9888-3314

*For service center location, please contact the phone number above.

NEW ZEALAND	⊕ Canon New Zealand Ltd. Akoranga Business Park, Akoranga Drive Northcote, Auckland, New Zealand	Phone: 0800-222-666* * Within New Zealand only (64) 09-489-0300

NON-IW MEMBERS

* Service facilities listed below are not "International Warranty Members"
They do not accept any warranty repair but may assist you when the repair charge is acceptable.

ASIA

BRUNEI	• Interhouse Company No.5 & 6, Bunut Jaya Complex, Simpang 574, Km 7 1/4, Jalan Tutong, Bandar Seri Begawan 2690, Brunei Darussalam	Phone: (673) 02-653001
BANGLADESH	• J.A.N. Associates LTD. 13/1, Fatema Arcade, Road 5, Dhanmondi, Dhaka-1205, Bangladesh	Phone: (880) 2-8611444 Fax: (880) 2-8610410
CAMBODIA	• Royal Cambodia Co., Ltd. 437 Preah Monivong Boulevard, Phnom Penh, Kingdom of Cambodia	Phone: (855) 023-428955 Fax: (855) 023-722961
CHINA	• Canon (China) Co., Ltd. 15F Jinbao Building No.89 Jinbao Street, Dongcheng District, Beijing 100005, China	Phone: (86) 010-9517-7178
INDIA	• Canon India Pte. Ltd. 2nd Floor, Tower A & B Cyber Greens, DLF Phase III Gurgaon-122 002, Haryana, India	Phone: 18001803366 (*) 39010101 * Prefix city code call from mobile phone Fax: (91)0124-4160011
INDONESIA	• PT Datascrip Jl. Angkasa no 18 BD,Jakarta, Indonesia	Phone: (62) 021-424-4204 Fax: (62) 021-424-7017
KOREA	• Canon Korea Consumer Imaging Inc. Kangnam Finance Center 17F. 737, Yeoksam-Dong, Kangnam-Ku, Seoul 135-984, Korea	Phone: (82) 2-2191-8500 Fax: (82) 2-2191-8598
MYANMAR	• Accel International Co., Ltd. Level 6, FJV Commercial Centre, 422~426 Strand Road, Botataung, Township, Yangon	Phone: (95) 01-202-092 Fax: (95) 01-202-079
NEPAL	• Primax International Inc. 3rd Floor, Maitry Bhavan, New Road, Kathmandu, Nepal	Phone: (977) 01-422-4079 Fax: (977) 01-422-9358
PAKISTAN	• Mega Business Machines 407, Techno City, Hasrat Mohani Road 1.1. Chundrigar Road, Karachi, Pakistan	Phone: (92) 21-2276926-8 Fax: (92) 21-2276930
SRI LANKA	• Homebase (Pvt.) Limited No.85 Braybrooke Place, Colombo 02, Sri Lanka	Phone: (94) 01-12437797 Fax: (94) 01-12448980

EUROPE / MIDDLE EAST / AFRICA

CIS	• Canon Representative Office Kosmodamianskaya nab. 52, Building 3, 5th Floor 113054 Moscow	Phone: (7) 095-258600
ESTONIA	• AS KTK Overall http://www.canon.ee	Phone: (372) 630-0530
KUWAIT	• Naser Mohammed, Al Sayer Comm.Co. P.O. Box 974 Safat 13008	Phone: (965) 2-44810315
LATVIA	• Canon North-East Oy http://www.canon.lv	Phone: (371) 720-4444
LEBANON	• Image System sal 460 Corniche Al-Nahr, Beirut	Phone: (961) 01-582-000
LITHUANIA	• Canon North-East Oy http://www.canon.lt	Phone: (370) 8700-555-78
MALTA	• P. Cutajar http://www.pcutajar.com.mt	Phone: (356) 448466
OMAN	• GENETCO P.O. Box 3139, Ruwi 112	Phone: (968) 706153
UAE	• Khoory Electronics P.O.Box 284 Dubai	Phone: (971) 04-3534168